The
father
factor

**Unsuspecting fathers
...and unexpected husbands!**

D0542385

By
Request™

The
father
factor

RELUCTANT FATHER
by
Diana Palmer

ALMOST AN ANGEL
by
Debbie Macomber

PASSION'S CHILD
by
Ann Major

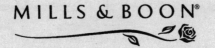

MILLS & BOON®

*All the characters in this book have no existence outside the imagination
of the author, and have no relation whatsoever to anyone bearing the same
name or names. They are not even distantly inspired by any individual
known or unknown to the author, and all the incidents are
pure invention.*

*All Rights Reserved including the right of reproduction in whole or in part
in any form. This edition is published by arrangement with Harlequin
Enterprises II B.V. The text of this publication or any part thereof may not
be reproduced or transmitted in any form or by any means, electronic or
mechanical, including photocopying, recording, storage in an
information retrieval system, or otherwise, without the written
permission of the publisher.*

*This book is sold subject to the condition that it shall not, by way of trade
or otherwise, be lent, resold, hired out or otherwise circulated without the
prior consent of the publisher in any form of binding or cover other than
that in which it is published and without a similar condition including this
condition being imposed on the subsequent purchaser.*

*MILLS & BOON and MILLS & BOON with the Rose Device
are registered trademarks of the publisher.*
*Harlequin Mills & Boon Limited,
Eton House, 18-24 Paradise Road, Richmond, Surrey, TW9 1SR*

THE FATHER FACTOR
© 1998 by Harlequin Books SA

Reluctant Father and *Passion's Child* were first published
in Great Britain by Silhouette Books in 1989.
Almost an Angel was first published in Great Britain
by Mills & Boon Limited in 1994.

Reluctant Father © Diana Palmer 1989
Almost an Angel © Debbie Macomber 1989
Passion's Child © Ann Major 1988

ISBN 0 263 81131 X

05-9808

*Printed and bound in Great Britain
by Caledonian Book Manufacturing Ltd, Glasgow*

Diana Palmer got her start in writing as a newspaper reporter and columnist, where she says she acquired many of her writing skills during her sixteen-year tenure. With over ten million copies of her books in print around the world, this perennially favourite writer has been named one of America's top ten romance authors by *Affaire de Coeur* magazine.

Always on the watch for new and exciting experiences, Diana recently added a college degree to her list of achievements. 'College was very important to me,' she says. 'I never had the opportunity or the wherewithal to go when I was younger. Then suddenly I was in school with teenagers. They treated me like another book bag walking down the hall, and I loved the anonymity.'

Now formally educated in anthropology and history, Diana remains a highly prolific author, averaging a book about every two months. She resides in the north mountains of her home state of Georgia with her husband, James, and their son, Blayne Edward.

RELUCTANT FATHER
by
DIANA PALMER

For Margaret, with love

One

Blake Donavan didn't know which was the bigger shock—
the dark-haired, unsmiling little girl at his front door or the
news that the child was his daughter by his ex-wife.

Blake's pale green eyes darkened dangerously. It had
been a hell of a day altogether, and now this. The lawyer
who'd just imparted the information stepped closer to the
child.

Blake raked his fingers through his unruly black hair
and glared down at the child through thick black lashes.
His daughter? The scowl grew and his expression hardened, emphasizing the harsh scar down one lean, tanned
cheek. He looked even taller and more formidable than he
really was.

"I don't like him," the little girl murmured, glaring at
Blake as she spoke for the first time. She thrust her lower
lip out and moved closer to the lawyer, clinging to his
trouser leg. She had green eyes. That fact registered al-

most immediately—that and her high cheekbones. Blake had high cheekbones, too.

"Now, now." The tall, bespectacled man cleared his throat. "We mustn't be naughty, Sarah."

"My wife," Blake said coldly, "left me five years ago to take up residence with an oilman from Louisiana. I haven't seen or heard from her since."

"If I might come in, Mr. Donavan . . . ?"

He ignored the attorney's plea. "We only cohabited for a month—just long enough for her to find out that I was up to my neck in legal battles. She cut her losses and got out quick with her new lover." He smiled crookedly. "She didn't expect me to win. But I did."

The lawyer glanced around at the elegant, columned front porch, the well-kept gardens, the Mercedes in the driveway. He'd heard about the Donavan fortune and the fight Blake Donavan had when his uncle died and left him fending off numerous greedy cousins.

"The problem, you see," the attorney continued, glancing worriedly at the clinging child, "is that your ex-wife died earlier this month in an airplane crash. Understandably her second husband, from whom she was estranged, didn't want to assume responsibility for the child. Sarah has no one else," he added on a weary sigh. "Your wife's parents were middle-aged when she was born, and she had no brothers or sisters. The entire family is dead. And Sarah is your child."

Blake stared down at the little girl half-angrily. He hadn't even kept a photograph of Nina to remind him of the fool he'd been. And now here was her child, and they expected him to want her.

"I don't have room in my life for a child," he said curtly, furious at the curve fate had thrown him. "She can be put in a home somewhere, I suppose. . . ."

And that was when it happened. The child began to cry. There wasn't a sound from her. She went from belligerence to heartrending sorrow in seconds, with great tears rolling from her green eyes down her flushed round cheeks. The effect was all the more poignant because of her silence and the stoic look on her face, as if she hated giving way to tears in front of the enemy.

Blake felt a stirring inside that surprised him. His mother had died soon after he was born. She hadn't been a particularly moral woman, according to his uncle, and all he knew about her was what little he'd been told. His uncle had taken him in and had adopted him. He, like Sarah, had been an extra person in the world, unwanted by just about everyone. He had no idea who his father was. If it hadn't been for his very wealthy uncle, he wouldn't even have a name. That lack of love and security in his young life had turned him hard. It would turn Sarah hard, too, if she had nobody to protect her.

He looked down at the little girl with a headful of angry questions, hating those tears. But the child had grit. She glared at him and abruptly wiped the tears away with a chubby little hand.

Blake lifted his chin pugnaciously. Already the kid was getting to him. But he wasn't going to be taken in by some scam. He trusted no one. "How do I know she's mine?" he demanded to the lawyer.

"She has your blood type," the man replied. "Your ex-wife's second husband has a totally different blood group. As you know, a blood test can only tell who the father wasn't. It wasn't her second husband."

Blake was about to remark that it could have been any one of a dozen other men, but then he remembered that Nina had married him for what she thought was his soon-to-be-realized wealth. He reasoned that Nina was too shrewd to have risked losing him by indulging in a fling. And after she knew what a struggle it was going to be to get that wealth, she hadn't wanted her newest catch to know she was already pregnant.

"Why didn't she tell me?" Blake asked coldly.

"She allowed her second husband to think the child was his," he said quietly. "It wasn't until she died and Sarah's birth certificate was found that he discovered she was yours. Nina had apparently decided that Sarah had a right to her own father's name. By then her second marriage was already on the rocks, from what I was told." He touched the child's dark hair absently. "You have the resources to double-check all this, of course."

"Of course." He stared down his broken nose at the little girl's face. "What's her name again? Sarah?"

"That's right. Sarah Jane."

Blake turned. "Bring her inside. Mrs. Jackson can feed her and I'll engage a nurse for her."

Just that quickly, he made the decision to keep the child. But, then, he'd been making quick decisions for a long time. When his uncle had attempted to link him with Meredith Calhoun, Blake had quickly decided to marry Nina. And as a last effort to force Blake into marrying Meredith, his uncle had left Meredith twenty percent of the stock in the real-estate conglomerate Blake was to inherit.

That had backfired. Blake had laughed at Meredith, in front of the whole family gathered for the reading of the will. And he'd told them all, his arm protectively around a smiling Nina, that he'd rather lose his inheritance and a leg than marry a skinny, plain, repulsive woman like Meredith. He was marrying Nina and Meredith could take her stock and burn it, for all he cared.

His heart lay like lead in his chest as he remembered the harsh words he'd used that day to cut Meredith down. She hadn't even flinched, but he'd watched something die in her soft gray eyes. With a kind of ravished dignity, she'd walked out of the room with every eye on her straight back. That had been bad enough. But later she'd come to offer him the stock and he'd been irritated by the faint hunger in her soft eyes. Because she disturbed him, he'd kissed her roughly, bruising her mouth, and he'd said some things that sent her running from him. He regretted that most of all. He planned to marry Nina, but despite his feeling for her, Meredith had been a tiny thorn in his side for years. He hadn't really meant to hurt her. He'd only wanted to make her go away. Well, he had. And he hadn't seen her since. She'd become internationally famous with her women's novels, one of which had been adapted for television. He saw her books everywhere these days. Like Meredith, they haunted him.

It hadn't been until after Nina had left him that he'd found out the reason for Meredith's haste in getting away. She'd been in love with him, his uncle's attorney had told him ruefully as he handed Blake the documents to sign that would give him full control of the Donavan empire. His uncle had known it and had hoped to make Blake see what a good catch she was.

Blake remembered vividly the day he'd discovered his hunger for Meredith. It had shocked them both. His uncle had come into the stable just in time to break up what might have been a disastrous confrontation between them. Blake had lost control and frightened Meredith, although she'd been so sweetly responsive at first that he hadn't seen her fear until the sound of a car driving up had brought him to his senses. Even a blind man couldn't have missed the faint swell of Meredith's mouth, the color in her cheeks and the way she was trembling. That was probably when the old man got the idea about the stock.

What irony, Blake thought, that what he'd wanted most
in life was just a little love. He'd never had his mother's.
He'd never known his father. And his uncle, though fond
of him, was a manipulative man interested in the survival
of his empire through Blake. Blake had actually married
Nina because she'd flattered him and played up to him and
sworn that she loved him. Now, looking back, he could see
that she'd loved his money, not him. Once there was any
possibility of the fortune being lost, she'd walked out on
him. But Meredith had genuinely loved Blake, and he'd
been cruel to her. That had haunted him all these years—
that he'd hurt the one human being on earth who'd ever
wanted to love him.

Meredith's father had worked for Blake's uncle, but the
two men were good friends, as well. Uncle Dan had been
at Meredith's christening as her godfather, and when she'd
grown into her teens and expressed an interest in writing
local history for the school newspaper, Uncle Dan had
opened his library to her and spent hours telling her stories
he'd heard from his grandfather about the old days. Meredith would sit and listen, her big eyes wide, her mouth
faintly smiling. And Blake would brood, because his uncle
had never given him that kind of time and affection. Blake
was useful, but his uncle loved Meredith. He felt as if she'd
usurped the only place in the world he had, and he'd resented her bitterly. And it was more than just that. He'd
already learned that he couldn't trust people. He knew that
Meredith and her parents were dirt poor, and he often
wondered if she might not have some mercenary reason for
hanging around the Donavan house. Too late, he discovered that she hung around because of him. Knowing the
truth put salt in an old wound.

Plain Meredith, with her stringy dark hair and her pale
gray eyes and her heart-shaped face. His uncle had loved

her. Blake had almost despised her, especially after what had happened in the stable when he lost control with her. But under the resentment was an obsessive desire for Meredith that angered him, until it reached flash point the day his uncle's will was read. He'd given his word to Nina that he'd marry her and he couldn't honorably go back on it, but he'd wanted Meredith. God, how he'd wanted her, for years!

She'd loved him, he thought wearily as he led the lawyer and child into the study. Nobody else ever had felt that way about him. His uncle had enjoyed their battles; they'd been friends. His death had been a terrible, unexpected blow, made worse by the fact that he'd always felt that his uncle might have cared for him if Meredith hadn't always been underfoot. Not that it was love that had caused his uncle to adopt him. That had been business.

Maybe his mother would have loved him if she'd lived, although his uncle had described her as a pretty, self-centered woman who simply liked men too much.

So it had come as a shock to find out what shy young Meredith had felt for him. It didn't help to remember how he'd cut her to pieces in public and private. Over the years since she'd left for Texas in the middle of the night on a bus, without a goodbye to anyone, he'd agonized over what he'd done to her. Twice, he'd almost gone to see her when her name started cropping up on book covers. But the past was best left in the past, he'd decided finally. And he had nothing to give her, anyway. Nina had destroyed that part of him that was capable of trust. He had no more to give—to anyone.

He dragged his thoughts away from the past and looked at the child, who was staring plaintively and a little apprehensively at the door, because the lawyer had just smiled and was now making his way out, patent relief written all over his thin features. Sarah sat very still on the edge of a blue wing chair, biting her lower lip, her eyes wide and frightened, although she tried to hide her fear from the cold, mean-looking man they said was her father.

Blake sat down across from her in his own big red leather armchair, aware that he looked more like a desperado in his jeans and worn chambray shirt than a man of means. He'd been out in the pasture helping brand cattle, just for the hell of it. At least when he was working with his hands on the small ranch where he ran purebred Hereford cattle, he could let his mind go. It beat the hell out of the trying board meeting he'd had to endure at his company headquarters in Oklahoma City that morning.

"So you're Sarah," he said. Children made him uncomfortable, and he didn't know how he was going to cope with this one. But she had his eyes and he couldn't let her go to strangers. Not if there was one chance in a million that she really was his daughter.

Sarah lifted her eyes to his, then glanced away, shifting restlessly. The lawyer had said she was almost four, but she seemed amazingly mature. She behaved as if she'd never known the company of other children. It was possible that she hadn't. He couldn't picture Nina entertaining children. It was totally out of character, but he hadn't realized that when he'd lost his head and married her. Funny how easy it was to imagine Meredith Calhoun with a lapful of little girls, laughing and playing with them, picking daisies in the meadow....

He had to stop thinking about Meredith, he told himself firmly. He didn't want her, even if there was a chance in hell that she'd ever come back to Jack's Corner, Oklahoma. And he knew without a doubt that she certainly didn't want him.

"I don't like you," Sarah said after a minute. She shifted in the chair and glanced around her. "I don't want to live here." She glared at Blake.

He glared back. "Well, I'm not crazy about the idea, either, but it looks like we're stuck with each other."

Her lower lip jutted, and for an instant she looked just like him. "I'll bet you don't even have a cat."

"God forbid," he grumbled. "I hate cats."

She sighed and looked at her scuffed shoes with something like resignation and a patience far beyond her years. She appeared tired and worn. "My mommy isn't coming back." She pulled at her dress. "She didn't like me. You don't like me, either," she said, lifting her chin. "I don't care. You're not really my daddy."

"I must be." He sighed heavily. "God knows, you look enough like me."

"You're ugly."

His eyebrows shot up. "You're no petunia yourself, sprout," he returned.

"The ugly duckling turns into a swan," she told him with a faraway look in her eyes.

She twirled her hands in her dress. He noticed then, for the first time, that it was old. The lace was stained and the dress was rumpled. He frowned.

"Where have you been staying?" he asked her.

"Mommy left me with Daddy Brad, but he had to go out a lot, so Mrs. Smathers took care of me." She looked up, and the expression in her green eyes was old for a little girl's. "Mrs. Smathers says that children are horrible," she said dramatically, "and that they belong in cages. I cried when Mommy left, and she locked me up and said she'd leave me there if I didn't hush." Her lower lip trembled, but she didn't cry. "I got out, too, and ran away." She shrugged. "But nobody came to find me, so I went home.

Mrs. Smathers was real mad, but Daddy Brad didn't care. He said I wasn't his real child and it didn't matter if I ran away.''

Blake could imagine that "Daddy Brad" was upset to find that the child he'd accepted as his own was somebody else's, but taking it out on the child seemed pretty callous.

He leaned back in his chair, wondering what in hell he was going to do with his short houseguest. He didn't know anything about kids. He wasn't sure he even liked them. And this one already looked like a handful. She was outspoken and belligerent and not much to look at. He could see trouble ahead.

Mrs. Jackson came into the room to see if Blake wanted anything, and stopped dead. She was fifty-five, a spinster, graying and thin and faintly intimidating to people who didn't know her. She was used to a bachelor household, and the sight of a child sitting across from her boss was vaguely unnerving.

"Who's that?" she asked, without dressing up the question.

Sarah looked at her and sighed, as if saying, oh, no, here's another sour one. Blake almost laughed out loud at the expression on the child's face.

"This is Amie Jackson, Sarah," Blake said, introducing them. "Mrs. Jackson, Sarah Jane is my daughter."

Mrs. Jackson didn't faint, but she did go a shade redder. "Yes, sir, that's hard to miss," she said, comparing the small, composed child's face with its older male counterpart. "Her mother isn't here?" she added, staring around as if she expected Nina to materialize.

"Nina is dead," Blake said without any particular feeling. Nina had knocked the finer feelings out of him years ago. His own foolish blindness to her real nature had helped her in the task.

"Oh, I'm sorry." Mrs. Jackson rubbed her apron between her thin hands for something to do. "Would she like some milk and cookies?" she asked hesitantly.

"That might be nice. Sarah?" Blake asked more curtly than he'd meant.

Sarah shifted and stared at the carpet. "I'd get crumbs on the floor." She shook her head. "Mrs. Smathers says kids should eat off the kitchen floor 'cause they're messy."

Mrs. Jackson looked uncomfortable, and Blake sighed heavily. "You can get crumbs on the floor. Nobody's going to yell at you."

Sarah glanced up hesitantly.

"I don't mind cleaning up crumbs," Mrs. Jackson said testily. "Do you want cookies?"

"Yes, please."

The older woman nodded curtly and went to get some.

"Nobody smiles here," Sarah murmured. "It's just like home."

Blake felt a twinge of regret for the child, who seemed to have been stuck away in the housekeeper's corner with no thought for her well-being. And not just since her stepfather had found out that she was Blake's child, apparently.

His eyes narrowed and he asked the question that was consuming him. "Didn't your mother stay with you?"

"Mommy was busy," Sarah said. "She said I had to stay with Mrs. Smathers and do what she said."

"Wasn't she home from time to time?"

"She and my daddy—" she faltered and grimaced "—my *other* daddy yelled at each other mostly. Then she went away and he went away, too."

This was getting them nowhere. He stood and began to pace, his hands in his pockets, his face stormy and hard.

Sarah watched him covertly. "You sure are big," she murmured.

He stopped, glancing down at her curiously. "You sure are little," he returned.

"I'll grow," Sarah promised. "Do you have a horse?"

"Several."

She brightened. "I can ride a horse!"

"Not on my ranch, you can't."

Her green eyes flashed fire. "I can so if I want to. I can ride any horse!"

He knelt in front of her very slowly, and his green eyes met hers levelly and without blinking. "No," he said firmly. "You'll do what you're told, and you won't talk back. This is my place, and I make the rules. Got it?"

She hesitated, but only for a minute. "Okay," she said sulkily.

He touched the tip of her pert nose. "And no sulking. I don't know how this is going to work out," he added curtly. "Hell, I don't know anything about kids!"

"Hell is where you go when you're bad," Sarah replied matter-of-factly. "My mommy's friend used to talk about it all the time, and about damns and sons of—"

"Sarah!" Blake burst out, shocked that a child her age should be so familiar with bad words.

"Do you have any cows?" she added, easily diverted.

"A few," he muttered. "Which one of your mummy's friends used language like that around you?"

"Just Trudy," she said, wide-eyed.

Blake whistled through his teeth and turned just as Mrs. Jackson came in with a tray of milk and cookies for Sarah and coffee for Blake.

"I like coffee," Sarah said. "My mommy let me drink it when she had hers in bed and she wasn't awake good."

"I'll bet," Blake said, "but you aren't drinking it here. Coffee isn't good for kids."

"I can have coffee if I want to," Sarah returned belligerently.

Blake looked at Mrs. Jackson, who was more or less frozen in place, staring at the little girl as she grabbed four cookies and proceeded to stuff them into her mouth as if she hadn't eaten in days.

"You quit, or even try to quit," Blake told the housekeeper, who'd looked after his uncle before him, "and so help me God, I'll track you all the way to Alaska and drag you back here by one foot."

"Me, quit? Just when things are getting interesting?" Mrs. Jackson lifted her chin. "God forbid."

"Sarah, when was the last time you ate?" Blake inquired, watching her grab another handful of cookies.

"I had supper," she said, "and then we came here."

"You haven't had breakfast?" he burst out. "Or lunch?"

She shook her head. "These cookies are good!"

"If you haven't eaten for almost a day, I imagine so." He sighed. "You'd better make us an early dinner tonight," Blake told Mrs. Jackson. "She'll eat herself sick on cookies if we're not careful."

"Yes, sir. I'll go and make up the guest room for her," she said. "But what about clothes? Does she have a suitcase?"

"No, that lawyer didn't bring anything. Let her sleep in her slip tonight. Tomorrow," he added, "you can take her into town to do some shopping."

"Me?" Mrs. Jackson looked horrified.

"Somebody has to be sacrificed," he told her pithily. "And I'm the boss."

Mrs. Jackson's lips formed a thin line. "I don't know beans about little girls' clothes!"

"Well, take her to Mrs. Donaldson's shop," he muttered. "That's where King Roper and Elissa take their little girl to be outfitted. I heard King groan about the prices, but that won't bother us any more than it bothers them."

"Yes, sir." She turned to leave.

"By the way, where's the weekly paper?" he asked, because it always came on Thursday morning. "I wanted to see if our legal ad got in."

Mrs. Jackson shifted uncomfortably and grimaced. "Well, I didn't want to upset you..."

His eyebrows arched. "How could the weekly paper possibly upset me? Get it!"

"All right. If you're sure that's what you want." She reached into the drawer of one of the end tables and pulled it out. "There you go, boss. And I'll leave before the explosion, if you don't mind."

She exited, and Sarah took two more cookies while Blake stared down at the paper's front page at a face that had haunted him.

"Author Meredith Calhoun to autograph at Baker's Book Nook," read the headline, and underneath it was a recent picture of Meredith.

His eyes searched over it in shock. The plain, skinny woman he'd hurt bore no resemblance to this peacock. Her brown hair was pulled back from her face into an elegant chignon. Her gray eyes were serene in a high-cheekboned face that could have graced the cover of a magazine, and her makeup enhanced the raw material that had always been there. She was wearing a pale suit coat with a pastel blouse, and she looked lovely. More than lovely. She looked soft and warm and totally untouched at the age of twenty-five, which she had to be now.

Blake put the paper down after scanning what he already knew about her skyrocketing career and her latest book, *Choices*, about a man and a woman trying to manage careers, marriage and parenthood all at once. He'd read it, as he secretly read all Meredith's books, looking for traces of the past. Maybe even for a cessation of hostilities. But her feelings for him were buried and there was never a single trait he could recognize in her people that reminded him of himself. It was as if she sensed that he might look at them and had hidden anything that would give her inner feelings away.

Sarah Jane was standing beside him without his knowing it. She looked at the picture in the paper. "That's a pretty lady," Sarah said. She leaned forward and picked out a word in the column below the photograph. "*B...o...o...k*. Book," she said proudly.

"So it is." He pointed to the name. "How about that?"

"*M...e...r*...Merry Christmas," she said.

He smiled faintly. "Meredith," he corrected. "That's her name. She's a writer."

"I had a book about the three bears," Sarah told him. "Did she write that?"

"No. She writes books for big girls. Finish your cookies and you can watch television."

"I like to watch *Mr. Rogers* and *Sesame Street*," she said.

He frowned. "What?"

"They come on television."

"Oh. Well, help yourself."

He moved out of the room, ignoring the coffee. Which was sad, because Sarah Jane discovered it in the big silver pot and proceeded to help herself to the now cool liquid while he was on the telephone in the hall. Her cry caused him to drop the receiver in mid-sentence.

She was drenched in coffee and screaming her head off. She wasn't the only wet thing, either. The carpet and part of the sofa were saturated and the tray was an inch deep with black liquid.

"I told you to stay out of the coffee, didn't I?" Blake said as he knelt to see if she had been burned. Which, thank God, she hadn't; she was more frightened than hurt.

"I wanted some," she murmured tearfully. "I ruined my pretty dress."

"That isn't all that's going to get ruined, either," he said ominously, and abruptly tugged her over his knee and gave her bottom a slap. "When I say no, I mean no. Do you understand me, Sarah Jane Donavan?" he asked firmly.

She was too surprised to cry anymore. She stared at him warily. "Is that my name now?"

"It's always been your name," he replied. "You're a Donavan. This is your home."

"I like coffee," she said hesitantly.

"And I said you weren't to drink it," he reminded her.

She took a deep breath. "Okay." She picked up the coffeepot, only to have it taken from her and put on the table. "I can clean it up," she said. "Mommy always made me clean up my mess."

"This is more than you can cope with, sprout. And God only knows what we're going to put on you while those things are washed."

Mrs. Jackson came in and put both hands to her mouth. "Saints alive!"

"Towels, quick," Blake said.

She went to get them, muttering all the way.

Minutes later the mess was gone, Sarah Jane was bundled up in a makeshift towel dress and her clothes were being washed and dried. Blake went into his study and locked the door, shamelessly leaving Mrs. Jackson to cope with Sarah while he had a few minutes' peace. He had a feeling that it was going to be more and more difficult to find any quiet place in his life from now on.

He wasn't sure he was going to like being a father. It was a whole new kind of responsibility, and his daughter seemed to have inherited his strength of will and stubbornness. She was going to be a handful. Mrs. Jackson knew no more about kids than he did, and that wasn't going to help, either. But he didn't feel right about sending Sarah off to a boarding school. He knew what it was like to be alone and unwanted and not too physically appealing. He felt a kind of kinship with this child, and he was reluctant to push her out of his life. On the other hand, how in hell was he going to live with her?

But over and above that problem was the newest one. Meredith Calhoun was coming to Jack's Corner for a whole month, according to that newspaper. In that length of time he was sure to see her, and he had mixed feelings about opening up the old wounds. He wondered if she felt the same way, or if, in her fame and wealth, she'd left the memories of him in the past. He wanted to see her all the same. Even if she still hated him.

Two

Blake and Mrs. Jackson usually ate their evening meal with a minimum of conversation. But that was another old custom that was going to change.

Sarah Jane was a walking encyclopedia of questions. One answer led to another why and another, until Blake was ready to get under the table. And just the mention of bedtime brought on a tantrum. Mrs. Jackson tried to cajole the child into obeying, but Sarah Jane only got louder. Blake settled the matter by picking her up and carrying her to her new room.

Mrs. Jackson helped her undress and get into bed and Blake paused at her bedside reluctantly to say good-night.

"You don't like me," Sarah accused.

He almost bristled at her mutinous expression, but she was a proud child, and he didn't want to break her spirit. She'd need it as she grew older.

"I don't know you," he replied reasonably. "Any more than you know me. People don't become friends on the spur of the moment. It takes time, sprout."

She considered that as she lay there, swallowed whole by the size of the bed under her and the thick white coverlet over her. She watched him curiously. "You don't hate little children, do you?" she asked finally.

"I don't hate kids," he said. "I'm just not used to them. I've been by myself for a long time."

"Did you love my mommy?"

That question was harder to answer. His broad shoulders rose and fell. "I thought she was beautiful. I wanted to marry her."

"She didn't like me," Sarah confided. "Can I really stay here? And I don't have to go back to Daddy Brad?"

"No, you don't have to go back. We'll have to do some adjusting, Sarah, but we'll get used to each other."

"I'm scared with the light off," she confessed.

"We'll leave a night-light on."

"What if a monster comes?" she asked.

"I'll kill it, of course," he reassured her with a smile.

She shifted under the covers. "Aren't you scared of monsters?"

"Nope."

She smiled for the first time. "Okay." She stared at him for a minute. "You have a scar on your face," she said, pointing to his right cheek.

His fingers touched it absently. "So I do." He'd long ago given up being sensitive about it, but he didn't like going into the way he'd gotten it. "Good night, sprout."

He didn't offer to read her a story or tell her one. In fact, he didn't know any he could tell a child. And he didn't tuck her in or kiss her. That would have been awkward. But Sarah didn't ask for those things or seem to need them.

Perhaps she hadn't had much affection. She acted very much like a child who'd been turned loose and not bothered with overmuch.

He went back downstairs and into his study, to finish the day's business that had been put on hold while he'd coped with Sarah's arrival. Tomorrow Mrs. Jackson would have to handle things. He couldn't steal time from a board meeting for one small child.

Jack's Corner was a medium-sized Oklahoma city, and Blake's office was in a new mall complex that was both modern and spacious. The next day, he and his board were just finalizing the financing for an upcoming project, when his secretary came in, flustered and apprehensive.

"Mr. Donavan, it's your housekeeper on the phone. Could you speak with her, please?"

"I told you not to interrupt me unless it was urgent, Daisy," he told the young blond woman curtly.

She hesitated nervously. "Please, sir?"

He got up and excused himself, striding angrily out into the waiting room to pick up the phone with a hard glare at Daisy.

"Okay, Amie, what's wrong?" he asked shortly.

"I quit."

"Oh, my God, not yet," he shot back. "Not until she starts dating, at least!"

"I can't wait that long, and I want my check today," Mrs. Jackson snorted.

"Why?"

She held out the receiver. "Do you hear that?"

He did. Sarah Jane was screaming her head off.

"Where are you?" he asked with cold patience.

"Meg Donaldson's dress shop downtown," she replied. "This has been going on for five minutes. I wouldn't let her buy the dress she wanted and I can't make her stop.''

"Smack her on the bottom," Blake said.

"Hit her in public?" She sounded as if he'd asked her to tie the child to a moving vehicle by her hair. "I won't!"

He said something under his breath. "All right, I'm on my way."

He hung up. "Tell the board to go ahead without me," he told Daisy shortly, grabbing his hat off the hat rack. "I have to go administrate a small problem."

"When will you be back, sir?" Daisy asked.

"God knows."

He closed the door behind him with a jerk, mentally consigning fatherhood and sissy housekeepers to the netherworld.

It took him ten minutes to get to the small children's boutique in town, and as luck would have it, there was one empty space in front that he could slide the Mercedes into. Next to his car was a sporty red Porsche with the top down. He paused for a moment to admire it and wonder about the owner.

"Oh, thank God." Mrs. Jackson almost fell on him when he walked into the shop. "Make her stop."

Sarah was lying on the floor, her face red and tear stained, her hair damp with sweat, her old dress rumpled from her exertions. She looked up at Blake and the tantrum died abruptly. "She won't buy me the frilly one," she moaned, pouting with a demure femininity.

My God, Blake thought absently, they learn how to do it almost before they can walk.

"Why won't you buy her the frilly one?" he asked an astonished Mrs. Jackson, the words slipping out before he could stop them, while Meg Donaldson smothered a smile behind her cupped hands at the counter.

Mrs. Jackson looked taken aback. She cleared her throat. "Well, it's expensive."

"I'm rich," he pointed out.

"Yes, but it's not suitable for playing in the backyard. She needs some jeans and tops and underthings."

"I need a dress to wear to parties," Sarah sobbed. "I never got to go to a party, but you can have one for me, and I can make friends."

He reached down and lifted her to her feet, then knelt in front of her. "I don't like tantrums," he said. "Next time Mrs. Jackson will spank you. In public," he added, glaring at the stoic housekeeper.

She turned beet red, and Mrs. Donaldson bent down beside the counter as if she were going to look for something and burst out laughing.

While Mrs. Jackson was searching for words, the shop door opened and two women came in. Elissa Roper was immediately recognizable. She was married to King Roper, a friend of Blake's.

"Blake!" Elissa smiled. "We haven't seen you lately. What are you and Mrs. Jackson doing in here? And who's this?"

"This is my daughter, Sarah Jane," Blake said, introducing the child. "We've just been having a tantrum."

"Speak for yourself," Mrs. Jackson sniffed. "I don't have tantrums. I just resign from jobs that have gotten too big for me."

"You're resigning, Mrs. Jackson? That would be one for the books, wouldn't it?" a soft, amused voice asked, and Blake's heart jumped.

He got slowly to his feet, oblivious to Sarah's curious stare, to come face to face with a memory.

Meredith Calhoun looked back at him with gray eyes that gave away nothing except faint humor. She was wearing a blue dress with a white jacket, and she looked expensive and sophisticated and lovely. Her figure had filled out over the years, and she was tall and exquisite, with full, high breasts and a narrow waist flaring to hips that were in exact proportion for her body. She had long legs encased in silk hose, and elegant feet in white sandals. And the sight of her made Blake ache in the most inconvenient way.

"Merry!" Mrs. Jackson enthused, and hugged her. "It's been so long!"

And it had been since Mrs. Jackson had made cake and cookies for her while she visited Blake's uncle, who was also her godfather.

She and the housekeeper had grown close. "Long enough, I guess, Amie," Meredith said as they stepped apart. "You haven't aged a day."

"You have," Mrs. Jackson said with a smile. "You're grown up."

"And famous," Elissa put in. "Bess—you remember my sister-in-law—and Meredith were in the same class at school and are still great friends. She's staying with Bess and Bobby."

"They've just bought the house next door to me," Blake replied, for something to say. He couldn't find the words to express what he felt when he looked at Meredith. So many years, so much pain. But whatever she'd felt for him was gone. That fact registered immediately.

"Has Nina come back with your daughter?" Elissa asked, trying not to appear poleaxed, which she was.

"Nina died earlier this year. Sarah Jane is living with me now." He dragged his eyes away from Meredith to turn his attention to his child. "You look terrible. Go to the rest room and wash your face."

"You come, too," Sarah said mutinously.

"No."

"I won't go!"

"I'll take her," Mrs. Jackson said in her best martyred tone.

"No! You won't let me buy the frilly dress!" Sarah turned her attention to the two curious onlookers. "She's in the paper," she said, her eyes on Meredith. "She writes books. My daddy said so."

Meredith managed not to look at Blake. The unexpected sight of him after so much time was enough to knock her speechless. Thank God she'd learned to mask her emotions and hadn't given herself away. The last thing she wanted to do was let Blake Donavan see that she had any vulnerability left.

Sarah walked over to Meredith, staring up at her with rapt fascination. "Can you tell stories?"

"Oh, I guess I can," she said, smiling at the child who was so much like Blake. "You've got red eyes, Sarah. You shouldn't cry."

"I want the frilly dress and a party and other little children to play with. It's very lonely, and they don't like me." She indicated Blake and Mrs. Jackson.

"One day, and she's advertising to the world that we're Jekyll and Hyde." Mrs. Jackson threw up her hands.

"Which one are you?" Blake returned, glaring at her.

"Jekyll, of course. I'm prettier than you are," Mrs. Jackson shot back.

"Just like old times," Elissa said with a sigh, "isn't it, Merry?"

Meredith wasn't listening. Sarah Jane had reached up and taken her hand.

"You can come with me," the little girl told Meredith. "I like her," she said to her father belligerently. "She smiles. I'll let her wash my face."

"Do you mind?" Blake asked Meredith, speaking to her for the first time since she'd entered the shop.

"I don't mind." She didn't look at him fully, then turned and let Sarah lead her into the small bathroom in the back of the shop.

"She's changed," Mrs. Jackson said to Mrs. Donaldson. "I hardly knew her."

"It's been a long time, you know. And she's a famous woman now, not the child who left us."

Blake walked away uncomfortably, staring at the dresses. Elissa moved closer to him while the other two women talked. She'd been a little afraid of Blake when she'd first met him years ago, but she'd gotten to know him better. He and King were friends and visited regularly.

"How long has Sarah been with you?" she asked him.

"Since yesterday afternoon," he replied dryly. "It seems like years. I guess I'll get used to her, but it's hard going right now. She's a handful."

"She's just frightened and alone," Elissa replied. "She'll improve when she has time to settle down and adjust."

"I may be bankrupt by then," he mused. "I had to walk out of a board meeting. And all because Sarah Jane wanted a frilly dress."

"Why don't you buy it for her and she can come to my Danielle's birthday party next week? It will be nice for her to meet children her own age."

"She'll sit on the cake and wreck the house," he groaned.

"No, she won't. She's just a little girl."

"She wrecked my living room in just under ten minutes," he assured her.

"It takes mine five minutes to do that." Elissa grinned. "It's normal."

He stared toward the bathroom. Meredith and Sarah Jane were just coming out. "There are people in the world who have more than one," he murmured. "Do you suppose they're sane?"

Elissa laughed. "Yes. You'll understand it all one day."

"Look what Merry gave me!" Sarah enthused, showing Blake a snowy white handkerchief. "And it's all mine! It has lace!"

Blake shook his head as she turned abruptly and grabbed the dress she'd been screaming about. "It's mine. I want it. Oh, please." She changed tactics, staring up pie eyed at her daddy. "It will go so nicely with my new handkerchief."

Blake laughed and then caught himself. He looked at Mrs. Jackson. "What do you think?"

"I think that if you buy Sarah Jane that dress I'm going to put it on you," the older woman replied in a hunted tone.

"You really shouldn't give in because children have tantrums, Blake," Mrs. Donaldson volunteered. "I know. I raised four."

He stared at Mrs. Jackson. "You started this. Why would you tell her she couldn't have the damned thing in the first place?"

"I told you, it was too expensive for her to play in."

"She'll need a dress to come to Danielle's party," Elissa broke in.

"Now see what you've done," Blake growled at Mrs. Jackson.

"I won't take her shopping ever again. You can just let somebody else run your company and do it yourself," Mrs. Jackson grumbled.

"I don't know what to think of a woman who can't manage to buy a dress for one small child."

"That isn't just one small child, that's one small Donavan, and nobody could say she isn't your daughter!" Mrs. Jackson said.

Blake felt an unexpected surge of pleasure at the words. He looked down at the child who looked so much like him and had to agree that she did have some of his better qualities. Stubborn determination. Not to mention good taste.

"You can have the dress, Sarah," he told her, and was rewarded by a smile so delightful he'd have sold his Mercedes to buy the damned thing for her no matter what it cost.

"Oh, thank you!" Sarah gushed.

"You'll be sorry," Mrs. Jackson said.

"You can shut up," he told her. "It's your fault."

"You said to take her shopping, you didn't say what to buy," she reminded him huffily. "And I'm going home."

"Then go on. And don't burn lunch," he called after her.

"I couldn't burn a bologna sandwich if I tried, and that's all you'll get from me today!"

"I'll fire you!"

"Thank God!"

Blake glared at Mrs. Donaldson and Elissa, who were trying not to smile. This byplay between Blake and Mrs. Jackson was old hat to them, and they found it amusing. Meredith's expression was less revealing. She was looking at Sarah and Blake wished he could see her eyes.

But she turned away. "We'd better get on," she told Elissa. "Bess will be waiting for us to pick her up at the beauty parlor."

"Okay," Elissa grinned. "Just let me get those socks for Danielle and I'll be ready."

She did, which left Meredith stranded with Blake and his daughter.

"Isn't it pretty?" Sarah sighed, pirouetting with the dress held in front of her. "I look like a fairy princess."

"Not quite," Blake said. "You'll need shoes, and some clothes to play in, too."

"Okay." She ran to the other racks and started looking through them.

"Is it normal for them to be so clothes conscious at this age?" Blake asked, turning his attention to Meredith.

"I don't know," she said uncomfortably. His unblinking green-eyed gaze was making her remember too much pain. "I haven't been around children very much. I must go. . . ."

He touched her arm, and was astonished to find that she jerked away from his touch and stared fully at him with eyes that burned with resentment and pain and anger.

"So, you haven't forgotten," he said under his breath.

"Did you really think I ever would?" she asked on a shaky laugh. "You were the reason I never came back here. I almost didn't come this time, either, but I was tired of hiding."

He didn't know what to say. Her reaction was unexpected. He'd imagined that she might have some bitterness, but not this much. He searched what he could see of her face, looking for something he knew he wasn't going to find anymore.

"You've changed," he said quietly.

Her eyes looked up into his, and there was a flash of cold anger there. "Oh, yes, I've changed. I've grown up. That should reassure you. I won't be chasing after you like a lovesick puppy this time."

The reference stung, and she'd meant it to. He'd accused her of chasing him and more, after the reading of the will.

But being reminded of the past only made him bitter, and he hit back. "Thank God," he said with a mocking smile. "Could I have that in writing?"

"Go to hell," she said under her breath.

That, coming from shy little Meredith, floored him. He didn't even have a comeback.

Sarah came running up with an armload of things. "Look, aren't they pretty! Can I have them all?" she asked the scowling man beside Meredith.

"Sure," he said absently.

Meredith turned away from him, smiling. It was the first time in memory that she'd ever fought back—or for that matter, said anything to him that wasn't respectful and worshipful. What a delightful surprise to find he no longer intimidated her.

"Ready to go?" Meredith asked Elissa.

"Sure am. See you, Blake!"

"But you can't go." Sarah ran to Meredith and caught her skirt. "You're my friend."

The child couldn't know how that hurt—to have Blake's child, the child she might have borne him, cling to her. She knelt in front of Sarah, disengaging the small hand. "I have to go now. But I'll see you again, Sarah. Okay?"

Sarah looked lost. "You're nice. Nobody else smiles at me."

"Mrs. Jackson will smile at you tonight, I promise," Blake told the child. "Or she'll never smile again," he added under his breath.

"You don't smile," Sarah accused him.

"My face would break," he assured her. "Now get your things and we'll go home."

She sighed. "Okay." She looked up at Meredith. "Will you come to see me?"

Meredith went white. Go into that house again, where Blake had humiliated and hurt her? God forbid!

"You can come to see Danielle, Sarah," Elissa interrupted, and Meredith knew then that Elissa had heard the whole story from King. She was running interference, bless her.

"Who's Dan—Danielle?" Sarah asked.

"My daughter. She's four."

"I'm almost four," Sarah said. "Can she say nursery rhymes? I know all of them. 'Humpty Dumpty sat on the wall, Humpty Dumpty—'"

"I'll give your Daddy a call and he can bring you down to Bess's house, where Meredith is staying. Bess is my sister-in-law, and Danielle and I go to see her sometimes."

"I'd like to have a friend," Sarah agreed. "Could we do that?" she asked her father.

Blake was watching Meredith shift uncomfortably. "Sure we can," he said, just to irritate her.

Meredith turned away, her heart going like an overwound watch, her eyes restless and frightened. The very last thing she wanted was to have to cope with Blake.

"Bye, Merry!" Sarah called.

"Goodbye, Sarah Jane," she murmured, and forced a smile, but she wouldn't look at Blake.

He said the appropriate things as Elissa followed Meredith out the door, but the fact that Meredith wouldn't look at him cut like a knife.

He watched Meredith climb in under the wheel of the red Porsche. It didn't seem like the kind of car she'd drive, but she wasn't the girl she'd been. His eyes narrowed. He wondered if she was still as innocent as before, or if some man had taught her all the sweet ways to make love. His face hardened at the thought. No one had touched her until he had. But he'd been rough and he'd frightened her.

He hadn't really meant to. The feel and taste of her had knocked him off balance, and at the time he hadn't been experienced himself. Nina had been his first woman, but his first real intimacy, even if it had been relatively chaste, had been with Meredith. Even after all the years in between, he could feel her mouth, taste its sweetness. He could see the soft alabaster of her breasts when he'd unbuttoned the top of her dress. He groaned silently. That was when he'd lost his senses—seeing her like that. He wondered if she knew how green he'd been in those days, and decided that she was too inexperienced herself to realize it. He'd wanted Meredith to the point of madness, and things had just gotten out of hand. But to a shy young virgin, his ardor must have seemed frightening.

He turned back to his daughter with memories of the past darkening his eyes. It seemed so long ago that the rain had found him in the stable and Meredith had come in looking for his uncle....

Three

It had been late spring that day five years ago, and Blake had been helping one of the men doctor a sick horse in the stable. Meredith had come along just in time to see the second man leave. Blake was still there. She'd come to ask where his uncle was, but it was a rainy day, and she and Blake had been caught in the barn while it stormed outside.

Blake had hungrily watched Meredith as she stood on her tiptoes to look toward the house. She was wearing a white sundress that buttoned up the front, and as she stretched, every line of her body had been emphasized and her dress had ridden up, displaying most of her long legs.

The sight of those slim, elegant legs and the sensuous curve of her body had caught him in the stomach like a body blow, and he'd stood there staring. It shouldn't have affected him. He had Nina, who was blond and beautiful and who loved him. Meredith was plain and shy and not at all the kind of woman who could attract him. But as he'd looked at her, his body had quickened and the shock of it had moved him helplessly toward where she stood in the wide doorway, just out of the path of the rain.

Meredith had heard him, or perhaps sensed him, because she turned, her eyes faintly covetous before she lowered them. "It's really coming down, isn't it?" she asked hesitantly. "I was just about to go home, but I needed to ask your Uncle Dan some more questions."

"You're always around these days," he'd remarked, half-angry because his body was playing cruel tricks on him.

She'd blushed. "He's helping me with some articles for the school paper, and I'm going to do a book with the same information," she'd begun.

"Book!" He scoffed at that. "You're barely twenty. What makes you think you've learned enough to write books? You haven't even started to live."

Her head came up and there had been a flash of anger in her pale gray eyes, which was instantly disguised. "You make me sound like a toddler."

"You look like one occasionally," he remarked with faint humor, noting the braid of her hair, which she'd tied with a ribbon. "And I'm almost twelve years older than you are." He pushed away from the barn door, noticing the faint hunger in her face as he went toward her.

The hunger was what touched him. It hadn't occurred to him that women besides Nina might find him physically attractive. He had that damned scar down one cheek, thanks to Meredith, and it made him look like a renegade. His arrogance didn't soften the impression.

He looked down his nose at Meredith when he was less than a foot from her, watching the expressions play across her face. It was a pretty good bet that she was innocent, and if she'd been kissed, probably it hadn't been often or seriously. That, at least, made him feel confident. She didn't have anyone to compare him with.

His eyes went to her soft bow of a mouth, and with an impulse he didn't even understand at the time, he tilted her chin up with a lean hand and bent to brush his lips over hers.

"Blake . . . !" she gasped.

He hadn't known if it was fear or shock . . . hadn't cared. The first contact with her mouth had caused a frightening surge of desire in his lean body. "Don't back away now," he bit off against her soft lips. "Come here."

He'd pulled her against him and his mouth had grown rough and hungry. Even now, five years later, he could feel the soft yielding of her body in his arms, smell the scent of her as she strained upward and gave him her mouth with such warm eagerness. He could hear the rain beating on the stable roof, and the soft sounds of a cow settling down in the darkness beyond where they stood silhouetted against the driving rain.

Blake had been amazed by the tentative response he got from her lips. That shy nibbling drove him over the edge. He eased her back against the wall of the barn, out of sight, with his mouth still covering hers. Then he let his body slide down against her so that his hips were pressing feverishly against hers, his chest crushing her soft young breasts.

He felt her quickened breathing, heard the soft "no!" as he felt for and found one firm breast and touched it through her clothing. The feel of her made him wild. He remembered the white-hot flames that had consumed him with the intimate touch. He'd wanted her with a shuddering passion and his mouth had grown more and more demanding. She gave in to him all at once, her body relaxing, shivering, her mouth shyly responding. His tongue pushed gently inside her lips and she stiffened, but she didn't try to pull away.

Confident now, his fingers worked at buttons and he lifted his head just fractionally to look down at what they uncovered. Her breasts were bare under the dress and he groaned as he bent to brush his mouth against them. He felt her gasp and her hands gripped his arms hard. The silky taste of her body stripped him of control entirely, the feel of her skin against his face made him wild. His hands grew roughly intimate in passion and his mouth closed hungrily over one firm breast.

What might have happened then was anyone's guess. He hardly heard Meredith's frantic voice. It wasn't until he caught the sound of a car driving up that his sanity returned.

He lifted his head, breathing fiercely, in time to see Meredith's eyes full of fear. He realized belatedly what he'd done. He took a sharp breath and levered himself back up, away from her, his body in torment with unsatisfied desire, his eyes smoldering as they met hers.

She blushed furiously as she fumbled buttons into buttonholes, making herself decent again. And only then did he realize how intimate the embrace had gotten. He didn't know what had possessed him. He'd frightened her and himself, because it was the first time he'd ever lost control like that. But, then, he hadn't been experienced, he realized now. Not until he and Nina were married. His first taste of sensual pleasure had been with Meredith that day in the stable.

He didn't speak—he was too shocked. The sudden arrival of his uncle had been a godsend at the time, but later it dawned on him that his uncle had guessed what had happened between Blake and Meredith and had altered his will to capitalize on it. His favorite godchild and his nephew—he would have considered them a perfect match. But Blake hadn't thought of it at the time. He'd been so drunk on Meredith's soft mouth that he'd almost gone after her when she mumbled some excuse and ran out into the rain as he and his uncle watched her.

Then, within days, his uncle was dead of a heart attack. Blake had been crushed. The sense of loneliness he felt when it happened was almost too great for words. Meredith had been around, with her parents, but he'd hardly noticed with Nina clinging to him, pretending sympathy. And then, suddenly they were reading the will. Blake was engaged to Nina, but still trying to cope with the turbulent emotions Meredith had aroused in him. The will was read, and he learned that Uncle Dan had left twenty percent of the stock in his real estate companies to Meredith. The only way Blake could have it would be by marrying her.

He had forty-nine percent of the stock, but his cousins had thirty-one shares between them. And although one of the cousins down in Texas would have sided with him in a proxy fight if Meredith sided against him, he could lose everything. Nina had laughed. He still remembered the look on her face as she scrutinized Meredith in a manner too contemptuous for words.

Blake had done much worse. The realization that his uncle had tried to control his life even from the grave and the embarrassment of having his haughty cousins snicker at him was just too much.

"Marry her?" he'd said slowly after the will had been read, rising out of his chair to confront Meredith in the dead silence that followed. "My God, marry that plain, dull, shadow of a woman? I'd rather lose the real estate companies, the money and my left leg than marry her!"

He'd moved closer to Meredith, watching her cringe and go pale at the humiliation of having him say those things so loudly in front of the family. "No dice, Meredith," he said with venom. "Take the stock and go to hell with it. I don't want you!"

He'd expected her to burst into tears and run out of the room, but she hadn't. Deathly pale, shaking so hard she could barely stand, she lowered her eyes, turned away and walked out with dignity far beyond her twenty years. It had shamed him later to remember her stiff pride and his own loss of control that had prompted the outburst. The cousin from Texas had glared at him with black eyes and walked out without another word, leaving him alone with Nina and the other cousins, who subsequently filed suit to take control of the real estate companies from him.

But Nina had smiled and clung to him and promised heaven, because she was sure he'd get the stock back somehow. She'd advised him to talk to the lawyer.

He had. But the only way to get the stock back, apparently, was to marry Meredith or break the will. Both were equally impossible.

He was still smoldering when he found Meredith coming out the back door. She'd been in the kitchen saying goodbye to Mrs. Jackson.

She was pale and unusually quiet, and she looked as if she didn't want to stop. But he'd gotten in front of her in the deserted, shaded backyard and refused to let her pass.

"I don't want the shares," she said, without looking at him. "I never did. I knew nothing about what your uncle had planned, and I wouldn't have gone through with it if I had."

"Wouldn't you?" he demanded coldly. "Maybe you saw a chance to marry a rich man. Your family is poor."

"There are worse things than being poor," she replied quietly. "And people who marry for money earn it, as you'll find out one day."

"I will?" He caught her arms roughly. "What do you mean?"

"I mean that Nina wants what you have, not what you are," she replied with a sad smile.

"Nina loves me," he said.

"No."

"What does it matter to you, anyway?" he growled. "I haven't been able to turn around without running into you for the past two months. You're always here, getting in the way! What's the matter, did you decide that one kiss wasn't enough, and you're hot for more?"

In fact, it had been the other way around. He'd wanted her so desperately that his mind had gone into hiding, behind the anger he used to disguise the hunger that was driving him mad.

He pulled her into his arms, angry at life and circumstances, ignoring her faint struggles. "God forbid that you should go away with nothing," he added. And he kissed her with all his fury and frustration in his lips. He accused her of chasing him, of wanting his uncle's money. And then he turned around and walked off, leaving her in tears.

His eyes closed as he came back to the present, hating the memory, hating his cruelty. He'd been a different man then, a colder, less feeling man. It had irritated him that Meredith disturbed him physically, that he could be aroused by the sound of her voice, by the sight of her. Because of what he thought he felt for Nina, he'd pushed his growing attraction to Meredith out of his mind. Nina loved him and Meredith just wanted what he had—or so he'd been sure at the time. Now he knew better, and it was too late.

Those few minutes he'd made love to Meredith in the stable that long-ago afternoon had been the sweetest and saddest of his entire life. He'd been cruel after the will was read because he'd felt betrayed by his uncle and by her. But he'd also been sad, because he wanted Meredith far more than Nina. He'd given his word to Nina that he was going to marry her, and honor made him stick to it. So he'd forced Meredith to run away to remove the temptation from his path. He'd known deep inside that he couldn't have resisted Meredith much longer. And he had no right to her.

It struck him as odd that he'd lost control with Meredith. He'd never lost it with Nina, although he'd had a lukewarm kind of feeling for her that had grown out of her adoration and teasing. But what he'd felt with Meredith had been fire and storm. The last time he'd seen her, he'd raged at her that she'd tempted him by following him around like a lovesick puppy, and that had been the last straw. She'd run then, all right, and she hadn't stopped. Not for five years. A week after she left, an attorney brought him the stock, legally signed over to him without a single request for money. Nina had been delighted, and she'd led him right to the altar. He'd been so cut up by his own conscience about what he'd done to Meredith that he hadn't protested, even though his yen for Nina had all but left him.

He went through the motions of making love to Nina, but it wasn't at all satisfying to him. And she always smiled at him so lovingly when they were in bed together. Smiling. Until the day the court battle started, initiated by his cousins, and he was backed into a corner that Nina didn't think he'd get out of. So she left him and divorced him, and he'd had years to regret his own foolishness.

Meredith's attitude toward him in the shop hadn't really come as a surprise. He knew how badly he'd hurt her that day, frightened her. Probably she'd never had a lover or wanted one, because if appearances were anything to go by, he'd left some bad scars. He felt even guiltier about that. But it didn't seem as if he were going to get close enough to tell her the truth about what had happened—even if his pride would allow it.

And anyway, she'd made her feelings about the house clear. She wouldn't voluntarily set foot in it. He sighed heavily. Incredible, he thought, how a man could become his own worst enemy. Looking back, he knew his uncle had been right. If he'd married Meredith, she'd have loved him, and in time he might have been able to love her back. As things stood, that was something he'd never know.

Down the road at Bobby and Bess's house, Meredith Calhoun was halfheartedly watching a movie on Bess's VCR as she tried to come to grips with the unexpected confrontation with Blake.

She felt shaky inside. The sight of Blake, with his jet black hair, green eyes and arrogant, mocking smile, had twisted her heart. Over the years she'd tried to force herself to go out on dates, see other men. But it hadn't worked. She couldn't bear for any man to do more than kiss her, and even the kisses were bitter and unpleasant after Blake's. One part of her was afraid of Blake because of what he'd done to her, but another part remembered the first kiss in the stable, the sweet, slow hunger that had flared between them like summer lightning. And because of that kiss, no other man had ever been able to stir her.

Blake's daughter had come as the biggest surprise. Meredith hadn't known about the child. It seemed, from what Elissa said, that nobody had. Sarah Jane was a quirk of fate, and she wondered if Blake still loved Nina. If he did, Sarah Jane would be a comfort to him. But when he'd said that Nina was dead, it had been without a scrap of emotion in his face or his eyes. He didn't seem to care one way or another. That was strange, because he'd been so adamant about marrying Nina, so certain that she loved him.

Meredith got up, oblivious to the television, and began to wander restlessly around Bess's big living room. She stopped in front of the picture window. Beyond it, on a rise a few hundred yards away, was Blake's house. She sighed, remembering the happy times she'd had there before the will had been read. Blake had always seemed to resent her, but that day in the stable had been full of soft magic. Because of it, she'd actually expected something more from him than anger. She'd dreamed afterward that he'd left Nina and discovered that he loved Meredith and couldn't live without her. Dreams.

She laughed with a new cynicism. That would be the day, when Blake Donavan would feel anything but dislike for her. He hadn't been openly antagonistic today, but he'd verged on it just before she left the store. Sarah liked her and it was going to be difficult to keep the child at bay without hurting her. Meredith had a feeling that Sarah Jane's young life hadn't been a happy one. She didn't act like a contented child, and apparently she'd only been with Blake and Mrs. Jackson for a day or so. Meredith had wondered why, but hadn't dared ask Blake.

Sarah reminded her of herself at that age, a poor little kid from the wrong side of the tracks, with no brothers or sisters and parents who worked themselves into early graves trying to make a living with the sweat of their brows. Bess had been her only friend, and Bess had it even worse than she did at home. The two of them had become close as children and remained close as adults. So when Bess had invited Meredith, with Bobby's blessing, to come and stay for a few weeks, she'd welcomed the rest from work and routine.

She hadn't consciously considered that Blake was going to be a very big part of her visit. She'd actually thought she could come to Jack's Corner without having to see him at all. Which was silly. King and Elissa and Bess and Bobby all knew him, and Blake and King were best friends. She wondered if maybe she'd rationalized things because of Blake, because she'd wanted to see him again, to see if her fears had been real or just manifestations of unrequited love and sorrow. She wanted to see if looking at him could still make her knees go weak and her heart run away.

Well, now she knew. It could. And if she had any sense of self-preservation, she was going to have to keep some distance from him. She couldn't risk letting Blake get close to her heart a second time. Once had been enough—more than enough. She'd just avoid him, she told herself, and everything would be all right.

But avoiding him turned out to be a forlorn hope, because Sarah Jane liked Meredith and contrived to get her father to call Elissa about that visit she'd mentioned.

Blake listened to the request with mixed feelings. Sarah Jane was beginning to settle down a little, although she was still belligerent and not an overly joyful addition to the household. Mrs. Jackson was coping well enough, but she'd vanish the minute Blake came home from work, leaving him to try and talk to his sullen young daughter. He knew that the situation needed a woman's touch, but Mrs. Jackson wasn't the woman. Meredith already liked Sarah, and Sarah was drawn to her. If he could get Meredith to befriend the child, it would make his life easier. But in another way, he was uncertain about trying to force himself and Sarah on Meredith. After having seen how frightened she still was of him, how bitter she was about the past, he might open old wounds and rub salt in them. He didn't want to hurt Meredith, but Sarah Jane was driving him nuts, and he needed help.

"You have to call 'lissa," Sarah Jane said firmly, her mutinous mouth pouting up at him. "She promised I could play with her little girl. I want to see Mer'dith, too. She likes me." She glared at him, her eyes so like his only in her youthful face. "You don't like me."

"I explained that to you," he said with exaggerated patience as he perched on the corner of his desk. "We don't know each other."

"You don't ever come home," she said, sighing. "And Mrs. Jackson doesn't like me, either."

"She's not used to children, Sarah, any more than I am." A corner of his mouth twisted. "Look, sprout, I'll try to spend more time with you. But you've got to understand that I'm a busy man. A lot of people depend on me."

"Can't you call 'lissa?" she persisted. "Please?" she added. "Please?"

He found himself picking up the telephone. Sarah had a knack for getting under his skin. He was beginning to get used to the sound of her voice, the running footsteps in the morning, the sound of cartoons and children's programs coming from the living room. Maybe in time he and Sarah would get along better. They were still in the squaring off and glaring stages right now, and she was every bit as stubborn as he was.

He talked to Elissa, who was delighted to comply with Sarah's request. She promised to set things up for the following morning because it was Saturday and Blake could bring Sarah down to Bess's house. But first she wanted to check with Bess and make sure it was all right.

Blake and Sarah both waited for the phone to ring.
Blake wondered how Meredith was going to feel about it,
but apparently she didn't mind, because Elissa had called
back within five minutes and said that Bess would be
expecting the child about ten o'clock. Not only that, Sarah
was invited to spend the day.

"I can spend the day?" Sarah asked, brightening.

"We'll see." Blake was noncommittal. "Why don't you
find something to play with?"

Sarah shrugged. "I don't have any toys. I had a teddy
bear, but he got lost and Daddy Brad wouldn't let me look
for him before they brought me here."

His eyes narrowed. "Don't call him that again," he said
gruffly. "He isn't your father. I am."

Sarah's eyes widened at his tone, and he felt uncomfortable for having said anything at all.

"Can I call you 'Daddy'?" Sarah asked after a long
minute.

Blake's breath caught in his throat. He shifted. "I don't
care," he said impassively. In fact, he did care. He cared
like hell.

"Okay," she said, and went off to the kitchen to see if
Mrs. Jackson had any more cookies.

Blake frowned, thinking about what she'd said about
toys. Surely a child of almost four still played with them.
He'd have to ask Elissa. She'd know about toys and little
girls.

The next morning, Sarah dressed herself in her new frilly
dress and her shoes and went downstairs. Blake had to bite
his lip to keep from howling. She had the dress on backward and unbuttoned. She had on frilly socks, but one was
yellow and one was pink. Her hair was unruly, and the
picture she made was of chaos, not femininity.

"Come here, sprout, and let's get the dress on properly," he said.

She glared at him. "It's all right."

"No, it's not." He stood. "Don't argue with me, kid. I'm twice your size."

"I don't have to mind you," she said.

"Yes, you do. Or else."

"Or else what?" she challenged.

He stared down at her. "Or else you'll stay home today."

She grimaced and stared down at the carpet. "Okay."

He helped her turn the dress around and cursed under his breath while he did up buttons that were hard for his big, lean hands to work. He finally got them fixed, then took her upstairs, where he searched until he found matching socks and then brushed her straight hair until it looked soft and shiny.

She turned before he finished, looking small and oddly vulnerable on the vanity stool, and her green eyes met his. "I never had any little children to play with. My mommy said I made her nervous."

He didn't say anything, but he could imagine Nina being uncomfortable around children.

"Can I stay here?" Sarah asked unexpectedly, and there was a flash of real fear in her eyes. "You won't make me go away, will you?"

He had to bite down hard to keep back a harsh curse. "No, I won't make you go away," he said after a minute. "You're my daughter."

"You didn't want me when I was a baby," she accused mutinously.

"I didn't know about you," he said, sitting down and talking to her very seriously, as if she were already an adult. "I didn't know I had a little girl. Now I do. You're a Donavan, and this is your place in the world. Here, with me."

"And I can live here forever?"

"Until you grow up, anyway," he promised. His green eyes narrowed. "You aren't going to start crying or anything, are you?" he asked, because her eyes were glistening.

That snapped her out of it. She glared at him. "I never cry. I'm brave."

"I guess you've had to be, haven't you?" he murmured absently. He stood. "Well, if we're going, let's go. And you be on your best behavior. I'm going to tell Bess to swat you if you don't mind her."

"Mer'dith won't let her hit me," she said smugly. "She's my friend. Do you have any friends?"

"One or two," he said, holding her hand as they went down the long staircase.

"Do they come to play with you?" she asked seriously. "And could they play with me, too?"

He chuckled deep in his throat, trying to imagine King Roper sitting cross-legged on the living room carpet, dressing a doll.

"I don't think so," he replied. "They're grown-ups."

"Oh. Grown-ups are too big to play, I guess. I don't want to grow up. I wish I had a doll."

"What kind of doll?" he asked.

"A pretty one with long golden hair and pretty dresses. I could talk to her. And a teddy bear," she said sadly. "I want a teddy bear just like Mr. Friend. I miss Mr. Friend. He used to sleep with me. I'm ascared of the dark," she added.

"Yes, I know," he murmured, having had to help Mrs. Jackson get her to bed every night and chase out the monsters before she closed her eyes.

"Lots of monsters live in my room," she informed him. "You have to kill them every night, don't you?"

"So far, I'm ahead by one monster," he reassured her.

"You're awful big," she said, eyeing him with an unblinking scrutiny. "I bet you weigh one million pounds."

"Not quite."

"I'm ten feet tall," she said, going on tiptoe.

He led her out the door, calling goodbye to Mrs. Jackson. It seemed natural to hold her hand and smile at her chatter. There was magic in a child, even a hard case like this one. He wondered if security would soften her, and doubted it. She had spirit and inner strength. Those qualities pleased him. She'd need them if she lived with him.

Bess and Bobby's house was a split-level brick with exquisite landscaping and a small thicket of trees that separated their property from Blake's. In the driveway were Elissa's gray Lincoln, Meredith's red Porsche convertible and the blue Mercedes that Bess drove. Blake parked behind them on the long driveway and helped Sarah out.

She was at the front door before he reached it, excited as the door opened and a little blond girl about her age shyly greeted her.

"This is Danielle, Sarah. She's looked forward to meeting you," Elissa said with a smile. "Hi, Blake. Come on in."

He took off his gray Stetson and stood in the hall while Sarah went into the living room with Danielle, who'd brought a box of toys with her.

Sarah's eyes lit up like a Christmas tree, and she exclaimed over every single one of Danielle's things, as if she'd never seen toys before. She sat down on the carpet and handled each one gingerly, turning it over and examining it and telling Danielle how beautiful the dolls were.

"She doesn't have any toys," Blake told Elissa with a worried frown. "She seems so mature sometimes. I didn't realize..."

"Parenthood takes time," Elissa assured him. "Don't expect to learn everything at once."

"I don't think I've learned anything yet," he confessed. He frowned as he watched his daughter. "I expected her to push Danielle around and try to take her toys away. She isn't the easiest child to get along with."

"She's a frightened child," Elissa replied. "Underneath there are some sweet qualities. You see, she's playing very nicely, and she isn't causing trouble."

"Yet," Blake murmured, waiting for the explosion to come.

His head turned as Meredith came down the hall. She hesitated momentarily, then joined them.

"Bess is getting coffee," she said quietly. She was wearing a pale green sundress that slashed squarely over her high breasts, and her hair was loose, waving around her shoulders. She looked younger this way, and Blake almost sighed with memories.

"Will you stay and have a cup with us?" Elissa asked him.

"I guess so," he agreed. His eyes hadn't left Meredith.

She averted her gaze and started into the living room, too vulnerable to risk letting him see how easily he could get to her with that level, unblinking stare.

"Mer'dith!" Sarah jumped up, all eyes and laughing smile, and ran with her arms open to be picked up and hugged warmly. "Oh, Mer'dith, Daddy brought me to see Dani and he's going to get me another Mr. Friend and he says I can have a doll! Oh, he's just the nicest daddy...!"

Blake looked as if someone had poured ice into his shirt. He stared at the child blankly. She'd just called him

'Daddy' for the first time, and something stirred in the region of his heart, making him feel warm and needed. It was a new feeling, as if he weren't totally alone anymore.

"That's nice, darling," Meredith was telling the child. She let her down and knelt beside her, smiling as she pushed back Sarah's unruly hair. "You look very pretty this morning. I like your new dress."

"It's very pretty," Danielle agreed. She was dressed in slacks and a shirt for playing, but she didn't make fun of Sarah's dress. She was a quiet child and sweet natured.

"I put it on backward, but Daddy fixed it for me." She smiled at Meredith. "Can you stay and play with us? We can play with dolls."

"I wish I could," Meredith said, nervous because Blake was watching her so closely. She was frantic for a way out of the house, away from him. "But I have to go into town to the library and do some research."

"I thought this was supposed to be a holiday," Bess said as she came in with a tray of coffee and cake. "You're here to rest, not to work."

Meredith smiled at her lovely blond friend. "I know. But I'm not comfortable if I don't have something to do. I won't be long."

"I could drive you," Blake volunteered.

She blanched and started to refuse, but Elissa and Bess jumped in and teased and cajoled until they made it impossible for her to turn down his offer.

She wanted to scream. Alone with Blake in his car? What would they say to each other? What could they say to each other that wouldn't involve them in another terrible argument? The past was very much in Meredith's thoughts, and she wasn't about to risk a repeat of it. But she'd allowed herself to be manipulated by him, and it looked as though she wasn't going to be able to get out of going to town with him. Now, she thought, what are you going to do?

Four

―――――

Blake could sense the nervousness in Meredith as she sat stiffly in the seat beside him while he started the car. In the old days, he might have made some cutting remark about it, but the days were gone when he'd deliberately try to hurt her.

"Fasten your seat belt," he said, noticing that she hadn't.

"Oh." She did it absently. "I usually remember in my own car," she said with faint defensiveness.

"Don't you ever ride with other people?"

"Not if I can help it," she murmured, glancing at his hard profile as he backed the car out of the driveway and pulled onto the highway.

"Are your friends bad drivers," he asked, "or is it that you just don't like being out of control?"

"Who drives you, if we're going to throw stones?" she asked with a pleasantly cool smile.

His mouth twitched. "Nobody."

She toyed with her white leather purse, twisting the thin strap around her fingers while she stared out the window at the green crops and grazing cattle on the way to Jack's Corner. The flat horizon seemed to stretch forever, just as it did back in Texas.

"Sarah engineered this get-together," he remarked. "She damned near drove me crazy until I phoned Elissa to arrange it." His green eyes touched her stiff profile and went back to the road. "She likes you."

"I like her, too," she said quietly. "She's a sweet child."

" 'Sweet' isn't exactly the word I'd choose."

"Can't you see what's under the belligerence?" she asked solemnly, and turned in the seat slightly so that she could look at him without having to move her head. "She's frightened."

"Elissa said that, too. What is she frightened of? Me?" he asked.

"I don't know what," she said. "I don't know anything about the situation, and I'm not prying." She stared at the clasp on her purse and unsnapped it. "She doesn't look like a happy child. And the way she enthused over Danielle's things, I'd almost bet she's hardly had a toy in her life."

"I'm a bachelor," he muttered angrily. "I don't know about children and toys and dresses. My God, until a few days ago I didn't even know I was a father."

Meredith wanted to ask why Nina had kept Sarah's existence a secret, but she didn't feel comfortable talking about such personal things with him. She had to remember that he was the enemy, in a very real sense. She couldn't afford to show any interest in his life.

He was already figuring that out by himself. She either didn't care about how he'd found out, or she wasn't going to risk asking him. He wished he smoked. She made him nervous and he didn't have anything to do with his hands except grip the steering wheel as he drove.

"Mrs. Jackson is one of your biggest fans," he said, moving the conversation away from Sarah.

"Is she? I'm glad."

"I guess you make a fair living from what you do, if that Porsche is any indication."

She lifted her eyes to his face, letting them run over his craggy features. The broken nose was prominent, as was that angry scar down his cheek. She felt a surge of warmth remembering how he'd come by that scar. Her eyes fell.

"I make a good living," she replied. "I'm rather well-to-do, in fact. So if you think I came home looking for a rich husband, you're well off the mark. You're perfectly safe, Blake," she added coldly. "I'm the last woman on earth you'll have to ward off these days."

He had to clamp down hard on his teeth to keep from saying what came naturally. The past was dead, but she had every reason for digging it up and throwing it at him. He had to remember that. If she'd done to him what he'd done to her, he'd have wanted a much worse revenge than a few pithy remarks.

"I don't flatter myself that you'd come looking for me without a loaded gun, Meredith," he returned. He glanced at her, noting the surprise on her face.

She looked out the window again, puzzled and confused.

He pulled the Mercedes into the parking lot behind the library and shut off the engine.

"Don't do that. Not yet," he said when she started to open the door. "Let's talk for a minute."

"What do we have to say to each other?" she asked distantly. "We're different people now. Let the past take care of itself. I don't want to remember—" she stopped short when she realized what she'd blurted out.

"I know." He leaned back against his door, his pale green eyes under thick black lashes searching her face. "I guess you think I was rough with you in the stable deliberately. And I said some cruel things, didn't I?"

She flushed and averted her eyes, focusing on his chest. "Yes," she said, taut with embarrassment and vivid memories.

"It wasn't planned," he replied. "And what I said wasn't what I felt." He sighed heavily. "I wanted you, Meredith. Wanted you with a passion that drove me right over the edge. But I'm sorry I hurt you."

"Nothing happened," she said icily. In her nervousness her hands gripped her purse like talons.

"Only because my uncle came driving up at the right moment," he said bitterly. He studied her set features. "You'll never know how it's haunted me all these long years. I was deliberately rough with you the day the will was read because guilt was eating me up. I'd promised to marry Nina, my cousins were talking lawsuits...and on top of all that, I'd just discovered that I wanted you to the point of madness."

"I don't want to talk about it," she said under her breath. Her eyes closed in pain. "I can't...talk about it."

His eyes narrowed. "I thought Nina loved me," he said gently. "She said she did, and all her actions seemed to prove it. I thought you only wanted the inheritance, that I was a stepping stone for you, a way to escape the poverty you'd lived in all your young life." He ran his fingers lightly over the steering wheel. "It wasn't until after...that day, that the lawyer told me why my uncle had wanted me to marry you." His eyes slid to catch hers and hold them. "I didn't know you were in love with me."

Her face lost every vestige of color. She sat and stared at him, her pride in rags, her deepest secret naked to his scrutiny.

"It wouldn't have made the slightest bit of difference," she choked out. "Nothing would have changed. Except that you'd have used the information to humiliate me even more. You and Nina would have laughed yourselves sick over that irony."

The cynicism in her tone made him feel even guiltier. She'd grown a shell, just like the one he'd lived inside most of his life. It kept people from getting too close, from wounding too deeply. Nina hadn't managed to penetrate it, but Meredith very nearly had. He'd pushed her out of his life at exactly the right moment, because it wouldn't have taken much to give her a stranglehold on his heart. He'd known that five years ago, and did everything he could to prevent it.

Now he was seeing the consequences of his reticence. His life had altered, and so had Meredith's. Her fame must have been poor recompense for the home and children she'd always wanted, for a husband to love and take care of and be loved by.

He couldn't answer her accusation without giving himself away, so he ignored it and let her think what she liked.

"You never used to be sarcastic," he said quietly. "You were quiet and shy—"

"And dull and plain," she added for him with a cold smile. "I still am all those things. But I write books that sell like hotcakes and I've got my own small following of loyal readers. I'm famous and I'm rich. So now it doesn't matter if I'm not a blond bombshell. I've learned to live with what I am."

"Have you?" He searched her eyes for a long moment. "You've learned to hide yourself away from the world so that you won't get hurt. You draw back from emotion, from involvement. Even today you were thinking of ways to keep Sarah from having any time with you. That's the whole point of this trip to the library. Your damned research could have been anytime, but you preferred not to be around while Sarah and I were at Bess's house.''

"All right, maybe I did!" she said, goaded into telling the truth. "Sarah is a sweet child, and I could love her, but I don't want to have to look at you, much less be dragged up to that house when you're there. Mars wouldn't be far enough away from you to suit me!"

He was grateful that he'd learned to keep a poker face. She couldn't have known how those words hurt him. She had every reason to want to avoid him, to hate him. But he didn't want to avoid her, and hatred was the last emotion he felt for her now.

"So Sarah's going to have to pay because you don't want to be around me," he replied.

She glared at him. "Oh, no, you don't," she said. "You aren't laying any guilt trips on me. Sarah has you and Mrs. Jackson—"

"Sarah doesn't like me and Mrs. Jackson," he interrupted. "She likes you. She's done nothing but talk about you."

She turned away. "I can't," she said huskily.

"She could have been our child," he said unexpectedly. "Yours and mine. And that's what's eating you alive, isn't it?"

She couldn't believe he'd said that. She looked back at him with tears welling in her gray eyes, blinding her. "Damn you!"

"I saw it in your face this morning when you looked at her," he went on relentlessly, driven to make her admit it. "It isn't fear of me that's stopping you—it's fear of admitting that Sarah reminds you too painfully of what you wanted and couldn't have.''

She cried out as if he'd slapped her. She pushed the door open and ran toward the library, almost stumbling in her haste to get away from him. She made it to the lobby and stood there shaking, grateful that the librarian was away from the desk as she tried to get her composure back. She fumbled a handkerchief out of her purse and wiped her eyes. Blake was right. She was avoiding Sarah Jane because of the pain the child caused her. But knowing the truth didn't help. It only made things worse that he should be perceptive enough to sense what she was thinking.

She put the handkerchief away and went back to the reading room to pore over volumes on southwestern history. She didn't know how she was going to get back home. Blake would have gone and she'd just have to call Elissa or Bess.

An hour later, calmer and less flustered, she put the notebook she'd been scribbling in back in her purse, returned the reference books to the shelf and walked outside to find a public telephone.

Blake was there, leaning comfortably against the wall, waiting.

''Are you ready to go?'' he asked pleasantly as if nothing at all had happened.

She stared at him. ''I thought you'd gone.''

His broad shoulders rose and fell. ''It's Saturday,'' he said. ''I don't usually work on Saturday unless I have to.'' His eyes narrowed as he searched her face. ''Are you all right?'' he added quietly.

She nodded, her eyes avoiding him.

''I won't do that again, Meredith,'' he said deeply. ''I didn't mean to upset you. Let's go.''

She sat rigidly beside him on the ride home, afraid that he might start on her again despite what he'd said. But he didn't. He turned on the radio and kept it playing until he pulled into Bess's driveway again.

"You don't have to worry," he said before she got out of the car, and there was a resigned expression on his face. "I won't try to force you into a relationship with Sarah. She's my responsibility, not yours."

And that was that. Meredith went back into the house, and after he'd explained to Elissa and Bess that they could call him when Sarah was ready to come home, he drove off.

He didn't know what he was going to do as he drove away. He hadn't expected Meredith to react like that to his words. What he'd said had only been a shot in the dark, but he'd scored a hit. Sarah disturbed her. The child reminded her of Blake's cruelty, and Meredith was going to keep Sarah at a distance no matter what it took.

That was going to be sad for both of them. Meredith had grown cold and self-contained. She could use a child's magic to bring her back into the sunlight. Sarah likewise would profit from Meredith's tenderness. But it wasn't going to happen and he had to face it. He'd hoped that he might reach Meredith again through Sarah, but she wanted no part of him. She hated him.

He went back to the house and locked himself in his study with his paperwork, forcing his mind not to dwell on Meredith's anger. He had no one to blame but himself. And only time would tell if she could ever forgive him.

Later that afternoon, Meredith sat with Bess and Elissa and watched the little girls play.

"Isn't she the image of Blake?" Elissa smiled as she watched Sarah. "I guess it's hard for him, trying to raise a child on his own."

"He needs to marry again," Bess agreed.

"Well, he's rich enough to attract a wife," Meredith replied with cool disinterest.

"Another Nina would be the end of him," Elissa said. "And think of Sarah. She needs to be loved, not pushed aside. She looks as if she's never really been loved."

"She won't be with Blake," Meredith said. "He isn't a loving man."

Elissa looked at her curiously. "Considering his life so far, is that surprising? He's never been loved, has he? Even his uncle manipulated him, used him for the good of the real estate corporation. Blake has been an outsider looking in. He hasn't known how to love. Maybe Sarah will teach him. She's not the little terror she makes out to be. There's an odd softness about her, especially when she talks to Blake. And have you noticed how unselfish she is?" she added. "She hasn't fought with Dani or tried to take her toys away or break them. She's not what she seems."

"I noticed that, too," Meredith said reluctantly. She looked at the child who was so much like Blake and so little like her beautiful blond mother. Her heart ached at the sight of the little girl who could have been her own. If only Blake could have loved her. She smiled sadly. Oh, if only.

Sarah seemed to feel that scrutiny, because she got up and went to Meredith, her curious eyes searching the woman's. "Can you write a book about a little girl and she can have a daddy and mommy to love her?" she asked. "And it could have a pony in it, and lots of dolls like Dani has."

Meredith touched the small, dark head gently. "I might do that," she said, smiling involuntarily.

Sarah smiled back. "I like you, Merry."

She went back to play with Danielle, leaving a hopelessly touched Meredith staring hungrily at her. Tears stung her eyes.

"Merry, could you watch the girls for a bit while Elissa and I run down to the ice cream shop and get some cones for them?" Bess asked with a quickly concealed conspiratorial wink at Elissa.

"Of course," Meredith agreed.

"We won't be a minute," Bess promised. "Do you want a cone?"

"Yes, please. Chocolate." Meredith grinned.

"I want chocolate, too," Sarah pleaded. "A big one."

"I want vanilla," Danielle said.

"Forty-eight flavors, and we live with purists." Bess sighed, shaking her head. "Okay, chocolate and vanilla it is. Won't be a minute!"

Of course it was more than a minute. They were gone for almost an hour, and when they got back, Meredith was sitting in the middle of the carpet with Sarah and Danielle, helping them dress one of Danielle's dolls. Sarah was sitting as close as she could get to Meredith, and her young face was for once without its customary sulky look. She was laughing, and almost pretty.

The ice cream was passed out and another hour went by before Elissa said reluctantly that she and Danielle would have to go.

"I hate to, but King's bringing one of his business associates home for supper, and I have to get Danielle's bath and have her in bed by the time they get home," Elissa said. "But we'll have to do this again."

"Do you have to go?" Sarah asked Danielle sadly. "I wish you could come live with me, and we could be sisters."

"Me, too," Danielle said.

"I like your toys. I guess your mommy and daddy like you a lot."

"Your daddy likes you, too, Sarah," Meredith said gently, taking the child's hand in hers. "He just didn't know that you wanted toys. He'll buy you some of your own."

"Will he, truly?" Sarah asked her, all eyes.

"Truly," she replied, hoping she was right. The Blake she'd known in the past wouldn't have cared overmuch about a child's needs. Of course, the man she'd glimpsed today might. She could hardly reconcile what she knew about him with what she was learning about him.

"That's right," Bess agreed, smiling down at Sarah. "Your dad's a pretty nice guy. We all like him, don't we, Meredith?"

Meredith glared at her. "Oh, we surely do," she said through her teeth. "He's a prince."

Which was what Sarah Jane told her daddy that very night over the supper table. He'd picked her up at Bess's house, but Meredith's car was gone. She was avoiding him, he supposed wearily, and he listened halfheartedly to Sarah all the way home. Now she was telling him about the wonderful time she'd had playing dolls with Meredith, and he turned his attention from business problems to stare at her blankly as what she was saying began to register.

"She did *what*?" he asked.

"She played dolls with me," she said, "and she says you're a prince. Does that mean you used to be a frog, Daddy?" Sarah added. "Because the princess kisses the frog and he turns into a prince. Did my mommy kiss you?"

"Occasionally, and no, I wasn't a frog. Meredith played dolls with you?" he asked, feeling a tiny glow deep inside himself.

"She really did." Sarah sighed. "I like Mer'dith. I wish she was my mommy. Can't she come to live with us?"

He couldn't explain that very easily. "No," he said simply. "You'd better get ready for bed."

"But, Daddy..." she moaned.

"Go on. No arguments."

"All right," she grumbled. But she went.

He looked after her, smiling faintly. She was a handful, but she was slowly growing on him.

He stayed home on Sunday and took Sarah Jane out to see the horses grazing in the pasture. One of the men, a grizzled old wrangler named Manolo, was working a gelding in the corral, breaking him slowly and gently to the saddle. Blake had complained that Manolo took too long to break horses, especially when he was doing it for the remuda in spring before roundup. The cowhands had to have a string of horses when they started working cattle. But Manolo used his own methods, despite the boss's arguments. No way, he informed Blake, was he going to mistreat a horse just to break it to saddle, and if Blake didn't like that, he could fire him.

Blake hadn't said another word about it. The horses Manolo broke were always gentle and easily managed.

But this horse was giving the old man a lot of trouble. It pranced and reared, and Blake was watching it instead of Sarah Jane when the lacy handkerchief Meredith had given her blew into the corral.

Like a shot, she climbed through the fence to go after it, just as the horse broke away from Manalo and came snorting and bucking in her direction.

Blake saw her and blinked, not believing what his eyes were telling him. All at once he was over the fence, just as Manolo yelled.

Sarah was holding her handkerchief, staring dumbly at the approaching horse.

Blake grabbed her and sent her through the fence, following her with an economy of motion. He thanked God for his own strength as it prevented what would have been a total disaster.

Sarah Jane clung to his neck tightly, crying with great sobs.

He hugged her to him, his eyes closed, a shudder running through his lean, fit body. Another few seconds and it would have been all over. Sarah would have become a tragic memory. It didn't bear thinking about. Worse than that, it brought back an older memory, of another incident with a bronc. He touched his lean cheek where the scar cut across his tan. How many years ago had it been that he'd saved Meredith just as he'd saved Sarah? A long time ago—long before the sight of her began to make him ache.

The fear he'd experienced, added to the unwanted memories, made him furious. He let go of Sarah and held her in front of him, his green eyes glittering with rage.

"Don't you know better than to go into the corral with a wild animal?" he snapped. "Where's your mind, Sarah?"

She stared at him as if he'd slapped her. Her lower lip trembled. "I had to get my...my hankie, Daddy." She held it up. "See? My pretty hankie that Mer'dith gave me...."

He shook her. "The next time you go near any enclosure with horses or cattle in it, you stay out! Do you understand me?" he asked in a tone that made her small body jerk with a sob. "You could have been killed!"

"I'm so—sorry," she faltered.

"You should be!" he jerked out. "Now get in the house."

She started crying, frightened by the way he looked. "You hate me," she whimpered. "I know you do. You yelled at me. You're mean and ugly...and...I don't like you!"

"I don't like you, either, at the moment," he bit off, glaring down at her, his legs still shaking from the exertion and fear. "Now get going."

"You mean old daddy!" she cried. She turned and ran wildly for the house as Blake stared after her in a blind rage.

"Is she all right, boss?" Manolo asked from the fence. "My God, that was quick! I didn't even see her!"

"Neither did I," Blake confessed. "Not until it was damned near too late." He let out a rough sigh. "I didn't mean to be so hard on her, but she's got to learn that horses and cattle are dangerous. I wanted to make sure she remembered this."

"She'll remember," Manolo said ruefully, and turned away before the boss could see the look on his face. Poor little kid. She needed hugging, not yelling.

Blake went in the house a few minutes later and looked for Sarah, but she was nowhere in sight. Mrs. Jackson had heard her come in, but she hadn't seen her because she was working in the front of the house.

He checked Sarah's bedroom, but she wasn't there, either. Then he remembered what she'd said about being locked in the closet when she was bad....

He jerked open the closet door and there she sat, her face red and tear stained, sobbing and looking as if she hadn't a friend in the world.

"Go away," she sniffed.

He got down awkwardly on one knee. "You'll suffocate in here."

"I hate you."

"I don't want anything to happen to you," he said. "The horse could have hurt you very badly."

She touched the dusty lace handkerchief to her red eyes. "You yelled at me."

He grimaced. "You scared me," he muttered, averting his gaze. "I never thought I'd get to you in time."

She sniffed and got up on her knees under the hanging dresses and blouses and slacks. "You didn't want me to get hurt?"

"Of course I didn't want you to get hurt," he snapped, green eyes flashing.

"You're yelling at me again," she said, pouting.

He sighed angrily. "Well, I've been doing it for a lot of years, and I won't change. You'll just have to get used to my temper." He stared at her half-angrily. "I thought I was getting the hang of it, and you had to go crawl in with a bucking bronco and set me back."

"Everybody used to yell at me," she told him solemnly. "But they didn't do it just if I got hurt. They didn't like me."

"I like you. That's why I yelled," he muttered.

She smiled through her tears. "Really and truly?"

He grimaced. "Really and truly." He got up. "Come out of there."

"Are you going to spank me?" she asked.

"No."

"I won't do it again."

"You'd better not." He took her hand and led her downstairs. When Mrs. Jackson found out what had happened, she took a fresh coconut cake out of the pantry, sliced it up and poured Sarah a soft drink. She even smiled. Sarah dried her eyes and smiled back.

On Monday Blake took two hours off at lunch and went to a toy store. He bought an armful of dolls and assorted girlish toys and took them to the house without fully understanding his motives. Maybe it was relief that Sarah was all right or guilt because he'd hurt her.

But she sat down in the living room with her new friends—which included a huge stuffed teddy bear—and the way she handled her toys was enough to bring a tear to the eye. She hugged the teddy bear, then she hugged Blake, who was half delighted and half embarrassed by her exuberance.

"You're just the nicest daddy in the whole world," Sarah Jane said, and she was crying again. She wiped her eyes with her hands. "I have a new Mr. Friend now, and he can help you fight monsters."

"I'll keep that in mind. Behave yourself." He went out the door quickly, more moved than he wanted to admit by his daughter's reception to the impromptu toy surprise.

On the way back to work, he remembered what Sarah had said about Meredith playing dolls with her. Meredith had been trying to keep Sarah at arms' length, so he wondered at her actions. Had he been wrong about Meredith's motives? Had he misjudged what he thought was her reason for avoiding Sarah?

He remembered all too well the feel of Meredith's soft, innocent mouth under his that day in the stable, the wonder in her eyes when he'd lifted his head just briefly to look down at her. And then he'd lost control and frightened her, turning the wonder to panic.

That she'd loved him didn't bear thinking about. At least he and Sarah were closer than ever. But she needed more than a father. Sarah needed a mother. Someone to read her stories, to play with her. Someone like Meredith. It made him feel warm to think of Meredith doing those things with his daughter. In time she might even get over the past and start looking ahead. She might fall in love with him all over again.

His body reacted feverishly to that thought, and as quickly his mind rejected it. He didn't want her to love him. He felt guilt for the way he'd treated her and he still wanted her, but *love* wasn't a word in his vocabulary anymore. It hurt too much.

Letting her get close would be risky. Meredith had every reason in the world to want to get even with him. He scowled. Would Meredith want revenge if he could bring himself to tell her the truth about why he'd been so rough with her?

Not that *he* needed her, he assured himself. It was only that Sarah liked her and needed her. But Meredith wouldn't come to the house. She wasn't going to let him, or Sarah, get close to her, and that was the big hurdle. How, he wondered, could he overcome it?

He worried the thought for two days and still hadn't figured out a solution, when he had to fly to Dallas on business for the day. But fate was on his side.

While he was gone, Mrs. Jackson's only living sister had a heart attack and a neighbor called asking Amie to come to Wichita, Kansas, and help look after her. That left Mrs. Jackson with nobody to look after Sarah. She couldn't take the child with her while she tried to care for a heart patient. She called Elissa, but she and her husband and child were out of town. Bess wouldn't be able to cope with the angry little girl. That left only one person in Jack's Corner who might be willing to try.

Without hesitation, Mrs. Jackson picked up the phone and called Meredith Calhoun.

Five

Sarah Jane was almost dancing with pleasure when Meredith came in the door. She ran to her, arms outstretched, and Meredith instinctively picked her up and hugged her warmly. Maternal instincts she hadn't indulged since Blake had sent her running came to the fore, making her soft.

"Now don't you give Meredith any trouble, young lady," Mrs. Jackson cautioned Sarah Jane. "Meredith, this is my sister's phone number, but I'll call as soon as I know something and tell Mr. Blake what's going on. I hope he won't mind."

"You know very well he won't," Meredith said. "I'm sorry about your sister, but I'm sure she'll be all right."

"Well, we can hope, anyway," Mrs. Jackson said, forcing a smile. "There's my cab. I'll be back as soon as I can."

"Bye, Mrs. Jackson," Sarah called.

She turned at the door and smiled at the little girl. "Goodbye, Sarah. I'll miss you. Thanks again, Merry."

"No problem," Meredith said as the housekeeper left.

"We can play dolls now, Merry," Sarah said enthusiastically, repeating the nickname she'd heard for Meredith as she struggled to be put down. She then led Meredith by the hand into the living room. "Look what my daddy bought me!"

Meredith was pleasantly surprised by the array of dolls. There must have been two dozen of them, surrounding a huge, whimsical tan teddy bear who was wearing one of Blake's Stetsons on his shaggy head.

"He's supposed to be my daddy," Meredith said, pointing to the bear, "since my daddy's away. But actually he's Mr. Friend. My old Mr. Friend got lost, so Daddy bought me a new one."

Meredith sat down on the sofa, smiling as Sarah introduced every one of her new toys to her older friend.

"I dropped the pretty hankie you gave me inside the fence," Sarah explained excitedly, "and a big horse almost ran over me, but my daddy saved me. He yelled at me and I cried and hid in the closet, and he came to find me. He said I mustn't *ever* do it again because he liked me." She laughed. "And then he went to the store and brought me ever so many toys."

Meredith was feeling cold chills at the innocent story. She could imagine how Blake had felt, the fear that had gripped him. She remembered so well the day he'd had to rescue her from a wild horse. She wondered if it had brought back memories for him, too.

Sarah looked up at Meredith. "My daddy has an *awful* temper, Merry."

Meredith knew that already. She remembered his temper very well. A lot of things could spark it, but embarrassment, fear, or any kind of threat were sure to ignite it. She could imagine how frightened Sarah had been of him, but apparently toys could buy forgiveness. She chided herself for that thought. Blake could be unexpectedly kind. It was just that he seemed so cold and self-contained. She wondered if Nina had ever really touched him during their brief marriage, and decided that it was unlikely.

Meredith got down on the floor with Sarah, grateful, as they sprawled on the carpet, that she'd worn jeans and a yellow blouse instead of a dress. She and Sarah dressed dolls and talked for a long time before Meredith got the small girl ready for bed, tucked her in and helped her say her prayers.

"Why do I have to say prayers?" Sarah asked.

"To thank God for all the nice things He does for us." Meredith smiled.

"Daddy talks to God all the time," Sarah said. "Especially when I turn things over or get hurt—"

Meredith fought to keep her expression steady. "That's not what I meant, darling. Now you settle down and we'll talk."

"Okay, Merry." She moved her dark head on the pillow. "Merry, do you like me?"

Meredith looked down at the child she might have had. She smiled sadly, touching Sarah's dark hair gently. "Yes, I like you very much, Sarah Jane Donavan," she replied, smiling.

"I like you, too."

Meredith bent and kissed the clean, shiny face. "Would you like me to read you a story? Have you any books?"

The small face fell. "No. Daddy forgot."

"That's all right, then. I can think of one or two." She sat down on Sarah's bed and proceeded to go through several, doing all the parts in different pitches of her voice, while Sarah giggled.

She was just in the middle of "The Three Bears," doing Baby Bear's voice when Sarah sat up, smiling from ear to ear and cried, "Daddy!"

Meredith felt her face burn, her heart start to pound, as he came into the room, dressed in a gray business suit, sparing her a curious glance as he handed something to Sarah.

"Something from Dallas," he told the child. "It's a puppet."

"I love him, Daddy!"

It was a duck puppet, yellow and white, and Sarah wiggled it on her hand while Blake turned to Meredith with a cool smile.

"Where's Amie?" he asked.

She told him, adding that Amie had promised to phone as soon as she knew something. "She couldn't get Elissa, and there wasn't anyone else, so she asked me."

"We had lots of fun, Daddy!" Sarah told him. "Merry and me played dolls and watched TV together!"

"Thank you for taking the time," Blake said, his whole attitude antagonistic. He'd done nothing but think about the irritating woman for days. And there she sat, looking as cool as a cucumber without a hint of warmth in her cold gray eyes, while his body had gone taut and started throbbing at the very sight of her.

Meredith got to her feet, avoiding him. "I didn't mind. Good night, Sarah," she said, running a nervous hand through her loosened dark hair to get it out of her face.

"Good night, Merry. Will you come back to see me again?"

"When I can, darling," she replied absently, without noticing the reaction that endearment had on Blake. "Sleep tight."

"Go to sleep now, young lady," Blake told his daughter.

"But, Daddy, what about the monsters?" Sarah wailed when he started to turn out the light at the door.

He stopped and looked uncomfortable. He wasn't about to start chasing monsters from under the bed and dragging them out of the closet in front of Meredith. Sarah loved the pretend housecleaning and he'd grown used to doing it to amuse her, but a man had to have his secrets. He cleared his throat. "When I walk Meredith to her car, okay?"

That pacified Sarah. She smiled. "Okay, Daddy." She looked at Meredith. "He kills the monsters every night so they won't hurt me. He's very brave and he weighs one million pounds!"

Meredith glanced at Blake and her face went red as she tried to smother laughter. He glared at her, breaking the spell. She rushed out into the hall and kept going.

He caught up with her downstairs and walked her out onto the porch.

"I'm sorry Amie involved you," he said curtly. "Bess would have kept Sarah."

"Bess and Bobby were going out," she replied. "I didn't mind."

"You didn't want to come here, though, even while I was away," he said perceptively. "You don't care for this house very much, do you?"

"Not anymore," she said. "It brings back some painful memories." She moved away from him, but he followed.

"Where's your car?" he asked, searching for it.

"I walked. It was a beautiful night and it's only a short walk."

He glared down at her from his superior height. In his gray suit and pearl-colored Stetson, he looked enormously tall and imposing. He never seemed to smile, she thought, searching his hard features in the light that shone from the windows onto the big, long porch.

"If you're looking for beauty, you won't find it," he said, his mouth twisting into a mocking smile. "The scar only makes it worse."

She gazed at it, the long white line that marred his lean cheek all the way from his high cheekbone to his jaw. "I remember when you got it," she said quietly. "And how."

His expression became grim. "I don't want to talk about it."

"I know." She sighed gently, her eyes searching over his dark face with more poignancy than she knew. "But you were always handsome to me, scar and all," she mused, turning away as the memories came flooding back. "Good night ... Blake!"

He'd whipped her around, his lean hands biting into her arms. She was wearing a sleeveless lemon yellow blouse with her jeans, and it made her skin look darker than it was. Where his fingers held her, the flesh went white from the pressure.

"I..." He eased his hold a little, although he didn't release her. "I didn't mean to do that." He drew in a silent breath. "I don't suppose you'll ever get over the fear I caused you in the past, will you?" he added, watching her eyes widen, her body stiffen.

"It was my first intimacy," she whispered, flushing. "And you made it ... you were very rough."

"I remember," he replied. His pride fought him when he tried to tell her the truth, although he wanted to. He wanted to make her understand his roughness.

"As you said, it was a long time ago," she added, pulling against his hold gently.

"Not that long. Five years." He searched her eyes. "Meredith, surely you've dated men. There must have been one or two who could stir you."

"I couldn't trust them," she said bitterly. "I was afraid to take a chance with anyone else."

"Most men aren't as rough as I am," he replied coldly.

Her breath was sighing out like a whisper. He made her nervous, and the feel of his hands was affecting her breathing. "Most men aren't as much a man as you are," she breathed, closing her eyes as forgotten sensations worked down her spine and made her ache.

His pride burned with what she'd said. Did she think him masculine, handsome? Or was that all in the past, part of the love he'd killed?

He drew her closer and held her against him warmly but chastely, her legs apart from his. He didn't want her to feel how aroused he already was.

"I'm not much gentler now than I used to be, Meredith," he said deeply, as his head bent toward her. "But I'll try not to frighten you this time...."

She opened her mouth to protest, but his lips met hers. They probed her soft mouth while his lean, strong hands slid up to frame her face.

She stiffened, but only for a minute. The taste of him made her dizzy with pleasure. She liked what he was doing to her too much to protest. After a minute she relaxed, letting his mouth do what it wanted to hers.

"God, it's sweet," he whispered roughly, biting at her lips with more instinct than expertise. His voice was shaking and he didn't care if she heard it. "Oh, God, it's so sweet!"

His mouth ground into hers and his arms slid completely around her. He pulled her body up against his so that his legs touched hers, and he felt her sudden shocked tautness.

He let her move away, his eyes glittering, his breath rustling out of his throat. "I shouldn't have done that," he said gruffly. "I didn't mean to let you feel how aroused I was."

Having him mention it shocked her more than the feel of his body, but she tried not to let him see her reaction. She stepped back, touching her mouth with light fingers. Yes, it had been sweet, as she'd heard him whisper feverishly. Just as it had been five years ago in the stable, when he'd put his mouth on hers and she'd ached to have him touch her.

"I have to get back to Bess's house," she said unsteadily.

"Just a minute." He took her hand and pulled her farther into the light. He held her gaze so that he could see the fear mingled with desire that lingered in her eyes, the swollen softness of her mouth.

"What are you looking for?" she asked huskily.

"You're still afraid of me," he said, his jaw going taut.

"I'm sorry." She lowered her eyes to his chest, to its quick, hard rise and fall. "I can't help it."

"Neither can I," he replied bitterly. He let her go, turning away. "I'm not much good at lovemaking, if you want the truth," he said through his teeth.

That was true. He had the patience, but not the knowledge. Nina had taught him a few things, but she'd been indifferent to his touch and her response to him had always been just lukewarm. She hadn't known he was innocent, but she had known he was inexperienced, and at the end of their relationship she'd taunted him with his lack of expertise. It was one of the things he hated remembering. Better to let Meredith think he was brutal than to have her know how green he was.

Watching him, Meredith was surprised by the admission. She'd always considered him experienced. If he wasn't, it would explain so much.

Suddenly, she understood his fierce pride a little better. She went closer to him, reaching out to lightly touch his sleeve. He jerked a little, as if that impersonal contact went through him like fire.

"It's all right, Blake," she said hesitantly.

He looked down at the slender hand that rested lightly on his sleeve. "I'm like a bull in a china shop," he said unexpectedly, looking into her eyes. "With women."

She felt a surge of emotion at that rough admission. He'd never been more approachable than he was right now. Part of her was wary of him, but another part wanted once, just once, to give in without a fight.

She went up on her tiptoes and pulled his head down to hers. He stiffened and she stopped dead.

"No!" he whispered huskily when she started to draw back in embarrassment. "Go ahead. Do what you want to."

She couldn't believe that he really wanted her to kiss him, but he was giving every indication that he did. She didn't know a lot about it, either, since all she'd ever done with men was kissing.

She drew her lips lightly over Blake's hard ones, teasing them gently. Her breath shook at his mouth while she held his head within reach, but she didn't relent. Her fingers slid into the thick, cool hair at the nape of his strong neck and her nails slid against his skin while her mouth toyed softly with his.

"I can't take much of that," he whispered roughly. His hands held her hips now, an intimacy that she should have protested, but she was too weak. "Do it properly."

"Not yet," she whispered. Her teeth closed softly on his lower lip, tugging at it sensuously. She felt him tremble as her tongue traced his upper lip.

"Meredith," he bit off, and his hands hurt her for an instant.

"All right." She knew what he wanted, what he needed. She opened her mouth on his and slid her tongue inside it, and the reaction she got from him was electrifying.

He cried out. His arms swallowed her, bruising her against his hard chest. He was trembling. Meredith felt the soft tremors with exquisite awareness, with pride that she could arouse him that easily after a beauty like Nina.

"Blake," she whispered under his mouth, and closed her eyes as she gave him the weight of her body, the warmth of her mouth.

She felt him move. Her back was suddenly against the wall and he was easing down over her body.

Her eyes flew open and his head lifted fractionally, and all the while his body overwhelmed hers, his hips lying heavy and hard against hers, pressing against her.

She could feel the full strength of his arousal now, and it should have frightened her, but it didn't. He was slow and gentle, not impatient at all as his hands slid to her hips, holding her.

"This should really frighten the hell out of you, shouldn't it?" he asked huskily, searching her eyes. "You can feel what I want, and I'm not quite in control right now."

"You aren't hurting me," she whispered. "And I started it this time."

"So you did." He moved down, letting his mouth repeat the soft, arousing movements hers had made earlier. "Like that, Meredith?" he whispered at her lips. "Is that how you like it?"

"Yes," she whispered back, excitement making her voice husky. Her hands were against his shirt and she could feel the heat from his body under the fabric.

"I want to open my shirt and let you touch me," he whispered roughly. "But that might be the straw that breaks the camel's back, and there's a long, comfortable sofa just a few feet inside the door."

The thought was more than tempting. She could already feel his skin against hers, his body overwhelming hers. She wanted him, and there wasn't really any reason to say no. Except that her pride couldn't take the knowledge that he wanted only her body and nothing else about her.

"I can't sleep with you," she said miserably. She let her head rest against him, drowning in the feel of his body over hers. "Blake, you have to stop," she groaned. "I'm going crazy...!"

"So am I." He pushed himself away from her, breathing roughly. His darkened green eyes looked down into hers. "You wanted me," he said, as if he were only just realizing it.

She flushed and looked up at his hard face. "I don't understand what you want from me."

"Sarah needs a woman's companionship," he said tersely.

"That isn't why you made love to me," she returned, searching his eyes.

He sighed deeply. "No, it isn't." He walked to the edge of the porch and leaned against one of the white columns, looking out over the wide expanse of flat land. The only trees were right around the house, where they'd been planted. Beyond was open land, dotted with a few willows at the creek and a few straggly bushes, but mostly flat and barren all the way to the horizon.

"Why, Blake?" she asked. She had to know what he was after.

"Do you know what an obsession is, Meredith?" he asked a minute later.

"Yes, I think so."

"Well, that's what I feel for you." He shifted so that he could see her. "Obsessed," he repeated, letting his green eyes slide over her sensually. "I don't know why. You aren't beautiful. You aren't even voluptuous. But you arouse me as no other woman ever has or ever will. I couldn't even feel for Nina what I feel for you." He laughed coldly. "After she left me, there wasn't anyone else. I couldn't. I don't want anyone but you."

She didn't know if she was still breathing. The admission knocked the wind out of her, took the strength from her legs. She looked at him helplessly.

"You haven't...seen me in five years," she said, trying to rationalize.

"I've seen you every night," he ground out. "Every time I closed my eyes. My God, don't you remember what I did to you that day in the stable? I stripped you...." He closed his eyes, oblivious to her scarlet face and trembling body. "I looked at you and touched you and put my mouth on you." He bit back a curse and opened his eyes again, tormented. "I see you in my bed every damned night of my life," he breathed. "I want you to the point of madness."

She caught the railing and held on tight. She couldn't believe what she was hearing. It wasn't possible for a man to feel that kind of desire, she told herself. Not when he didn't feel anything emotional for the woman. But Blake was different. As Elissa said, he'd never been loved, so he didn't know what it was. But all men felt desire. A man didn't have to love to want.

"Don't worry—" he laughed mockingly "—I'm not going to force you into anything. I just wanted you to know how I felt. If that sensuous little kiss was some sort of game, you'd better know how dangerous it is. I'm not sane when I touch you. I wouldn't hurt you deliberately for the world, but I want you like hell."

Her swollen lips parted. "I wasn't playing," she said with quiet pride. "It was no game. You..." She hesitated. "You seemed so disturbed because you'd been rough. I wanted to show you that you hadn't made me afraid."

He watched her unblinkingly. "You weren't, were you?" he said then, scowling. "Not even when I brought you close and let you feel what you were doing to me."

She shifted. "You shouldn't have," she murmured evasively.

"Why hide it?" he asked. He moved toward her, encouraged by her response and her lack of bitterness. He was taking a hell of a chance by being honest with her, but it might be his only way of reaching her. "You might as well know it all."

She lifted her face as he stood over her. "Know what?"

"Nina was my first woman," he said bluntly. "And the only woman."

She wanted to sit down, but there was no chair. She leaned against the banister, her eyes searching his hard face. He wasn't kidding. He meant it.

"That's right," he said, nodding when he saw the memories replaying in her eyes. "The day we were in the stable together, I was as inexperienced as you were. That's why I was rough. It wasn't deliberate. I didn't know how to make love."

Her lips opened on a slow breath. "No wonder..." she whispered.

"Yes, no wonder." He brushed a strand of loosened hair from her pale cheek. "Why don't you laugh? Nina did."

She could feel the hurt under that mocking statement. What it must have done to his pride! "Nina was a—" She bit back the word.

He laughed coldly. "She certainly was," he agreed. "She taunted me with it toward the end," he added, his eyes bitter and cynical. "I didn't want to risk that kind of ridicule again, so there weren't any more women."

"Oh, Blake," she whispered, closing her eyes on a wave of pain. "Blake, I'm so sorry!"

"I don't want pity. I wanted you to know the truth. If you're ever tempted to give in to me, you're entitled to know what you'd be up against. My God," he said heavily, moving away, "I don't even know the basics. Books and movies don't make up for experience. And Nina wasn't interested in tutoring me."

"I wish I'd known," she said huskily. "I wish I'd known five years ago."

He looked back at her, his thick eyebrows raised. "Why?"

"I wouldn't have fought you," she said simply. "I thought you were terribly experienced." She lowered her eyes. "I'm sorry. I guess I hurt your ego as much as you frightened me."

He studied her in a tense silence. "You don't have a thing to apologize for. I'm the one who's sorry." He waited until she lifted her head, and he caught her eyes and held them. "You haven't wanted anyone, in all this time?"

"I wanted you," she said frankly. "I...couldn't feel that for anyone else. I'd rather have been frightened by you than pleasured by the greatest lover living." She laughed coldly. "So I guess I'm in the same boat that you are." She clutched her purse. "I really do have to go," she said after a long, quiet moment during which he stared at her without saying anything at all.

He escorted her down the porch steps. "All right. I'll walk you to the woods and watch you through them. Sarah Jane will be all right until I get back, and the house is in full view the whole way."

"Sarah is very much like you," she said.

"Too much like me," he replied. His fingers brushed hers as they walked, accidentally or deliberately she didn't know, making her all too aware of him. "She almost got trampled the other day, climbing into the corral to retrieve a handkerchief."

"She told me. I suppose you were livid."

"Mild word," he said. "I blew up. Scared her. I found her hiding in the closet, and I felt like a dog. I went to town the next day and bought her half a toy store to make up for yelling at her." He sighed. "She scared me blind. I kept thinking what could have happened if my reflexes had been just a bit slower."

"But they weren't." She smiled. "You were always quick in an emergency."

He looked down at her and his fingers lazily entangled themselves in hers. "Luckily for you," he murmured darkly, watching her flush. "I haven't had an easy life," he said then. "I had to be tough to survive. They weren't good days before I came here to live with my uncle. I got in a lot of fights because of my illegitimacy."

"I never heard you talk about that," she said.

"I never could." His fingers tightened in hers as they got to the small wooded area and stopped. "I can't talk about a lot of things, Meredith. Maybe that's why I'm so damned alone."

She glanced toward Bess's house. Bess and Bobby must have come home, because their car was in the driveway next to hers. She hesitated, not eager to leave Blake in this oddly talkative mood. "You've got Sarah now," she reminded him gently.

"Sarah is getting to me," he confessed ruefully. "God, I don't know what I'd do if I could sit down in a chair without crushing a stuffed toy, or go to bed without running monsters out of closets." He smiled mockingly. "It cut me to pieces when she started crying after I raged at her about getting in with the horse."

"She doesn't seem that sensitive at first glance, but she is," she replied. "I noticed it that first day, at the children's shop, and again when she played with Danielle. I gather she was neglected a lot before they sent her to you."

"I got the same feeling. She had a nightmare just after she came here," he recalled quietly. "She woke up in the early hours, screaming her head off, and when I asked what was the matter, she said they wouldn't let her out of the closet." His face hardened, and for an instant he looked relentless. "I've still got half a mind to send my lawyers after that housekeeper."

"A woman that cruel will make her own hell," Meredith said. "Mean people don't get away with anything, Blake. It may seem that they do, but in the end their meanness ricochets back at them."

"The way mine did at me?" he asked with a mirthless laugh. "I scarred you and pushed you out of my life, married Nina, and settled down to what I thought would be wedded bliss. And look where it got me."

"You've got everything," she corrected. "Money, power, position, a sweet little girl."

"I've got nothing except Sarah," he said shortly. His green eyes glittered in the faint light. "I thought I needed money and power to make people accept me. But I'm no more socially acceptable now than I was when I was poor and illegitimate. I've just got more money."

"Acceptance doesn't have anything to do with money." She stared down at the big, warm hand clasping hers. "You're not the world's most sociable man. You keep to yourself and you don't smile very much. You intimidate people." She smiled gently, her eyes almost loving despite her reluctance to give herself away. "That's why you don't get a lot of social invitations. This isn't the Dark Ages. People don't hold the circumstances of their birth against each other anymore. It's a much more open society than it was."

"It stinks," he returned coldly. "Women propositioning men, kids neglected and abused and cast off...."

"They don't burn witches anymore, though," she whispered conspiratorially, going up on tiptoe. "And the stocks have been eliminated, too."

His face cracked into a reluctant smile. "Okay. You've got a point."

"Who propositioned you?" she added.

He cocked his head a little to study her. "A woman at the workshop in Dallas I just came back from. I didn't believe she meant it until she put her room key in an ashtray beside my coffee cup."

"What did you do?" she asked, because she had to know.

He smiled faintly. "Took it out and handed it back." He touched her cheek gently, running a lean finger down it. "I told you on the porch. I don't want anyone but you."

She lowered her eyes to his chest. "I can't, Blake."

"I'm not asking you to." He let go of the hand he was holding. "I'm archaic in my notions, in case it's escaped your notice. I don't seduce virgins."

Her body tingled at the thought of making love with Blake. It was exciting and surprising to know how much he wanted her. But her own conscience wasn't going to let her give in, and he knew that, too.

"I guess you'd rather I got my autographing over and left town . . ." she began.

He tilted her chin up so he could see her face. "Sarah and I are going on a picnic Saturday. You can come."

The suddenness of the invitation made her blink. "Saturday?"

"We'll pick you up at nine. You can wear jeans. I'm going to."

Her eyes lifted to his. "Blake . . ."

"I like having things out in the open, so there aren't any more misunderstandings," he said simply. "I want you. You want me. But that's as far as it goes, and there won't be any more of what happened on my porch tonight. I'll keep my hands off and we'll give Sarah a good time. Sarah likes you," he added quietly. "I think you like her, too. She could use a few good memories before you go back to the life you left in San Antonio."

So he was going to freeze her out. He wanted her, but he wasn't going to do anything about it. He wanted her for Sarah, not for himself, despite his hunger for her.

She hesitated. "Is it wise letting her get used to me?" she asked, her voice echoing the disappointment she felt.

His hand on her chin became faintly caressing. "Why not?" he asked.

"It will be another upset for her when I leave," she said.

His thumb moved over her lips, brushing them, caressing them. "How long are you going to stay?"

"Until the first of the month," she said. "I do the autographing a week from Saturday."

His hand fell just in time to keep her from throwing herself against him and begging him to kiss her. "Then you can spend some time with Sarah and me until you leave. I won't force you into any corners and we can help Sarah find her feet."

Her eyes searched his night-shadowed face. "Why do you want me around?"

"God knows," he muttered. "But I do."

She sighed audibly, fighting her need to be near him.

"Don't brood," he said. He didn't smile, but there was something new about the way he was looking at her. "Just take things one day at a time and stop analyzing everything I say."

"Was I doing that? Okay, I'll try." She wished there were more light. She managed a smile. "Good night, Blake."

"Go on. I'll watch you."

She left him standing there and went running down to the house, her heart blazing with new hope.

If there was any chance for her to have Blake, she'd take it willingly, no matter what the risk. She now understood the reasons for his actions. And if she went slowly and didn't ask for the impossible, he might even come to love her one day. She went to sleep on that thought, and her dreams were so vivid that she woke up blushing.

Six

___

Meredith was awake, dressed and ready to go by eight on Saturday morning, with an hour to kill before it was time for Blake and Sarah to pick her up.

Bess, an early riser herself these days, made breakfast and smiled wickedly at her friend.

"It must feel strange to have Blake ask you out after all these years."

"It does. But I'm not kidding myself that it's out of any great love for me," she said, neglecting to tell Bess that Blake's main interest in her was sensual. All the same, just remembering the way he'd kissed her Wednesday night made her tingle from head to toe. And he'd shared secrets with her that she knew he'd never tell anyone else. That alone gave her a bit of hope. But she was afraid to trust him too much just yet. She needed time to adjust to the new Blake. She sighed. "I haven't been on a picnic in years. And I'm looking forward to it," she confessed with a smile, "even if he only wants me along because Sarah likes me."

"Sarah's a cute little girl." Bess sighed. "Bobby and I are ready to start a family of our own, but I can't seem to get pregnant. Oh, well, it takes time, I guess. Do you want something to eat?"

"I'm too nervous to eat," Meredith said honestly, her eyes still soft with memories of the night before. "I hope I'm wearing the right thing."

Bess studied her. Jeans, sneakers, a white tank top that showed off her pretty tan and emphasized her full, high breasts, and her dark hair loose around her shoulders. "You look great," she said. "And there's no rain in the forecast, so you should be fine."

"I should have slept longer," Meredith wailed. "I'll be a nervous wreck . . . Oh!"

The jangling of the telephone startled her, but Bess only smiled.

"If I were a gambling woman," Bess said as she went to answer it, "I'd bet my egg money that Blake's as nervous and impatient as you are." She picked the receiver up, said hello, then glanced amusedly at Meredith, whose heart was doing a marathon race in her chest. "Yes, she's ready, Blake," she said. "You might as well come get her before she wears out my carpet. I'll tell her. See you."

"How could you say that!" Meredith cried. "My best friend, and you sold me out to the enemy!"

"He isn't the enemy, and I think Blake needs all the advantages he can get." Bess's smile faded. "He's such a lonely man, Meredith. He was infatuated with Nina and he let himself be suckered into marriage without realizing she only wanted his money. He's paid for that mistake enough, don't you think?"

"There are some things you don't know," Meredith said.

"I'm sure there are. But if you love him in spite of those things I don't know, then it's foolish to risk your future out of spite and vengeance."

Meredith smiled wearily. "I don't have the strength for vengeance," she replied. "I wanted to get even for a long time after I left here, but when I saw him again..." She shrugged. "It's just like old times. I can't talk straight or walk without trembling when he gets within a foot of me. I never should have come back. He's going to hurt me again if I give him an opening. After what Nina did to him, he's not going to make it easy for any woman to get close. Least of all me."

"Give it a chance," Bess advised. "Nothing comes to us without some kind of risk. I've learned a lot about compromise since Bobby and I almost split up a few years ago. I've learned that pride is a poor bedfellow."

"I'm glad you two are getting along so well."

"So am I. I went a bit bonkers over my sexy brother-in-law for a while, but Elissa came along and solved all my problems," Bess confessed with a grin. "King Roper has a gunpowder temper, if you remember." Meredith grinned, because she did. "I couldn't stand up to him, but Elissa didn't give an inch. Not that they do much fighting these days, but they had a rocky start."

"She's so sweet," Meredith murmured. "I liked her the minute I met her."

"Most people do. And King would die for her."

Those words kept echoing in Meredith's brain as she sat in the car, with Blake behind the wheel and Sarah chattering away in the back seat. She looked at Blake's taut profile and tried to imagine having him care enough to die for her. It was a forlorn hope that he'd ever love her. His reserved nature and Nina's cruelty wouldn't let him.

He glanced at her and saw that sadness in her eyes. "What is it?" he asked.

"Nothing." She smiled at Sarah, who was looking worried. "I'm just barely awake."

Blake lifted an eyebrow as the powerful car ate up the miles. "That explains why you were up and dressed at eight when I said we'd be at Bess's at nine."

"I couldn't sleep," she muttered.

"Neither could I," he replied. "Sarah was too excited to stay in bed this morning," he added, just when Meredith was breathless at the thought that the memory of the way he'd kissed her had been the reason he didn't sleep.

"I'm so glad you came, Merry," Sarah said, hugging her new Mr. Friend stuffed bear in the back seat. "We'll have lots of fun! Daddy says there's a swing!"

"Several," he returned. "Jack's Corner has added a new park since you were here," he told Meredith. "It has swings and a sandbox and one of those things kids love to climb on. We can sit on a bench and watch her. Then there are plenty of tables. I thought we'd pick up something at one of the fast food stores for lunch, since Amie wasn't around to fix a picnic basket."

"Did she call?"

"Yes. Her sister is recovering very well, but it will be at least two weeks more before Amie comes back."

"How are you managing?"

"Not very well," he confessed. "I'm no cook, and there are things Amie could do for Sarah that I'm not comfortable doing."

"Daddy won't bathe me," Sarah called out. "He says he doesn't know how."

A flush of color worked its way up Blake's cheekbones and Meredith felt the embarrassment with him. It would be hard for a man to do such things for a daughter when he'd rarely been around a woman and never around little girls.

"I could..." Meredith hesitated at his sharp glance and then plowed ahead. "I could bathe her for you tonight. I wouldn't mind."

"Oh, Merry, could you?" Sarah enthused.

"If your father doesn't mind," she continued with a concerned glance in Blake's direction.

"I wouldn't mind," he said, without taking his eyes from the road.

"And you can tell me some more stories, Merry," Sarah said. "I specially like 'The Ugly Ducking.'"

"Duckling," Blake corrected, and he smiled faintly at his child. "I guess that story fits both of us, sprout."

"Neither of you," Meredith interrupted. "You both have character and stubborn wills. That's worth a lot more than beauty."

"Daddy has a scar," Sarah piped up.

Meredith smiled at the child. "A mark of courage," she corrected. "And your father was always handsome enough that it didn't matter."

Blake felt his chest grow two sizes. His gaze darted to Meredith's face and he searched her eyes long and intently. As she was feeling the effect of that glance, he forced his eyes back to the road barely in time to avoid running the car into a ditch.

"Sorry," Meredith murmured with a grimace.

"No need." He turned the car down the street that led to the city park and pulled it into a vacant parking space.

"It's beautiful," Meredith said, looking at the expanse of wooded land with a children's playground and a gazebo. There was even a fountain. At this time of the day, though, the area was fairly deserted. Dew was still on the grass, and as they walked to the benches overlooking the playground, Meredith laughed as her sneakers quickly became soaked.

"Your feet are getting wet," Sarah said, laughing, too. "But I have my cowgirl boots on!"

"I think I can spare your feet," Blake murmured.

Before she realized what he intended, Blake bent and whipped Meredith off the ground, carrying her close to his chest without any sign of strain.

"Gosh, you're strong, Daddy," Sarah remarked.

"He always was," Meredith said involuntarily, and her eyes looked up into Blake's, full of memories, full of helpless vulnerability.

His arms contracted a fraction, but he didn't look at her. He didn't dare. He could already feel the effect that rapt stare had on his body. If he gazed at Meredith's soft, yielding face, he would start kissing her despite the small audience of one watching them so closely.

He put her down on the sidewalk without a word and moved to the bench to sit down, leaning back and crossing one booted foot over his jeans-clad knee. "Well, sit down," he said impatiently. "Sarah, play while you can. This place probably fills up in an hour or so."

"Yes, Daddy!" Sarah said and she ran for the swings. Meredith sat down beside Blake, still glowing and warm from the feel of his arms and savoring the warm, cologne-scented fragrance of his lean body. "She's already a different child," she commented, watching Sarah laugh as she pumped her little legs to make the swing go higher.

"She's less wild," Blake agreed. He took off his hat and put it next to him on the bench, pausing to run his hand through his thick black hair. "But she isn't quite secure yet. The nightmares haven't stopped completely. And I've had less time to spend with her lately. Business goes on. A lot of jobs depend on the decisions I make. I can't throw up my hands and stay home every day.''

"Sarah likes Amie, doesn't she?" Meredith asked.

"Amie won't be here for several weeks, Meredith," he said impatiently. "That's what I'm worried about. Monday morning I've got a board meeting. What do I do with Sarah, take her along?"

"I see your problem." Meredith sighed, fingering the face of her watch. "Well . . . I could keep her for you."

He didn't dare let himself react to that offer, even if it was the second time in a day that she'd volunteered to spend time with Sarah. It wouldn't do to get his hopes up too high.

"Could you?" he asked, and turned his head so that his green eyes pinned her gray ones.

"All I have to do is the autographing," she said. "And that's next Saturday. The rest of my time is vacation."

"You'd need to be at the house," he said with apparent unconcern. He pursed his lips, watching Sarah. "And considering how late I get home some nights, it's hardly worth rousing Bobby and Bess to let you in just for a few hours. Is it?"

She colored. "Blake, I don't care if this is the nineteen eighties, I can't move into your house. . . ."

He glanced at her and saw the rose-red blush. "I won't seduce you. I told you that Wednesday, and I meant it."

The blush deepened. She averted her gaze to Sarah and her heart shook her with its mad beat. "I know you won't go back on your word, Blake," she whispered. "But it's what people would think."

"And you're a famous author," he said, his eyes narrowing. "God forbid that I should tarnish your reputation."

"Don't start on me." She sighed miserably and got up. "This isn't a good idea. I shouldn't have come...!"

He got up, too, and caught her by the waist, holding her in front of him. "I'm sorry," he bit off. "I've never given a damn what people thought, but I guess when you aren't looked down on to begin with, reputations matter."

She looked up at him with soft, compassionate eyes. "I never looked down on you."

His jaw clenched. "Don't you think I know that now?" he asked huskily. He pulled her hand to his chest and smoothed over the neat pink nails, his eyes on her long fingers. "You were always defending me."

"And you hated it," she recalled with a sad smile. "I always seemed to make you mad—"

"I told you," he interrupted. "I wanted you, and I didn't know how to handle it. I knew it was impossible to seduce you, and I'd given my word that I was going to marry Nina." His shoulders lifted and fell. "It wasn't conscious, but afterward when I thought about what I did to you that day, I thought maybe it would be easier for you if I made you hate me." He looked up into her gray eyes with quiet sincerity.

Her face felt hot. She searched his hard expression for a long moment. "I suppose in a way it was," she said finally. "But it undermined my confidence. I couldn't believe any man would want me."

"Which worked to my advantage," he whispered, smiling faintly. "Because you weren't tempted to experiment with anyone else." The smile faded. "You're still a virgin. And your first man, Meredith, is going to be me."

Her heart stopped and then ran wild. "That's the most chauvinistic—"

He stopped her by simply lowering his head until his lips were almost touching hers. She could taste his coffee-flavored breath and the intimacy of it made her knees feel rubbery. "I am chauvinistic," he whispered. "And possessive. And hard as nails. I can't help those traits. Life hasn't been kind to me. Not until just recently."

His hands were on her shoulders, holding her in place, and his eyes were on her mouth in a way that made her breath rustle in her throat.

"Sa-Sarah Jane..." she stammered.

"Is facing the opposite direction and doesn't have eyes in the back of her head," he murmured. "So just give me your mouth without a struggle, little one, and I'll show you how gentle I can be when I try."

He felt her mouth accept his with the first touch, felt her body give when he drew her against his hard chest. She sighed into his mouth, and his brows drew together tightly over his closed eyes with the sheer pleasure of holding her.

She reached up under his arms to hold him and her body melted without a vestige of fear. Even when she felt the inevitable effect of her closeness on his powerful body, she didn't flinch or try to move away. He was her heart. Despite the pain and the anguish of years ago, he was all she knew or wanted of love.

His hands smoothed her hair as his hard mouth moved slowly on hers. She'd dreamed of this for so many years, dreamed of his mouth taking hers with exquisite tenderness, giving as much as he took. But the dreams paled beside the sweet reality. Her nails scraped against his back, loving the way the muscles rippled under her fingers.

His mouth lifted a fraction of an inch, and his breath was audible. "Who taught you to do that?" he whispered huskily.

"Nobody. I...guess it comes naturally," she whispered back.

His hands slid up her back to her hair and tangled gently in it. "Your mouth is very soft," he said unsteadily. "And it tastes of coffee and mint."

"I had Irish mocha mint coffee," she said.

"Did you?" He searched her eyes slowly. "Your legs are trembling," he remarked.

She laughed nervously. "I'm not surprised," she confessed. "My knees are wobbly."

He smiled, and the smile echoed in his eyes. "Are they?"

"Daddy, watch how high I can go!" a small voice called out.

Blake reluctantly loosened his hold on Meredith. "I'm watching," he called back.

Sarah Jane was swinging high and laughing. "I can almost touch the sky!" she said.

"Funny, so can I," Blake murmured. He glanced at Meredith, and he wasn't smiling.

She looked back, her heart threatening to burst. He took her hand in his, threading his fingers through hers so that he had them pressed in an almost intimate hold.

"To hell with your reputation," he said huskily. "Move in with us for a couple of weeks. Nobody will know except Bess and Bobby, and they're not judgmental."

She wanted to. Her worried eyes searched his. "Your company is an old and very conservative one. Your board of directors wouldn't like it at all."

"My board of directors doesn't dictate my private life," he replied. "We could sit close on the couch and watch television at night with Sarah. We could have breakfast together in the kitchen. If Sarah had nightmares, she could climb in with you. You could read her stories and I could listen." He smiled crookedly. "I don't remember anybody ever reading me a story, Meredith," he added. "My uncle wasn't the type. I grew up in a world without fairy tales and happy endings. Maybe that's why I'm so bitter. I don't want Sarah to end up like me."

"Don't run yourself down," she said softly. Her eyes searched over his face warmly. "I think you turned out pretty well."

He touched her hair with a big, lean hand. "I never meant to be as cruel to you as I was." He sighed wearily. "And I guess if it hadn't been for Sarah, you wouldn't have come near me again, would you?" he asked.

She lowered her eyes to his chest. "I don't know," she said honestly. "I was still bitter, and a little afraid of you when I came back. But when I saw you with Sarah…" Her eyes lifted. "You might not realize it, but you're different when she's around. She takes some of the rough edges off you."

"She's pretty special. No thanks to Nina," he added curtly. "God knows why she kept the child when she so obviously didn't want her."

"Maybe her husband did."

"If he did, he sure changed his tune when he found out she was mine. He turned his back on her completely. I'm damned if I could have done that to a child," he said coldly. "Whether or not we shared the same blood, there are bonds equally strong."

"Not everyone has a sense of honor," Meredith reminded him. "Your sense of honor was always one of your strongest traits."

"It still is." He sat down on the bench again, tugging her down beside him and drawing her closer while Sarah stopped the swing and ran to the sandbox. "She'll carry half that sand home with us," he murmured ruefully.

"Sand brushes off," Meredith reminded him.

He smiled. "So it does." He leaned back and his hand contracted on her shoulder. "She's crazy about you."

"I like her, too. She's a wonderful little girl."

"I hope you'll still think so after she's treated you to one of her tantrums."

"Most children have those," she reminded him. She leaned back against his arm and looked up at him. Impulsively she reached up and touched the white line of scar tissue on his face, noticing the way he flinched and grabbed her hand. "It's not unsightly," she said softly, and she smiled. "I told Sarah it was a mark of courage, and it is. You got it because of me. It was my fault."

His fingers curled around hers and pressed before he led them back to the scar and let her touch it. "Saving you from a wild bronc," he recalled, smiling because it was a lot like what had happened to Sarah in the corral. "You weren't after a lacy white handkerchief. Instead it was a kitten that had run into the corral. I got to you in the nick of time, but I ran face first into a piece of tin on the way out."

"You used words I'd never heard before or since," she murmured sheepishly. "And I deserved every one of them. But you let me patch you up, anyway. That was sweet," she said unthinkingly, and then lowered her eyes.

"'Sweet.'" His hard lips pursed as he studied her face. "You'll never know what I felt. The atmosphere was electric that day. I gritted my teeth and forced myself to glare at you. It kept me from doing what I really wanted to do."

"Which was?" she asked, curious, because she remembered too well the cold fury in his face and voice as she'd doctored him.

"I wanted to pull you into my lap and kiss the breath out of you," he said huskily. "You were wearing a cotton blouse with nothing, not a damned thing, under it. I could see the outline of your breasts under the blouse and I wanted to touch them so badly that I shook with longing. It wasn't more than a day later that I did just that, in the stable. You didn't know," he guessed, watching the expressions play across her face.

"No," she admitted breathlessly. "I had no idea. Of course, I was shaking a little myself, and trying so hard to hide my reaction from you that I didn't notice what you might be feeling."

"I lay awake all night, remembering the way you looked and sounded and smelled." He glanced at Sarah, watching her make a pointed castle in the sand and stack twigs around it for doors and windows. "I woke up aching. And then, days later, they read the will, and I went wild. Nina was clinging to me, I was confused about what I felt for you and for her." He shrugged. "I went crazy. That's why I said such cruel things to you. I wanted you so badly. When I saw you later, I couldn't resist one last chance to hold you, to taste you. So I kissed you. It took every last ounce of willpower I had to pull back."

"I really hated you for that," she said, remembering. "I knew you were getting even for the will, for what your uncle tried to do. I never realized that you really wanted me." She smiled self-consciously.

His lips twisted. "Do you think a man can fake desire?" he asked with a level stare.

She flushed and avoided his gaze. "No."

"At least I know now that I'm still capable of feeling it," he said heavily, his eyes going again to Sarah. "It's been a long dry spell. I couldn't bear the thought of having some other woman cut up my pride the way Nina did. And no one knows better than I do that I'm not much good in bed."

"I think that depends on who you're in bed with," she said, staring at his shirt. "When two people care about each other, it's supposed to be magic, even if neither of them has any experience."

"It wasn't magic for us, and we both fit into that category the day the will was read," he murmured softly.

"That's true. But I fought you. I didn't understand what was happening," she confessed.

He studied her down-bent head. "Do you think it might be different now that we've both had five years to mature?"

"I don't know," she said.

His lean hand touched her hair hesitantly and trailed down her cheek to her soft mouth. "I haven't learned a lot," he said, his voice quiet and deep. He drew in a slow breath. "And you knock me off balance pretty bad. I might frighten you if things got out of hand."

He sounded as if the thought tormented him. She lifted her eyes and looked up at him. "Oh, no," she said softly. "You wouldn't hurt me."

His heart stampeded in his chest when she looked at him that way. "Would you go that far with me?" he whispered.

She couldn't sustain that piercing green-eyed gaze. Her eyes fell to his hard mouth. "Don't ask me, Blake," she pleaded. "I would, but I'd hate both of us. All those years of strict upbringing don't just go away because we want them to. I'm not made for a permissive life. Not even with you.''

She made it sound as if he were the exception to the rule, and he felt a sting of pure unadulterated masculine pride at her words. She wanted to. He smiled slowly. That made things a little easier. Of course, the walls were all still up. The smile faded when he realized that those scruples of hers were going to stop him, because his own conscience and sense of honor wouldn't let him seduce her. Not even if she wanted him to.

''I guess I'm not either, if you want the truth.'' He sighed. ''You and I are a dying breed, honey.''

She heard the endearment with a sense of awe. It was the first time he'd used one with her, the very first time. She was aware of a new warmth deep inside her as she savored it in her mind.

''Daddy, look at my sand castle!'' Sarah Jane called. ''Isn't it pretty? But I'm hungry. And I want to go to the bathroom.''

Blake smiled involuntarily. ''Okay, sprout. Come on.'' He moved slightly away from Meredith. ''She doesn't settle for long. Her mind is like a grasshopper.''

''I think it's the age.'' Meredith smiled. She knelt and held out her arms for Sarah to run into, and she lifted the child, hugging her close. ''You smell nice,'' she said. ''What do you have on?''

''It's Daddy's,'' Sarah said, and Blake's eyebrows shot up. ''It was on his table and I got me some. Isn't it nice? Daddy always smells good.''

''Yes, he does.'' Meredith was fighting a losing battle with the giggles. She looked at Blake's astounded face and burst out laughing.

"So that's where it went," he murmured, sniffing Sarah and wrinkling his nose. "Sprout, that stuff's for me. It's not for little girls."

"I want to be like you, Daddy," Sarah said simply, and there was the sweetest, warmest light in her green yees.

Blake smiled at her fully for the first time, his white teeth flashing against his dark tan. "Well, well. I guess I'll have to teach you how to ride and rope, then."

"Oh, yes!" Sarah agreed. "I can ride a horse now. And I can rope anything. Can't I, Merry?"

Meredith almost agreed, but Blake's eyes were making veiled threats.

"You'd better wait a bit, until your daddy can teach you properly," Meredith said carefully, and Blake nodded in approval.

"I hate to wait," Sarah muttered.

"Don't we all," Blake murmured, but he didn't look at Meredith as he started toward the car. "Let's find someplace that sells food."

They found a small convenience store with rest rooms just a little way down the road, where they bought coffee and soft drinks and the fixings for sandwiches, along with pickles and chips. Blake drove them back to the park, which was beginning to fill up.

"I know a better place than this," he remarked. "Sarah, how would you like to wade in the river?"

"Oh, boy!" she exclaimed.

He smiled at Meredith, who smiled back. "Then let's go. We're between the Canadian and the North Canadian rivers. Take your pick."

"The North Canadian, then," Meredith said.

He turned the car and shot off in the opposite direction, while Sarah Jane asked a hundred questions about

Oklahoma, the rivers, the Indians and why the sky was blue.

Meredith just sat quietly beside Blake as he drove, admiring his lean hands on the wheel, the ease with which he maneuvered through Jack's Corner and out onto the plains. He didn't try to talk while he drove, which was good, because Sarah wouldn't have let him get a word in edgewise, anyway.

Sarah's chatter gave Meredith a breathing space and she used it to worry over Blake's unexpected proposal. He wanted her to move in with him and Sarah, and she was more tempted than he knew. She had to keep reminding herself that she had a lot to lose—and it was more than just a question of her reputation and his. It was a question of her own will and whether she could trust herself to say no to Blake if he decided to turn on the heat.

He wasn't a terribly experienced man, but that wouldn't matter if he started kissing her. She still loved him. If he wanted her, she wasn't sure that all her scruples would keep her out of his bed.

And being the old-fashioned man he was, she didn't know what would happen if she gave in. He'd probably feel obliged to offer to marry her. That would ruin everything. She didn't want a marriage based on obligation. If he grew to care about her, and wanted her for his own sake and not Sarah's...

She forced her mind back to the present. It didn't do to anticipate fate. Regardless of how she felt, it was Blake's feelings that mattered now. He had to want more than just her body before she could feel comfortable about the future.

Seven

Blake drove over the bridge that straddled the Canadian River, but he didn't stop on its banks. He kept driving until finally he turned off on a dirt road and they went still another short distance. He stopped the car under an oak tree and helped Meredith and Sarah Jane out into the shade.

"Where are we?" Meredith asked, disoriented.

He smiled. "Come and see." He took Sarah's hand and led them through the trees to a huge body of water. "Know where you are now?" he asked.

Meredith laughed. "Lake Thunderbird!" she burst out. "But this isn't the way to get to it! And this isn't the North Canadian or the Canadian. It's in between!"

"Don't confuse the issue with a lot of facts," he said with dry humor. "Isn't this a nice place for a picnic?" he went on. "We have shade and peace and quiet."

"Who owns this land?"

He pursed his lips. "Well, actually, it's part of what I inherited from my uncle. It's only fifteen acres, but I like it here." He looked around the wooded area with eyes that appreciated its natural beauty. "When I need to think out something, I come here. I guess that's why I've never built on it. I like it this way."

"Yes, I can see why," Meredith agreed. Birds were singing nearby, and the wind brushed leafy branches together with soft whispers of sound. She closed her eyes and let the breeze lift her hair, and she thought that with Sarah and Blake beside her, she'd never been closer to heaven.

"Sarah, don't go too near the edge," Blake cautioned.

"But you said I could go wading," the child protested, and began to look mutinous.

"So I did," he agreed. "But not here. After we eat, there's a nice place farther down the road where you can wade. Okay?"

For several long seconds, she matched her small will against his. But in the end she gave in. "Okay," she said.

Blake got out the cold cuts and bread, and a heavy cloth to spread on the grass. They ate in contented silence as Sarah offered crumbs to ants and other insects, fascinated with the variety of tiny life.

"Haven't you ever seen a bug before, Sarah?" Meredith asked.

"Not really," the little girl replied. "Mama said they're nasty and she killed them. But the man on TV says that bugs are bene . . . bene . . ."

"Beneficial," Blake said. "And I could argue that with the man on TV, especially when they get into the hides of my cattle."

Meredith smiled at him. He smiled back. Then the smiles faded and they were looking at each other openly, with a blistering kind of attraction that made Meredith's body go hot. She'd never experienced that electricity with anyone except Blake. Probably she never would, but she had to get a grip on herself before it was too late.

She forced her eyes down to the cloth. "How about another sandwich?" she offered with forced cheer.

After they finished the makeshift meal, Blake drove them down to the small stream. It ran across the dirt road, and Sarah tugged off her cowgirl boots in a fever to get to the clear, rippling water. Butterflies drifted down on the wet sand, and Blake smiled at the picture the child made walking barefoot through the water.

"I used to do that when I was a boy," Blake said, hands in his pockets as he leaned against the trunk of the car and watched her. "Kids who live in cities miss a hell of a lot."

"Yes, they do. I can remember playing like this, too. We used to get water from streams occasionally in oil drums, when the well went dry." Her eyes had a wistful, faraway look. "We were so poor in those days. I never realized how poor until I went to a birthday party in grammar school and saw how other kids lived." She sighed. "I never told my parents how devastating it was. But I realized then what a difference money makes."

"It doesn't seem to have changed you all that much, Meredith," he said, studying her quietly. "You're a little more confident than you used to be, but you're no snob."

"Thank you." She twisted the small gold-braid ring on her finger nervously. "But I'm not in your class yet. I get by and that's all."

"A Porsche convertible is more than just getting by," he mused.

"I felt reckless the day I bought it. I was thinking about coming back here and facing the past," she confessed. "I bought it to give me confidence."

"We all need confidence boosters from time to time,"
Blake replied quietly, his eyes on Sarah. "She's slowly
coming out of the past. I like seeing her laugh. She didn't
in those first few days with me."

"I guess she was afraid to," Meredith said. "She hasn't
really had much security in her young life."

"She's got it now. As long as I live, I'll take care of her."

The pride and faint possessiveness in his deep voice
touched Meredith. She wondered how it would feel to have
him say the same thing about her, and she blushed. Blake
might allow himself to become vulnerable with a small
child, but she had serious doubts about his ability to really
love a woman. Nina had hurt him too badly.

They stayed another few minutes, and then Sarah announced that she needed to find a bathroom again. With
an amused smile, Blake loaded them into the car and set
out for a gas station.

They drove around looking at the countryside until almost dark. Then they went home and Meredith helped
Sarah get a bath. After that, she settled down by the child's
bedside to tell her some stories before she fell asleep.

She was halfway through "Sleeping Beauty," when
Blake came into the room and sat down, legs crossed, in
the chair by the window to listen. He was a little intimidating, but Sarah laughed and encouraged Meredith, and
in no time she was lost in the fantasy herself.

She told the child two more stories and Sarah's eyelids
grew heavier by the second. By the time Meredith had
started on "Snow White," Sarah Jane was sound asleep.

Meredith got up, tucked the covers around the tired little body and bent impulsively to kiss Sarah good-night.

"That's another thing she's missed," Blake remarked as
he joined her by the bed. "Being kissed good-night." He
shifted, his hands in his pockets as he looked down at his

daughter. "Showing affection is difficult for me." He glanced at Meredith. "My uncle wasn't the kissing sort." He smiled a little. "And I guess you know that."

She laughed. "Yes. I remember. He was a sweet man, but he hated touching or being touched."

"So do I," Blake replied. His eyes slid over Meredith's soft oval face. "Except by you," he added quietly. "I used to love to get cut up when you were here because you always patched me up. I loved the feel of your hands on my skin. I remember how soft and caring they were." He sighed heavily and turned away. "We'd better get out of here before we wake her up."

It was obviously embarrassing to him to admit how much he'd enjoyed her doctoring. That was surprising. She hadn't realized until he'd said it just how many minor accidents he seemed to have had in the old days, when she was around. She smiled to herself. That was one more tiny secret to cherish in the years ahead, when these sweet days were just a memory and Blake was far out of her reach.

"Why are you smiling?" he asked curtly.

She looked across at him as she closed Sarah's door. "I was thinking how ironic it is. I loved it when you needed patching up because it gave me an excuse to get close to you." She colored a little as she averted her eyes.

"Isn't it amazing how green we both were?" he asked. "Considering our ages. We weren't kids."

"No."

The atmosphere was getting tenser by the second. She could almost feel the hard pressure of his mouth on her lips, and the way he was watching her, with that single-minded level stare, made her knees feel weak under her.

"How do you remember all those fairy tales?" Blake asked to relieve the tension that he was feeling.

"I don't know. It's a knack, I guess. Blake, you really do need to get her some storybooks," she said.

"You'll have to pick them out," he replied. "I don't know beans about what kids her age read."

"All right. I'll see if Mrs. Donaldson has any in her shop. I noticed some books in the back, but I didn't take time to look at them."

"I appreciate your help tonight," he said. "Some facets of being a parent are difficult. Especially dealing with frilly underwear and baths." He leaned against the wall, in no hurry to go downstairs, and his green eyes wandered slowly over Meredith's exquisite figure in the revealing button-up white tank top and well-fitting blue jeans. His eyes narrowed on that top because he didn't think there was anything under it and her breasts were hard tipped when they hadn't been a minute ago. "You're very maternal."

"I like children. Shouldn't we go downstairs?" she added nervously, because she felt the impact of his eyes on her breasts.

"Why? Do you suspect that I'm going to drag you into my bedroom and lock the door?"

"Of course not," she said too quickly.

"Pity," he remarked, shouldering away from the wall. "Because that's exactly what I'm going to do."

And he did, quickly, smoothly and with deadly efficiency. Before Meredith had time to say anything, he had her in his room. He paused to lock the door and then lowered her onto the middle of the king-size bed.

She lay there breathless, staring up at him, as he bent over her, one lean hand on either side of her head, his green eyes biting into hers.

"How afraid of me are you, Meredith?" he asked quietly. "If I start making love to you, are you going to kick and scream for help?"

Her lips parted as she looked up at him. She wasn't afraid of him at all. During the day, something had happened to both of them. The time they'd spent together had acted to bring them close. She knew more about him now than she ever had, and the thought uppermost in her mind was how much she loved him. Her eyes fell to his hard mouth, and she wanted it, and him, almost shockingly.

"No, I'm not frightened," she said. "Because I know you won't hurt me or force me to do anything I don't want to. You said so."

He seemed to relax a little. "That's true. I meant it, too." His eyes slid down her body, lingering on the thrust of her breasts against the tank top and the way her jeans clung to her rounded hips and long legs. "You can't imagine the effect you've had on me all day in that getup. Do you know how sexy you are?"

"Me?" she asked with a faint, delighted smile.

"You." He lifted his gaze back to collide with hers. "And you aren't getting out of here yet."

She felt tiny tremors shooting up and down her spine at the delicious threat. "I'm not?" she asked huskily.

He lowered himself down over her so that his chest was almost touching her breasts and his mouth was within an inch of hers. "No," he breathed. "You're not."

Her hands slid up around his neck and her eyes dropped to his mouth. He smelled of cologne and she loved the feel of his shoulders and back under her hands, the hard muscles under the thin shirt. Her breath jerked out of her throat as she felt the warm threat of his body and tasted his coffee-scented breath on her lips.

"Just relax," he whispered as his mouth brushed hers. "I won't hurt you."

Her hands slid into his thick hair and she let her body sink under the warm weight of his chest as it pressed against hers. His mouth was slow and hungry, and she didn't mind when it began to probe inside her own. She'd never kissed anyone except Blake this way, and she loved the sensuality of it. She let his tongue enter her mouth and her hands clung as the new sensations ran like fire along her nerves and made her weak.

She kissed him back, savoring the warm hungry mouth on hers. One of his hands supported her neck, but the other slid over her shoulder and suddenly covered her soft breast.

She took an audible breath and he lifted his head, but he didn't remove his hand.

"You're a woman now," he whispered. "And we've done this together once before. Except that this time, I'm not so green."

"Yes." She touched his fingers, lightly brushing them, while her eyes looked into his glittering ones with building excitement. Her swollen lips parted. "You could... unbutton it," she whispered shakily. "I'm not wearing anything under it."

She colored as she said it, and he realized how much courage it took for her to make him such an offer. Was she trying to prove that she trusted him, or could she feel the same hunger he did?

His fingers slid to the buttons and slowly began to slip them out of the buttonholes. And all the while, he searched her eyes, held them. "Why aren't you wearing anything underneath?" he asked when he'd finished and the edges were still touching.

"Don't you know, Blake?" she whispered with aching hunger. She arched just a fraction of an inch.

The invitation was as blatant as if she'd shouted it. He slowly peeled the edges of the tank top away from her full, firm breasts and let his eyes fall to them. They were as beautiful as they had been five years ago. A little fuller now, firmer. The color of seashells and rose petals, he thought dizzily as his eyes lingered on the hard tips that signaled her desire.

"Have you ever let any other man see you like this?" he whispered, because it was suddenly important.

"Only you," she replied, and her eyes were warm and soft, almost loving as they met his. "How could I let anyone else . . . ?" she asked huskily.

"Meredith, you're exquisite," he bit off. His fingers brushed over one perfect breast lightly, barely touching it, and she cried out.

The sound startled him. He stopped at once, scowling at her in open concern. "Did I hurt you?" he asked softly. "I knew you were delicate there. I didn't mean to be rough with you."

She stared at him curiously, biting her lower lip as she tried to control the tremors he'd set off. "Blake . . . it didn't hurt," she said hesitantly.

"You cried out," he said, his eyes steady and honestly worried.

She colored furiously. "Yes."

The scowl stayed as his hand moved again. His green eyes held hers the whole time while he stroked her gently, smoothed the hard tip between his fingers and cupped her in his lean, rough hand. And she whimpered softly and cried out again, her body shivering and lifting up to him.

"Damn Nina!" he whispered roughly.

Meredith was too drugged to understand what he'd said at first. Her whirling thoughts barely registered in her mind. "What?"

"Never mind," he whispered huskily. "Oh, God, Meredith...!" His mouth went down against her breast, and she moaned, arching under him. The sound and her trembling drove him crazy.

He kissed every soft inch of her above her hips, savoring both breasts, nibbling at her creamy skin, dragging the edge of his teeth with exquisite tenderness over her stomach and rib cage. And all the while his hands caressed her, adored her. He made a meal of her, and long before he lifted his head, she was crying and pleading with him for something more than he was giving her.

He dragged air into his lungs, his eyes wild, his chest rising and falling raggedly as he looked down into her abandoned eyes.

Her face fascinated him. She looked as if he was torturing her, but her hands were pulling at his head, her soft voice was begging for his mouth. She moaned, but not in pain. And the most exquisite sensations racked his lean body as he poised over her. "You want me," he whispered huskily.

"Yes."

"Badly," he continued.

"Yes!"

His hands smoothed over her breasts and she shuddered. His breath caught. "I never dreamed a woman could sound like that. I never knew..." He bent to her mouth and kissed it softly. "My God, she was suffering me, and I didn't even have the experience to realize it."

"What?"

He dragged himself into a sitting position, and when she made a halfhearted effort to cover herself he pulled her wrist away. "Don't do that," he said quietly. "You're the most beautiful thing I've ever seen in my life. I won't hurt you."

"I know that. I'm just...embarrassed," she faltered, flushing.

"You shouldn't be," he said firmly. "The first intimacy I ever shared with a woman was with you. And your first one was with me. I know what you look like. I've seen you every night in my dreams."

She relaxed a little, sighing as she sank back on the bed. "It's just new," she tried to explain.

"Yes, I know." He brushed his fingertips over a firm breast and watched her shiver with pleasure. "That's sweet," he breathed. "That's so damned sweet, Meredith."

Her breath sighed out. "Blake..."

"What do you want?" he asked, reading the hesitant curiosity in her eyes. "Tell me. I'll do anything you want."

"Could you...unbutton your shirt and let me look at you?" she whispered.

His blood surged in his veins. He flicked buttons open with a hand that was deftly efficient even as he trembled inside with the hunger she aroused. He moved the fabric aside, and when he saw the sheer delight in her eyes at the thick mat of hair over impressive muscle, arrowing down to his jeans, he stripped the whole damned shirt off and threw it on the floor to give her an unobstructed view.

She held out her arms, and he groaned as he went into them, shuddering when he felt her nipples press against his chest as he crushed her into the mattress.

"Blake," she moaned. Her arms clung and her lips searched blindly for his. She found them and kissed him with all her heart, feeling his mouth tremble as it increased its hungry pressure.

He slid over her. His hands found her hips and urged them up against his, moving them against his rhythmically, letting her experience the full surge of his arousal.

She was whimpering, and he felt his control giving. It would only take another few seconds...

"No!" he bit off. He jerked himself away from her and rolled over, but he couldn't get to his feet. He lay there doubled up, while Meredith managed to get her trembling arms to support her. But she didn't touch him. He was shivering and she wanted to cry because she knew it was hurting him that he'd had to stop.

"I'm sorry," she wept. "It's all my fault."

"No, it isn't," he said through his teeth. He drew in sharp breaths until he could get himself under control. His body relaxed and he lay there for a long moment, fighting the need to roll over and strip her and submerge himself in her soft warm body.

"I wouldn't have stopped you," she breathed.

"I know that, too." He finally dragged himself up and ran his hands through his damp hair. His eyes darted to her half-clad body, softening as they swept over her full breasts. "Button your top," he said gently. "Or I'm going to start screaming my head off."

She managed a shaky smile as she pulled her top together and buttoned it with trembling fingers. "You make me feel beautiful," she whispered.

"My God, you are," he returned. His darkened green eyes held hers. "I can't begin to tell you what those sweet little noises you were making did for my ego. I didn't know women made noise or looked like that when they made love."

She searched his eyes. "I don't understand."

"Meredith," he began heavily, "Nina smiled. All through it, all the time. She smiled."

It took a minute for that to get through to her. When it did, she went scarlet. "Oh!"

"I hurt you, that first time," he continued. "So I didn't get any passionate response. I didn't have any other experience when I married Nina, so I thought women were supposed to smile." A corner of his hard mouth lifted ruefully. "But now I know, don't I?"

Her face felt as if she might fry eggs on it. "I couldn't help it," she confessed self-consciously. "I never dreamed there was such pleasure in being touched by a man."

He caught one of her hands and pressed its soft palm hungrily to his mouth. "The pleasure was mutual," he said, his glittering gaze holding hers. "I almost lost it. You let me hold your hips against mine, and I went crazy."

"I'm sorry," she said softly. "I should have pulled away."

"Are you supposed to be superhuman?" he asked reasonably. "I couldn't stop, either. Together we start fires. I wanted nothing more in life than to feel you under me and around me, skin on skin, mouth on mouth, absorbing me into you."

She caught her breath and trembled at the words, seeing the quiet pride in his eyes when he realized the effect they had on her.

"I want to make love to you," he whispered roughly. "Here. Now. On my bed."

"I can't." She closed her eyes. "Please don't ask me."

"It isn't lack of desire. What, then? Scruples?"

She nodded miserably. "You know how I was raised, Blake. It's hard to forget the teachings of a lifetime overnight, even when you want someone very, very much."

"Then suppose you marry me, Meredith."

Her eyes opened wide. "What?"

"We get along well together. You like Sarah. You want me. You've got a career, so I know you don't need my money, and you know I don't need yours. We could build a good life together." He searched her shocked face. "I know I'm not the best matrimonial prospect going. I'm short-tempered and impatient, and I can be ruthless. But you know the worst of me already. There won't be any terrible surprises after the vows."

"I don't know..." she argued.

"You want hearts and flowers and bells ringing." He nodded. "Well, that doesn't always happen. Sometimes you have to settle for practicalities. Tell me you don't want to live with me, Meredith," he challenged with a faintly mocking smile.

"That would be a lie," she said, sighing, "so I won't bother. Yes, I want to live with you. And I'm very fond of Sarah Jane. Taking care of her wouldn't be any trial to me. But you're still not going to let your emotions get in the way of a good business deal, are you, Blake?" she returned. "You want me, but that's all you have to offer."

"For a man, lovemaking is one big part of a relationship," he said, choosing his words. "I don't know much about love. I've never had any." He lifted his eyes back to hers. "If it can be taught, you can teach me. I've never been in love, so you've got a good shot at it already."

She sighed at his summing-up of the situation, despite the ache in her heart for something he might never be able to give her. He was locked up emotionally, and nobody had a key.

He leaned down, his face poised just above hers. "Stop thinking, Meredith," he whispered. His mouth nibbled at her lower lip, smoothing over its delicate swell. His hands cupped her breasts, hot even through the fabric of her tank top and sensual as they caressed her. One long leg insinuated itself between both of hers and she felt it begin to move lazily.

"This isn't fair," she whispered shakily.

"I know. Unbutton your top again," he whispered, and proceeded to tell her exactly why he wanted her to and what he intended to do when she unfastened it.

Her body tingled with heat. She wanted him. Her moan was pure surrender, and he knew it. His heart leaped as he felt her fingers working at the buttons. And then she was all silky warmth under him, her breasts soft and yielding under his searching hands, his hungry mouth.

"You aren't...going to stop...this time, are you?" she whimpered as his mouth grew even bolder.

"That depends on you," he said in a strange, thick tone. "I'd never force you."

"I know." Her mind tumbled while she tried to decide what to do. Part of her knew it was a mistake. But it had been so many years, and she'd done little else but dream of him, of lying in his arms and loving him.

His hand slid to the fastening of her jeans and he lifted himself so that he could see her eyes. "If I start this, I'll have to finish it," he said gently. "I'll go all the way. You have to decide."

Her fingers lingered on his. "I don't know," she moaned. "Blake, I'm afraid. It's going to hurt ... !"

"Only a little," he whispered solemnly. "I'll be as slow and tender as I can. I'll do anything you want me to do to make it easier for you." He bent to her mouth, touching it lightly with his. "Meredith, don't you want to know all the secrets?" he asked huskily. "Don't you want to see how much pleasure we can give each other? My God, just kissing you makes my blood run like fire. Having you..." He groaned as he kissed her. "Having you ... would be unbearably sweet."

"For me, too." Her arms tightened around his neck, and she buried her face in his hair-roughened chest, savoring the smell and feel of him in her arms.

His hands smoothed down her hips and his weight settled over her, gently, so that he wouldn't frighten her. His mouth trembled as it found hers, and he kissed her with exquisite warmth and tenderness.

"This is how much I want you," he whispered as he moved sensuously against her.

She felt his need, and an answering hunger made her tremble. "Blake...what about...precautions?" she choked out. "I don't know how."

His lips lifted just above hers. "I'm going to marry you," he told her roughly. "But if precautions are important to you, I can use something."

Heat shot through her. She felt her nails digging into his back, heard her own wild cry as she lifted to him. His face hardened and she saw his eyes darken as his mouth came slowly back down to cover hers.

"We should . . ." she whimpered.

"Yes," he whispered. But his mouth grew demanding, and his last sane thought was that creating babies with Meredith was as natural as wading in country streams and walking in the park. He closed his eyes, shaking with the need to join his aching body to hers and give her the same sweet pleasure he felt when he touched her.

Eight

Meredith trembled, half blind with pleasure as Blake's mouth became more demanding. It was almost enough just to kiss him, to feel the exquisite weight of his body on hers as his hand worked at the fastenings of her clothes.

"The light," she whispered huskily.

He touched her mouth tenderly. "I know," he said deeply, reaching for it. "You might not believe it, little one, but I've got more hang-ups than you have."

The room was in darkness then, except for the faint moonlight seeping in through the white curtains. His hands smoothed down her breasts, savoring their warm fullness. She gasped and he searched for her mouth in the darkness.

"Meredith," he whispered huskily.

"What?" she breathed.

"One of us needs to do something if you don't want me to make you pregnant. You haven't really answered me."

She felt the heat in her cheeks. He was right, it was something they had to consider. She swallowed. "I'm not on the pill," she confessed.

"Do you want me to take care of it?"

Her fingers touched his face, involuntarily running down the scar, while visions of his son in her arms made her tremble with hunger. "I . . . I don't mind, either way," she said unsteadily.

"God!" He buried his face in her throat and shuddered. It was so profound to hear her say that. It would be all of heaven to see her grow big with his child, to share the sweetness of raising it.

"Blake?" she whispered, uncertain.

"I don't mind, either," he said roughly. "Come here."

He pulled her closer still and she melted against him with blinding hope as he began to tease her breasts with his hands. He trailed his fingers around the outer edges, feeling the tension in her body, the heat of her skin as he drew his caresses out, making her wait, building the need, until she caught his wrists and tried to make him touch her.

And he did, finally, so that it was like a tiny fulfillment, and she shuddered and arched into his warm, lean hands. He liked her reactions, delighted in her responses. She had to care about him, he thought dizzily as his hands smoothed away her clothing, to let him do these things to her and to feel such pleasure when he did.

He was slow. Deliberately slow. More patient than he'd ever dreamed of being. He loved the soft sounds that came whispering out of her throat, the way her hands were clinging to him. He loved the very texture of her skin, the sound of her quick breathing like a rustle in the darkness as he touched her more intimately.

He should be out of his mind with the need to have her, he thought in the back of his mind. But stronger than pas-

sion was the need for her to feel the same exquisite sensations that were rippling through his powerful body and
making him tremble with each new touch, each soft kiss.
He wanted much, much more than quick fulfillment. He
wanted to touch all that was Meredith, to join his body to
hers and feel the oneness that he'd read was possible between two people who cared for each other.

His lips smoothed over hers, barely touching, while his
hands found her where she was untouched and gently,
tenderly probed. She gasped under his mouth. Thank God
for books, he thought while he could. He hadn't known
anything about virgins until he'd done some reading the
other night.

"It's all right," he whispered tenderly. "I'm going to be
very gentle, Meredith. I just want to make sure that what
we do won't be any more painful than it has to be."

"I don't mind," she told him softly, clinging.
"Blake...I'd give you anything...!"

"Yes." His mouth whispered against hers. "I'd give you
anything, too, Meredith. I'd do anything to please you,
even forgo my own pleasure."

That didn't sound like lust. Neither did the exquisitely
slow movements of his hands, the gentle crush of his body.
He was hungry, she could feel his need, but he wouldn't
take his pleasure at her expense. That consideration, incredible given the length of abstinence for him, made her
want to cry. He had to care a little to be so...!

Her mind went crazy as his hand moved and she felt a
stab of pleasure so sweet that it lifted her and she cried out.

She clung to him, telling him without words that it was
pleasure, not pain, she was feeling. He warmed, remembering his own earlier withdrawal when she moaned or
gasped, because he'd never known how a woman re-
sponded when giving herself to pleasure.

He opened his mouth on hers and let his tongue gently stab inside her lips, aching at the implied intimacy, delighting in the way her soft, slender body turned in his hands when he did that. She was loving this, he thought dizzily. Loving every second of it, reveling in his mouth, his touch. He could feel her pleasure even as his built and built until he couldn't contain it any longer.

She was trembling now, and tiny whispers of excitement were moaning past her lips as she lay waiting for him, her body twisting sensually with mindless abandon.

He was heady with pride at his own latent abilities. He hadn't dreamed that with his inexperience he could bring her to this frenzy.

He stripped with quick, deft movements and slid onto the coverlet beside her, his hands moving on her body, holding her while he kissed her with whispery tenderness.

"Pl...ease." She managed the one word, and her voice broke on it.

"I want you, too, little one," he breathed against her mouth. "I want you so much."

He balanced his weight on his forearms and slid over her, trembling at the soft warmth of her legs tangling with his. She moved, helping him, and he let his hips ease down.

She felt the first hesitant probing and shuddered, but she didn't tense. She forced her body to relax, not to fight him.

He could feel that, and his mouth smoothed over her lips in silent reassurance.

His hands went to her face, holding it while he kissed her, and he felt her soft cry go into his mouth as he pushed gently against the veil of her womanhood.

And it was easy then. He felt the faint tension go out of her body, felt her sigh feather against his lips.

"I won't ever have to hurt you again," he murmured unsteadily. "I'm sorry it has to be this way for a virgin."

"But it wasn't bad," she whispered back. Her fingers slid into his cool, thick hair. "Oh, Blake..." she whimpered. She kissed him softly. "Blake, it's...incredible!"

"Yes." He touched her eyes, closing them; he touched her nose, cheeks and forehead with lips that were breathlessly tender. And all the while his body moved with equal tenderness, drowning her in the exquisite sensation of oneness. She pulled his mouth to hers as his movements began to lengthen and deepen with shuddering pleasure, her breath filling him, her tiny cries making him feverish with contained passion.

His hands slid under her, savoring the warm, soft skin of her back and hips, holding her to him.

"Meredith—" His voice broke on her name. His eyes closed. He felt the tension growing in his powerful body with each torturously slow movement, felt the control he had beginning to slip. But her control was going, too. She was trembling, clinging, her mouth ardent and hungry. He lifted her up and overwhelmed her with desperate tenderness, and when the spasms came, they were white hot, blinding, but with a gentleness that he couldn't have imagined.

She bit him in her passion, but he was riding waves of completion and he hardly felt her teeth. His hands contracted. He cried her name against her damp throat and the tide washed over him in pulsating shudders.

He heard her crying an eternity later and he managed to lift his head and search her face. "Meredith?" he whispered huskily. "Oh, God, I didn't hurt you, did I?"

"No!" She buried her face against his chest, kissing him there, kissing his throat, his face, everywhere she could reach, with lips that worshipped him. "Blake!" she moaned, her arms contracting around his neck. "Blake...!" She shuddered again and again, and when he realized why, he put his mouth gently against hers and began to move.

The second time was every bit as sweet, but slower, more achingly drawn out. He hadn't dreamed a man could hold out as long as he was managing to. But he adored her with his mouth, his hands, and finally, when she was crying with the tension he'd aroused, he adored her with the slow, worshipping motion of his body in one long, sweet pinnacle of fulfillment.

She couldn't seem to stop crying. She lay in his arms with her wet face pillowed on his chest where the thick hair was damp with sweat. She couldn't let go of him, either, and he seemed to understand that, because he held her even closer and gently brushed her hair away from her face while he kissed her tenderly and soothed her.

"I thought . . . passion was uncontrollable and . . . and quick . . . and men couldn't . . . men were rough," she told him.

"How could I be rough with you?" His mouth touched hers, brushing softly over her trembling lips. "Or make something that beautiful into raw sex?"

Her breath sighed out, making little chills against his damp skin. "I'm so glad I waited for you," she said simply, shaken by the experience. "I'm so glad I didn't give in to some man I didn't even like out of curiosity or because everybody else was doing it." She nuzzled her face against him. "You are so wonderful."

He drew her mouth up to his and kissed her possessively. "So are you," he whispered. "I didn't know what lovemaking was until tonight. I didn't know that there could be such pleasure in it," he murmured against her mouth.

"I thought men felt the pleasure with anyone," she replied.

"Apparently it's an individual thing," he said quietly. "Because I never felt anything approaching this before." He heard the words without realizing their importance, until it suddenly came to him that he'd hardly felt anything with Nina. But Meredith's soft young body had sent him spinning into oblivion and he'd done things with her and to her that had come naturally. Perhaps it was instinct. But what if it was something stronger?

He'd called it lovemaking, and it had been. Not sex, or the satisfaction of a need. And he couldn't imagine doing that with anyone except Meredith. Not that way. Not with such staggering tenderness. He hadn't even known he was capable of it.

"I wasn't sure I could wait for you," he confessed, nuzzling her face. "Was it enough?"

Her body burned with the memory, and she kissed his throat with breathless tenderness. "Yes. And...was it for you?" she asked, worried.

"Yes." Only the one word, but there was a wealth of unspoken pleasure in it.

She was beginning to feel self-conscious, and he seemed distant all of a sudden, as if he were withdrawing. Had he satisfied his hunger for her and now he was looking for a way out of what could become an embarrassing situation? Did he regret what they'd done? He had old-fashioned ideas about sex, after all. In fact, so did she, but they hadn't helped once he'd started kissing her. Her love for him had betrayed her into his bed.

"Blake, you don't...I mean, you don't think I'm easy...?" she asked suddenly.

"My God!" he exclaimed. He reached over and turned on the light, blinding her with stark illumination and embarrassment.

She fumbled for the cover, scarlet faced, but he stayed her hand.

"No," he said quietly, his eyes as solemn as his face. "Look at me, Meredith. Let me look at you."

Her eyes darted over him and she looked away quickly as the heat grew in her face, but he turned her eyes back gently.

"I'm not a monster," he said softly. "I'm just a man. Flesh and blood, like you. There's nothing to be frightened of."

She managed not to look away this time, and after the first shock, she found him beautiful, in a very masculine sense. He was looking, too, his eyes reconciling sweet memories of her five years ago with the reality of today.

"You've blossomed," he said after a minute, and there was no masculine mockery or teasing in his tone. It was deep and soft as he searched over her swollen breasts, her flat stomach, the curve of her hips, the elegant sweep of her long legs. "You're much more pleasing to my eyes than the Venus, Meredith," he said huskily. "The sight of you knocks the breath right out of me."

Her breath caught at the emotion in his voice. "You make it sound so natural," she said with faint curiosity.

"Isn't it?" he asked. His green eyes searched her soft gray ones. "We made love. I know your body as well as I know my own. We touched in more than just the conventional way, and you're part of me now. Isn't it natural that I should want to see the lovely body I've known so intimately?"

She colored, but she smiled. "Yes."

"And to answer your other question, Meredith, no, I don't think you're easy." He smoothed back her dark hair and his eyes slid over her face. "We both knew it wasn't going to be a casual encounter. I knew you were a virgin."

He brought her hand to his lips and kissed the palm tenderly. "We're going to get married and spend the rest of our lives together. That's the only reason I didn't pull away from you. If sex had been all I wanted, I could have had it long before now, and I wouldn't have seduced you in cold blood for my own pleasure."

She searched his darkened eyes. "It isn't just because of Sarah that you want to marry me, is it? Or just because you wanted me—"

He stopped the words with his mouth. "You talk too much. And worry too much. I want to marry you." He lifted his head. "Don't you want to marry me?"

Her eyes softened. "Oh, yes."

"Then stop brooding." He got up, stretching lazily while she watched him with shy fascination. He dug in his chest of drawers and pulled out a set of navy silk pajamas. He tugged the bottoms up over his hard-muscled legs and snapped them before he carried the pajama top to the bed, lifted Meredith into a sitting position and eased her arms into the sleeves.

"It's economical to share these," he murmured dryly when her eyes asked him why. "I used to sleep raw, but I have to wear something now that Sarah's here. Except that I never wear the tops." He looked down at the soft thrust of her breasts, swollen and dark tipped in the aftermath of passion. He bent slowly and brushed his lips over them, tautening as the tips went hard involuntarily. "I've never felt more like a man than I feel when I touch you," he said roughly, his eyes closing, his brows knitting in the most exquisite pleasure.

She held his dark head against her, loving the feel of his warm mouth. "Are we going to sleep together?" she asked.

"We have to," he murmured, sliding his lips slowly over her breast. "I can't let you go."

She slid her arms around his neck as he lifted his head. "But, Sarah..."

"Sarah will be the first to find out we're going to be married," he murmured. "I'll get the license. We can have a blood test on Monday morning and the service two days later. Will that give you enough time to close out your apartment in San Antonio and change your mailing address?"

"Yes." She was breathless with his impatience, but not irritated. She wanted to live with him, and the sooner the better, before he woke up to what he was doing and changed his mind. She couldn't bear it if he'd only proposed in the heat of the moment.

He read that fear in her eyes. "I'm not going to change my mind. I'm not going to back out at the last minute or decide that I've satisfied my hunger for you and I don't need you anymore. I want you, Meredith," he emphasized. "I want to live with you, and not in some modern way with no ties and no legal status. To me, living with someone involves a thing called honor. It's a lost word in this society, but it still means a hell of a lot to me. I care enough to give you my name."

"I'll try to be a good wife," she said solemnly. "You won't mind if I just sit and stare at you sometimes, will you?"

He searched her eyes quietly. "Do you love me?"

Her lips trembled and she averted her gaze, focusing on his bare chest.

"All right. I won't force it out of you." He brought her forehead to his lips, his chest swelling with the knowledge that she did love him, even if she wouldn't admit it. He could see it in her eyes, feel it in her body. Apparently love could survive the cruelest blows, because God knows he'd hurt her enough to kill anything less. He closed his eyes and nuzzled his cheek against her soft dark hair. "I'll take care of you all my life," he promised. "Don't be afraid."

She trembled a little, because she was. Afraid that he didn't care enough, that he might regret his decision. He might fall in love again someday with someone else like Nina, and what would she do? She'd have to let him go....

It was happening so fast. Almost too fast. She hesitated. "Blake, maybe we should just get engaged..." she began worriedly.

He lifted his head and searched her eyes. "No."

"But—"

He put a long finger over her lips. "Do you remember what we said to each other when we came in here? About precautions?"

She colored. "Yes."

"Marriage and children are synonymous to me," he said quietly. "I think they are to you, too. I'm illegitimate, Meredith. I won't let my child be called what I was."

She sighed. "Does it really bother you so much?"

"I'd like to know who my father was at least," he replied. "Half my heritage is lost forever, because I have no idea who he was or what his background is. I can't tell Sarah anything about him. She'll ask someday."

"She'll understand, too," she replied. "She's a very special little girl. She's so much like you."

His green eyes searched hers. "We could have another daughter," he said. "Or a son."

She held her breath while he touched her flat stomach under the long open pajama top. Her heart went crazy when he looked down, watching the tips of her bare breasts harden helplessly.

She tried to pull the fabric together, but he caught her hands and held them gently.

"No," he said. "You can't imagine the pleasure it gives me just to see you like that."

Her breath sighed past her parted lips. "It's hard."

"I know." He lifted his eyes back to hers, searching them in a long, static silence. "It was for me, too, believe it or not. But I let you look at me, and I wasn't embarrassed." He smiled faintly. "I couldn't let Nina."

She reached up and touched her lips to his. "I'm glad," she said huskily.

He pulled her against him, nudging the pajama top out of the way so that her breasts brushed slowly against his hair-roughened chest, and she caught her breath with pleasure at the exquisite friction.

"We've got a lot to learn about this," he said softly. "We can learn it together."

"Yes." She touched her mouth to his throat, his collarbone. He took her head and guided her lips to his own nipples, groaning at the pleasure that shot through him when he felt the moist suction of her mouth.

"God, that feels good!" he ground out, forcing her mouth closer.

"Let's take our clothes off and experiment some more," she suggested brazenly, teasing him for the first time.

It delighted him. "You hussy!" he accused, and tugged her head up. His eyes were playful, and his face had never looked less hard.

"You started it," she pointed out, smiling back.

"But I can't finish it," he said ruefully. He sighed over her breasts before he buttoned them out of sight. "It's too soon," he said, answering the question in her eyes. "I don't want to rush you. You're much too new to this for any more experimenting."

She studied his face quietly. "How do you know?"

"Simple logic." He touched her lips. "And a book I read," he confessed, brushing his mouth over them. "In case I ever got this far with you, I wanted to make sure I knew enough so that I wouldn't make you afraid of me again."

"Oh, Blake." She hugged him hard, nestling her face against him. "Blake, I adore you."

His heart skipped when she said it. He smiled, aglow with satiation and the knowledge that she cared. "Lie down with me. We'll sleep in each others' arms."

She tingled all over as he pulled back the cover and tucked her in, turning out the light before he climbed in beside her. He drew her to him with a long, warm sigh and kissed her.

"Good night, little one," he whispered.

"Good night, Blake."

He closed his eyes, sure that he'd never been happier in his entire life. He pulled her closer and sighed when he felt her arms go around him. For a beginning, it was perfect.

But the next morning, when he awoke and found Meredith lying asleep in his bed, the perfection waned. His body surged at the sight of her, and he realized belatedly that the hunger he'd thought assuaged last night had only grown with feeding. He wanted her more now than ever, with a fever that actually made him shake as he looked at her sleeping body.

The realization terrified him. He'd never been vulnerable. Even Nina hadn't really knocked him off balance very far, or tested his control over his emotions. But Meredith did. She was the very air he breathed, the sun in his sky. He felt a rush of possessiveness when he looked at her, a desperate need to keep her, to protect her. He got out of bed and stared at her as if he'd gone mad. He'd sworn that he would never let her get to his heart, but last night he'd given her a lien on it. This morning, she owned him lock, stock and barrel.

He swallowed down a wave of nausea. The tender loving of the night faded into cold fear with the dawn. He didn't trust women, and now that distrust had extended itself to Meredith all over again. As long as he could persuade himself that it was only physical, marriage hadn't bothered him. But what he was feeling this morning gave new meaning to the situation. He could care for her. He could go crazy over her after a few more nights like last night. He could be so enamored of her that he'd do anything she wanted just to feel her arms around him. And that realization was what caught him by the throat—that he might not be able to keep his pride, his independence. He was afraid of her because he might love her, and he couldn't trust her enough to give in to her. She might be just like Nina. How could he know before it was too late?

Like a trapped animal, he felt the need to run, to get away, to think it through.

He got up and got dressed, taking one long, hungry look at Meredith before he forced himself to jerk open the door and go out. Last night everything had been so simple, until he'd touched her for the first time. And now he was mired up to his neck in quicksand. He didn't know what to do. He had the most ridiculous urge to go out and get Meredith an armload of roses. God knows, it must be the first stages of insanity, he thought as he went down the stairs and out the back door.

Nine

Meredith woke up slowly, aware of new surroundings and light coming into her room from the wrong direction. Then she moved, and her body told her that the light wasn't the only difference.

She sat up. She was in Blake's bedroom, in Blake's bed, wearing Blake's pajama top. Her face burned. The night before came back with startling clarity. She'd given in. More than given in. She'd participated wildly in what she and Blake had done together.

Her breath came unsteadily as wave after wave of re-membered pleasure tingled in her sore body. She looked around, wondering if Blake was in the bathroom. But she spotted his pajama bottoms laid across the foot of the bed, and his boots were missing. They'd been sitting beside the armchair last night.

She got out of bed slowly, a little disoriented. "Bess!" she exclaimed, then remembered that she'd called Bess just after they'd gotten home last night to tell her that she was spending the night to help Blake with Sarah. Wouldn't Bess be grinning when she got back home this morning, she moaned to herself.

She put back on the clothes she'd taken off—the clothes that Blake had taken off for her, she corrected—and pulled on her socks and sneakers before she combed her hair.

In the mirror she could see the imprint of her head and Blake's on the pillows, and she blushed. Well, it was too late now for regrets. He'd said that they were getting married, so she might as well reconcile herself to her new status in his life. At least they were physically compatible and she loved him desperately. Perhaps someday he might learn to love her back. He was already different, mostly due, she was sure, to Sarah's gentle influence.

She opened the door and went to Sarah's room, but the little girl was nowhere in sight.

"If you're awake, breakfast is ready," Blake called from the foot of the staircase.

She looked down, thrilling to the sight of him, tall and dark headed, dressed in gray slacks and shirt with a light-weight tan sport coat and brown striped tie. He looked very elegant, and just a little somber.

That didn't bode well. She almost missed a step on her way down, nervous and shy with him after the night before. Her face was wildly colored and she couldn't look at him.

She paused two steps above him because his hand shot out and kept her there. His green eyes forced her to look at him, and he searched her face quietly.

"Come here," he said gently. "I've got something for you."

His big, lean hand curved possessively over hers and his fingers tangled in her cold ones as he led her into the hall and stopped her at the chair, which was covered with waxed paper that held dozens of small pink roses, their fragrance like perfume.

"For me?" she whispered, breathless.

"For you. I went out into the field and cut them early this morning."

She lifted them, burying her nose in their beautiful scent. "Oh, Blake," she moaned with pleasure, and looked up with her heart in her eyes.

He was glad then that he'd followed the crazy impulse in spite of his disturbing thoughts after waking. He bent and brushed his mouth over her forehead, his mood light. "I hoped you might like them," he murmured. "They looked as virginal as you did last night."

Her face felt like fire. "I'm not anymore," she said hesitantly.

He smiled slowly. "I'll carry last night in my heart until I die, Meredith Anne," he told her huskily. "It was everything it should have been. Magic."

She smiled into her roses, feeling all womanly and soft when he said things like that.

"Are you sorry that I took the choice away from you?" he asked unexpectedly, and his eyes were serious. "I carried you into my room without asking if it was what you wanted, and I didn't give you much chance to get away."

"Don't you think I could have gotten away if I'd really wanted to?" she asked honestly.

He smiled back at her. "No."

She traced rose petals. "Well, I could have. You didn't force me."

"In a way I did," he replied worriedly. "I didn't try to protect you. I don't want to force you into marriage with the threat of pregnancy."

Her eyebrows lifted. "Threat?" she picked up on the word. "Oh, no, it isn't that. A baby is..." Her breath caught as she searched his eyes and felt the hunger for a child. "Blake, a baby would be the sweetest thing in the world."

His heart began to race as he looked at her. "That's what I thought, too," he said. "That's why I didn't try to hold back." He smiled ruefully. "And the fact is, I don't think I could have. Years of abstinence makes it pretty hard for a man to keep his head."

Her eyes widened. "You meant it?" she exclaimed. "It was actually that long?"

He nodded. "Now I'm glad," he confessed. "It made it that much more intense with you." He framed her face with his lean hands and bent to savor her lips with his warm, moist ones. "So intense," he whispered roughly, "that I want it again and again and again. Every time I look at you, my body burns."

His mouth became demanding, and she felt the quick, violent response of his body to the feel of hers.

"So does mine," she whispered back, reaching up with her free hand to cling to his neck. "Blake," she moaned as his hands dropped to her hips and pulled her hard against him.

"God!" he groaned, and his mouth covered hers urgently.

Somewhere in the fever they were sharing, a door opened.

"Daddy? Meredith? Where are you?"

They broke apart with heated faces, trembling bodies and faintly crushed roses. "We're here," Blake said, recovering quickly. "We'll be there in a minute, Sarah. I was just giving Meredith her roses."

"Okay, Daddy. Aren't they nice, Merry?"

"Yes, darling," she murmured absently, but her eyes were on Blake as the child went back through to the kitchen.

"You aren't going home tonight," he said huskily. "I've got you and I'm keeping you, and to hell with gossip. I'll get the license tomorrow and arrange for blood tests with my doctor. I'll phone you from my office in the morning with the time. Meanwhile—" he smiled slowly "—you can go over to Bess's and get a change of clothes."

"What will I tell her?" she groaned.

"That we're getting married and you're taking care of Sarah while Mrs. Jackson's away," he said simply. He pulled her hand to his lips and kissed it warmly. "Sarah and I will even go with you to make things respectable. But first we'll have breakfast. Okay?"

She sighed with pure delight. "Okay. But I'll have to go to my apartment in San Antonio this week," she added.

"I'll take time off to go with you Tuesday. Sarah can come, too." He bent, half lifting her against his lean, hard body. "I'm not letting you out of my sight any more than I have to. You might decide to run for it."

"If you think that, you underestimate yourself," she murmured, and buried her face in his throat. "I don't have the strength to get away."

His hands contracted. "How sore are you?" he asked intimately.

She burrowed closer. "Blake . . . !"

"Is it bad?"

She grimaced and looked up at him, hesitating.

"Tell me the truth," he said. "It will spare us a lot of frustration later—if I start making love to you and have to stop."

"It's uncomfortable," she confessed finally, averting her eyes.

But he tilted her chin and forced her to look at him. "No secrets between us," he said. "Not ever. I want the truth, no matter how much it hurts, and you'll always get it from me."

"All right," she said. "I want it that way, too."

His eyes brushed over her soft features with lazy warmth. "You look very pretty without makeup," he remarked. "As pretty as these roses." He glanced at them and frowned. "We've bruised them a bit."

"They'll forgive us," she said. She reached up to kiss him softly. "Will your board of directors understand your taking two days off in one week?" she asked. "For a blood test and a license and then to go with me to Texas?"

"I haven't taken two days off in five years, so they'd better." He let her go. "Let's get breakfast. Then we'll go see Bess and Bobby."

She curled under his arm and, carrying her precious roses, let him guide her to the table.

It was cozy in the kitchen. Blake kept watching her and Meredith could hardly keep from bursting into song with the sheer joy of having him look at her that way. He might not love her, but he was already very, very possessive. And in time, love might come.

"Meredith and I are going to get married, Sarah," Blake said. "She's going to live with us and take care of you and write books."

Sarah's eyes lit up and the expression on the small face was humbling. "Are you, Merry? Are you going to be my mommy?" she asked, as if they were offering her the earth.

"Yes." Meredith smiled. "I'm going to be your mommy and hug and kiss you and tell you stories and—oh!"

Sarah ran to her like a whirlwind, almost knocking the breath out of her as she climbed onto her lap and clung, crying and mumbling things that Meredith couldn't understand.

"What is it, honey?" Blake asked, torn out of his normal calm by the child's totally unexpected reaction. He touched Sarah's dark hair gently. "What is it?" he repeated.

"I can stay now, can't I, Daddy?" Sarah asked him with wet red eyes. "I don't have to go. Merry is going to live with us and I'll be her little girl, too."

"Of course you can stay," Blake said shortly. "There was never any question of that."

"When I first came," she reminded him, "you said I could go to a...a home!"

"Damn my vicious tongue," Blake burst out. He got up, lifting Sarah out of Meredith's arms and into his own. He held her close, his green eyes steady on hers. "You'll never live in any home but mine," he said huskily. "You're my own flesh and blood, my own little girl. I..." He choked on the words. His jaw worked. "I...care for you—very much," he bit off finally.

Even at her age, Sarah seemed to realize what a difficult thing it was for him to say. She lowered her cheek to his shoulder with a sigh and smiled through her tears. "I love you, too, Daddy," she said.

Blake didn't know how he managed not to break down and cry. His arms contracted around her and he turned so that Meredith couldn't see his face. In all his life he'd never been so shaken.

"How about some more coffee?" Meredith asked gently. "I'll get it, okay?" She went to the stove to pour coffee from the percolator into the carafe, and her eyes were wet. She felt stunned by Blake's brief display of vulnerability, his hope for the future. If he could love Sarah, he could love others. She dabbed at her eyes and filled the carafe. Miracles did happen, after all.

When she turned back to the table, Sarah was sitting on Blake's lap. And she stayed there for the rest of breakfast, her small face full of love and wonder. Blake just looked smug.

"What about your work?" Blake asked when they'd finished breakfast and Sarah had excused herself to go and watch her eternal cartoons in the living room.

"I just need a place to set up my computer," she said.

His eyebrows arched. "What have you got?"

"An IBM compatible," she said. "Twin disk drives, over 600K memory, word processing software, a big daisy wheel printer and a modem."

"Come and look over my setup."

She let him take her hand and lead her into the study. "It's just like mine!" she exclaimed when she saw what he had on his desk.

He smiled at her. "A good omen?"

"Wonderful! Now we'll both have a spare," she said with a dancing glance.

"You can work here when I'm not home. And if you want to set up your equipment in the corner, we'll order another desk and some filing cabinets."

"It won't bother you?" she asked hesitantly. "I work odd hours. Sometimes, if I get on a streak, I may work into the small hours of the morning."

"I'm marrying you," he said. "That includes your job, your eccentricities, your bad habits and your temper. I don't mind what you do. You're entitled to a life that allows you the right to be your own person, to make your own dreams come true in business."

"I thought you were a chauvinist," she said. "That's the wrong attitude. You're supposed to refuse to let me work outside the home and say that no job is going to come before you."

He arched an eyebrow. "Okay, if that's what you want."

She hit his chest playfully. "Never mind. I like you better this way." She reached up and slid her arms around his neck. "Sarah says she won't mind if I hug and kiss her. So can I hug and kiss you, too?" she asked daringly.

His mouth quirked a little. "I guess so."

"You might show more enthusiasm," she said.

He bent his head and whispered, "I can't. You're sore."

She blushed and opened her mouth to protest just as his came down and settled over her lips. He kissed her gently, swinging her lightly in his arms from side to side as he held her mouth under his.

"That was nice," she told him huskily.

"I thought so, too." he let her go abruptly, the hardness back in his face. "I'll line up a charter flight to San Antonio for Tuesday. We can have your furniture sent out."

"It's a furnished apartment." She smiled. "All I have is my clothes, a few manuscripts and my computer stuff."

"Okay. We'll have that sent out."

"Blake, you're sure, aren't you?" she asked seriously.

"As sure as you are," he replied. "Now stop brooding over it. I'll get the license and set up the blood test for you tomorrow. Sarah can go with you to the doctor, because it will only take a minute."

"All right. It sounds like a nice day." She sighed.

"Every day is nice with you, Meredith," he said unexpectedly and with a wry smile.

But just as they started to go down to Bess's, a friend of Blake's arrived out of the blue, and Meredith went by herself, letting Sarah stay with her dad and his friend while she told Bess what was going on.

Bess was overwhelmed when she heard the news. "Congratulations!" She laughed. "It's the best thing that could have happened to both of you. You'll make a good marriage."

"Oh, I hope so." Meredith sighed. "I'll do my best, and at least Blake likes me."

"At least," Bess said, and laughed. "If you need witnesses, Bobby and I will be glad to volunteer. Elissa and King, too."

"You can all come," Meredith promised. "I'll need as much moral support as I can get." She shook her head. "It seems like a beautiful dream. I hope I don't wake up. Well, I'd better get my things and get back up to his place. I hope you don't mind, but he, uh, doesn't want me out of his sight until the ceremony Wednesday."

"Fast mover, isn't he?" Bess grinned and hugged her friend warmly. "I'm so happy for you, Merry. And for Blake and Sarah. You'll make a lovely family."

Meredith thought so, too. She carried her single suitcase out to the Porsche and drove up in front of Blake's house. Sarah Jane met her at the door as she set her case down, and Blake came out of the living room smiling.

"Well, what did she say?" he asked. He answered her silent glance into the living room. "He's gone. What did Bess say?"

"She said congratulations." Meredith laughed. "And that we'll make a lovely family."

"Indeed we will," Blake murmured gently.

"Merry, can I be a flower girl?" Sarah asked from behind her.

"You certainly can," Meredith promised, kneeling beside the child to hug her. "You can carry an armload of roses."

"But, Merry, they're all crushed."

"Daddy will cut some more," Meredith said, warming when she remembered how the roses had gotten crushed. She glanced at Blake and the look in his eyes made her blush.

The next two days went by in an unreal rush. The blood tests were done, the license obtained, and a minister was lined up to perform the ceremony at the local Baptist church where Meredith's parents had worshipped when she was a child. For reasons that Meredith still didn't understand, Blake had given her a guest room to sleep in until the wedding, and although he'd been friendly enough, he hadn't really attempted to make love to her. She preferred to think it was because she was still uncomfortable from their first time rather than because he had any regrets.

The ceremony was held late Wednesday afternoon, with King and Elissa Roper and Bess and Bobby for witnesses. Meredith said her vows with tears in her eyes, so happy that her heart felt like it would overflow.

She'd bought a white linen suit to be married in, with a tiny pillbox hat covered in lace. It was so sweet when Blake put the ring on her finger and lifted the veil to kiss her. She felt like Sleeping Beauty, as if she'd been asleep for years and years and now was waking to the most wonderful reality.

The reception was held at the Ropers' sprawling white frame house outside Jack's Corner, and Danielle and Sarah Jane played quietly while the adults enjoyed champagne punch and a lavish catered buffet.

"You didn't have to go to this kind of expense, for God's sake," Blake muttered to big King Roper.

King pursed his lips and his dark eyes sparkled. "Yes, I did. Having you get close enough to a woman to marry again deserved something spectacular." He glanced at Meredith, who was talking animatedly to Elissa and Bess

a few feet away while Bobby, the exact opposite in coloring to his half-brother, King, was watching the kids play.

"She's a dish," King remarked. "And we all know how
she felt about you when she left here." His dark eyes
caught Blake's green ones. "It's not a good thing to live
alone. A wife and children make all the difference. I know
mine do."

"Sarah likes her," Blake replied, sipping punch as his
eyes slid over Meredith's exquisite figure like a paint-
brush. "She's a born mother."

King smiled. "Thinking of a large family, are you?"

Blake glared at him. "I've only just got married."

"Speaking of which, why aren't you two going on a
honeymoon?"

"I'd like that," Blake confessed. "But neither Meredith nor I like the idea of leaving Sarah behind while we
have one. She's had enough insecurity for one month.
Anyway," he added, "Meredith's got that autographing
in town Saturday, and she doesn't want to disappoint the
bookstore."

"She always was a sweet woman," King remarked. "I
remember her ragged and barefoot as a child, helping her
mother carry eggs to sell at Mackelroy's Grocery. She
never minded hard work. In that," he added with a glance
at his friend, "she's a lot like you."

Blake smiled faintly. "I didn't have a choice. It was
work or starve in my case. Now that I'm in the habit, I
can't quit."

King eyed him solemnly. "Don't ever let work come before Meredith and Sarah," he cautioned. "Bobby had to
find that out the hard way, and he barely realized it in
time."

Blake was looking at Meredith with faint hunger in his
narrow eyes. "It would take more than a job to oversha-

dow Meredith," he said without thinking. He finished his punch. "And we'd better get going. I've got reservations at the Sun Room for six o'clock. You're sure you and Elissa don't mind having Sarah for the night?"

"Not at all. And she loves the idea of sleeping in Dan-- ielle's room," King assured him. "If she needs you, I promise we'll call, even if it's two in the morning. Fair enough?" he added when he saw the worry in Blake's eyes.

"Fair enough," Blake said with a sigh.

A few minutes later, Blake and Meredith said their goodbyes, kissed Sarah good-night and went to the Sun Room for an expensive wedding supper.

"I still can't quite believe it," Meredith confessed with a smile as she looked at her husband across the table. "That we're married," she added.

"I know what you mean," he said quietly. His eyes caressed her face. "I swore when Nina left that I'd never marry again. But it seemed the most natural thing in the world with you."

She smiled. "I hope I don't disappoint you. I can cook and clean, but I'm not terribly domestic, and when I'm writing, sometimes I pour coffee over ice and put mashed potatoes in the icebox and make coffee without putting a filter in it. I'm sort of absentminded."

"As long as you remember me once in a while, I won't complain," he promised. "Eat your dessert before it melts."

She picked up a spoon to start on her baked alaska. "Sarah was so happy." She sighed.

"You'll be good for her." He sipped his coffee and watched Meredith closely. "You'll be good for both of us."

Meredith felt as if she were riding on a cloud for the rest of the evening. The Sun Room had a dance band as well as a wonderful restaurant. They danced until late, and Meredith was concealing a yawn when they got home.

"Thank you for my honeymoon," she said with a mischievous smile when they were standing together in the hall. "It was wonderful."

"Later on I'll give you a proper one," he promised. "We'll go away for several days. To Europe or the Caribbean."

"Let's go to Australia and stay on a cattle station," she suggested. "I wrote about one of those in my last book, and it sounded like a great place to visit."

"Haven't you traveled?" he asked.

"Just to the Bahamas and Mexico," she said. "It was great, but no place is really exciting when you have to see it alone."

"I know what you mean." He pulled her against him and bent to kiss her. "You still taste of ice cream," he murmured, and kissed her again.

"You taste of coffee." She linked her arms around his neck and smiled at him. "I want to ask you something."

"Be my guest."

"Do you have any deeply buried scruples about intimacy after marriage?" she asked somberly. "I mean, I wouldn't want to cause you any trauma."

He smiled in spite of himself. "No," he replied. "I don't think I have any buried scruples about it. Why? Were you thinking of seducing me?"

"I would if I knew how," she assured him. She smiled impishly. "Could you give me a few pointers?"

He reached down and picked her up in his arms. "I think I might be able to help you out," he said. He started for the staircase with his lips brushing hers. "It might take a while," he added under his breath. "You don't mind, do you? You don't have any pressing appointments in the next few hours...?"

"Only one. With you," she whispered, and pressed her open mouth hungrily to his, shivering with delight as his tongue pushed softly inside it and tasted her. She moaned with the aching pleasure.

His lips drew back a little. "I like that," he whispered huskily. "Make a lot of noise. Tonight there's no one to hear you except me."

Her teeth tugged at his lower lip and she obliged him with a slow, sultry moan that caused his mouth to grow rough with desire. She smiled under the heat of the kiss, and when he lifted his head and saw her expression, for just an instant he wondered if, like Nina, she was pretending pleasure that she didn't feel. And then he saw her eyes. And all his doubts fell away as his mouth bit hungrily into hers. He thought that in all his life he'd never seen such a fierce passion in a woman's soft eyes....

This time he left the lights on. He undressed her slowly, drawing it out, making her dizzy with pleasure as he kissed every inch of her as he uncovered her body. When the clothes were off, his mouth smoothed over her adoringly, lingering on her soft, warm breasts. He'd never realized how infallible instinct was until now. Apparently it didn't matter how skilled he was. She cared for him, and that made her delightfully receptive to anything he wanted. His heart swelled with the knowledge.

By the time he'd undressed, she was trembling, her body waiting, her eyes so full of warm adoration that he felt like a lonely traveler finally coming home. This was nothing like the indifference Nina had shown when he'd touched her. He looked at Meredith's lovely face and wanted nothing more in life than her arms around him.

She raised her feverish eyes to his, drowning in their green glitter. His lips parted and she trembled, because he wasn't in any hurry.

His hard mouth brushed at hers while his hands touched her with reverence. His wife. Meredith was his wife, and she wanted him. He groaned softly. "Merry, love me," he whispered as his mouth bit hungrily into hers. "Love me."

She felt her body trembling with delight as she heard the soft words and wondered dizzily if he even realized what he was saying. Poor, lonely man. . . .

Her arms went around him hungrily and she kissed him back, willing to give him anything as tenderness and love welled up within her.

"You're . . . killing me," she bit off minutes later, when his slow, exquisitely tender caresses were making her shudder with need for him.

"Liar," he told her, smiling gently at her even through his own trembling need. He moved suddenly, and watched her eyes dilate, felt her body react. "That's it. Help me," he coaxed. "Show me what you want, little one. Let me . . . love you," he groaned when she lifted her body up into his.

Blinded with the passion they were sharing, she pulled his head down to her mouth and kissed him with all the lonely years and all her smothered love in her lips. She felt his powerful body tremble until it gave way under his hunger for her and he overwhelmed her with exquisite tenderness.

Her cry was echoed in his as unbearable pleasure bound them, lifted them together in a fierce buffeting embrace, and they clung to each other as the wave of fulfillment hit them together.

Meredith could barely breathe when she felt the full weight of Blake's body against her. He was shivering, and her arms contracted around him.

"Darling," she whispered. Her lips touched his cheek, his mouth, his throat, damp with sweat. "Darling, darling...!"

The endearment went through his weary body like an electric current. He returned her tender kisses, smoothing her bare body against his and loving the soft curves caressing him. His hands felt almost too rough to be touching her. He savored the warm silk of her skin, the cologne scent of her, the pleasure of just being close to her.

Somewhere in the back of his mind, he remembered whispering to her to love him. He buried his mouth in her throat, kissing it hungrily as his need broke through his reserve and made him just temporarily vulnerable.

He pulled her into the hair-roughened curve of his chest and thighs, holding her with a new kind of possessiveness. His mouth brushed her forehead and her closed eyes with breathless tenderness. He felt the tension of pleasure slowly relax in her soft body, as it had in his own.

"I've been alone all my life until now," he said quietly, his face solemn. "I never realized how cold it was until you warmed me."

Tears formed in her eyes. "I'll warm you all my life if you'll let me," she assured him huskily.

He searched her soft face and bent to take her mouth under his. "Warm me now," he breathed against her lips, and his hands slid to her hips. As he pulled her close, he heard her voice, heard the soft endearment that broke from her lips, and his heart almost burst with delight that she cared too much to be capable of hiding it.

Later, curled up together with the lights out, Blake lay

awake long after Meredith was enveloped in contented
sleep. He couldn't quite believe what had happened so
quickly in his life. He'd been alone, and now he had a
daughter and a loving wife, and the way it was affecting
him made him nervous.

Something had happened tonight with Meredith.
Something incredible. It hadn't been just the satisfying of
a physical desire anymore. It went much deeper than that.
There was something reverent about the way they made
love, about the tenderness they gave to each other. He was
being taken over by Meredith and he had cold feet. Could
he really trust her not to walk out on him as Nina had? If
he let himself fall in love with her, would she betray him?
He looked down at her sleeping face, and even in the
darkness he could see its warm glow. The distrust relaxed
out of him. He could trust her.

Of course he could, he told himself firmly. After all, he
could live with her profession and she'd have Sarah to keep
her busy. Her writing wasn't going to interfere in their
lives. He'd make sure of it.

Ten

But Meredith's job did interfere with their marriage. Her autographing session was the first indication of it. Blake and Sarah had gone to the bookstore Saturday to watch, and Blake had been fascinated by the number of people who'd come to have her sign their books. Dressed in a very sexy green-and-white ensemble, with a big white hat to match, Meredith looked very much the successful, urbane author. And she was suddenly speaking a language he didn't understand. Her instant rapport with people fascinated and disturbed him. He didn't get along well with people, and he certainly didn't seek them out. If she was really as gregarious as she seemed and started to expect to throw lavish parties and have weekend guests, things were going to get sticky pretty fast.

As it happened, she wasn't a party girl. But she did have to do a lot of traveling in connection with the release of her latest book.

Blake went through the ceiling when she announced her third out-of-state trip in less than three weeks.

"I won't have it," he said coldly, bracing her in the study.

"*You* won't have it?" Meredith replied with equal hauteur. "You told me when we married that you didn't mind if I worked."

"And I don't, but this isn't working. It's jet-setting," he argued. "My God, you're never here! Amie's spending most of her time baby-sitting Sarah because you're forever getting on some damned airplane!"

"I know," Meredith said miserably. "And I'm sorry. But I made this commitment to promote the book before I married you. You of all people wouldn't want me to go back on my word."

"Wouldn't I?" he demanded, and he looked like the old Blake, all bristling masculinity and outraged pride. "Stay home, Meredith."

"Or what?" she challenged, refusing to be ordered about like a child of Sarah's age. "What did you have in mind, tying me to a tree out in the backyard? Or moving to your club in town? You can't, you know, you don't have a club in town."

"I could use one," he muttered darkly. "Okay, honey. If you want the job that much, go do it. But until you come to grips with the fact that this is a marriage, not a limited social engagement, I'm sleeping in the guest room."

"Go ahead," she said recklessly. "I don't care. I won't be here!"

"Isn't that the gospel truth," he said, glaring at her.

She turned on her heel and went to pack.

From then on, everything went downhill between them. She felt an occasional twinge of guilt as Blake reverted to his old, cold self. He was polite to her, but nothing more. He didn't touch her or talk to her. He acted as if she were a houseguest and treated her accordingly. It was a nightmarish change from the first days of their marriage, when every night had been a new and exciting adventure, when their closeness in bed had fostered an even deeper closeness the rest of the time. She'd been sure that he was halfway in love with her. And then her traveling had started to irritate him. Now he was like a stranger, and Meredith tossed and turned in the big bed every night, all alone. In the back of her mind, the knowledge that she had failed to conceive ate away at her confidence. As the days went on, Blake was becoming colder and colder.

Only with Sarah was he different. That was amusing, and Meredith laughed at the spectacle of Blake being followed relentlessly every step he took by Sarah Jane. She was right behind him all weekend, watching him talk to the men, sitting with him while he did the books, riding with him when he went out over the fields in the pickup truck to see about fences and cattle and feed. Sarah Jane was his shadow, and he smiled tolerantly at her attempts to imitate his long strides and his habit of ramming his hands in his pockets and rocking back on his heels when he talked. Sarah was sublimely happy. Meredith was sublimely miserable.

She tried once to talk to Blake, to make him understand that it wouldn't always be this way. But he walked off even as she began.

"Put it in your memoirs, Mrs. Donavan," he said with a mocking smile. "Your readers might find it interesting."

In other words, he didn't. Meredith choked back tears and went to her computer to work on her next book. It was taking much longer than she'd expected, and the tense emotional climate in the house wasn't helping things along. It was hard to feel romantic enough to write a love scene when her own husband refused to touch her or spend five minutes in a room with her when eating wasn't involved, or watching the news on television.

"You're losing weight," Bess commented one day at lunch when Meredith had escaped to her house to avoid the cold silence at home.

"I'm not surprised." Meredith sighed. "It's an ordeal to eat over there. Blake glares at me or ignores me, depending on his mood. I tried to explain that it wasn't going to be like this every time a book came out, but he refuses to listen."

"Maybe he's afraid to listen," Bess said sagely. "Blake's been alone a long time, and he doesn't really trust women. Maybe he's trying to withdraw before he gets in over his head. In which case—" she grinned "—it could be a good omen. What if he's falling in love with you and trying to fight it? Wouldn't he act just that way?"

"No normal man would," Meredith grumbled.

"Bobby did. So did King, according to Elissa. Men are really strange creatures when their emotions get stirred up." She cocked her blond head and stared at Meredith. "You might put on your sexiest negligee and give him hell."

"There's a thought. But he'd probably toss me out the window if I dared."

"You underestimate yourself."

"All the same, it's his heart I want to reach. I can't really do that in bed," Meredith said with sad eyes. "He's always wanted me. But I want more. I'm greedy. I want him to love me."

"Give it time. He'll come around eventually."

"Meanwhile I'm miserable," Meredith said. "At least he and Sarah are getting along like a house on fire. They're inseparable."

"Camouflage," Bess said. "He's using her to keep you at bay."

"He wouldn't."

"You greenhorn." Bess sighed. "I wish I could make you listen."

"Me, too." Meredith got up. "I've got to go. I have to fly to Boston for a signing in the morning. And I haven't told Blake yet." She grimaced. "He's been in an explosive mood for two weeks. This will sure light the fuse, I'm afraid."

"Do you have to go?"

She nodded. "It's the very last trip, but I did promise, and the bookseller is a friend of mine. I can't let her down."

Bess searched Meredith's face. "Better Blake than her?" she asked quietly. "It seems to me, from an objective standpoint, that you're running as hard from this relationship as he is. Do you really have to make these trips, or are you doing it to spite him, to prove your independence?"

"I can't let him own me," Meredith said stubbornly.

"Good for you. But a man like that isn't going to be owned, either. You're going to have to compromise if you want to keep him."

Meredith felt herself going pale. "What do you mean, if I want to keep him?"

"Just that you could drive him away. He isn't like other men. He's been kicked around too much already. His pride won't take much more abuse. You see these trips as simple tours," she explained. "Blake sees that you prefer your work to him."

Meredith felt sick. "No. He couldn't think . . ."

"I did with Bobby," Bess said simply. "I was sure that he would walk over my dying body to get to the office. I very nearly left him because of it. I couldn't bear being second best." Her eyes narrowed. "Neither can Blake. So look out."

"I've been blind," Meredith groaned. She wrapped her arms around herself. "I thought it was important not to be led around like a dumb animal, so I was fighting for my independence." She closed her eyes. "I never dreamed he'd think I considered him less important than writing."

"If you want some expert advice, tell him while there's still time," Bess suggested.

Meredith hugged the blond-haired woman. "Thanks," she said huskily. "I love him so much, you know, and it was like a dream come true when he married me. Maybe I was afraid to let myself be happy with him, afraid of being hurt, of losing him again. I guess I just lost my perspective."

"Blake probably lost his for the same reason. Get over there and fight for what you have."

"Ever thought about joining the army?" Meredith murmured on her way out the door. "You'd make a dandy drill sergeant."

"The marines offered, but then I found out they expected me to take showers with the men." Bess grinned. "Bobby would never approve of that!"

Meredith laughed and waved as she got into her car and sped back up to the house. Bless Bess for making things so clear. It was going to be all right now. She'd tell Blake the real reason she'd insisted on the tours, and it would smooth over the tension.

She got out of the car and ran into the house, but there was no sound. Odd. She was sure Sarah had been playing in the living room.

She wandered into the kitchen, but there was no one there except Amie.

"Where is everybody?" Meredith asked, excitement shining in her eyes as she savored speaking to Blake.

Amie looked at her worriedly. "Surely Blake told you, Merry," she said hesitantly.

Meredith blinked. "Told me what?"

"Why, that he was taking Sarah to the Bahamas for a few days," Amie said, dropping the bombshell.

Meredith knew her face was like rice paper, but she managed to smile. "Oh. Yes. Of course. It slipped my mind."

"You're crying!" Amie put down her dishcloth and hugged Meredith. "Poor little thing," she mumbled, patting the weeping woman. "He didn't tell you, did he?"

"No."

"I'm sorry."

Meredith reached into her pocket for a tissue and wiped her red eyes. "I've given him a hard time lately," she said. "It's no more than I deserve." She took a deep breath. "I have to fly to Boston in the morning, but when I come back, that's the end of my traveling. I won't go on tour again. Not ever."

Amie searched her white face. "Don't do that," she said unexpectedly.

"What?"

"Don't do it. If you let him get the upper hand now, if you ever let him start ordering your life, you'll never be your own person again," she said simply. "He's a good man in many ways, but he has a domineering streak a mile wide. If you let him, he'll tell you how to breathe. I know you want peace with him, but don't sacrifice your freedom for it.''

Meredith felt torn. Bess had said give in, Amie was saying don't. She didn't know what to do anymore. Who was right? And what should she do?

Her heart shattered, she went upstairs to pack. What had begun as a beautiful marriage had turned sour. It was partly her fault, but Blake was as much to blame. She wondered if he was able to admit fault. Somehow she didn't think so.

Boston was lovely. She did her autographing and stayed an extra day to enjoy the historic places and spend a little time in the local library. But her heart was broken. Blake had gone away without her, without even asking if she wanted to go with him. She didn't know if she even wanted to go home again.

She did go home again, of course—to an empty house. She and Amie ate together and Meredith worked on her newest book because there was nothing else to do. And all the while she wondered what Blake and Sarah were doing. Most of all, she wondered if his eye was wandering to a more domestic kind of woman, one who would be content to stay at home and have his babies.

She stopped writing and sat with her head in her hands, daydreaming about having Blake's child. Even though they hadn't taken precautions she hadn't conceived. In a way that was a shame. A baby might have helped bring them together. On the other hand, if Blake decided to leave her, it would be better for both of them if there were no blood ties.

Leave her. She closed her eyes. *If Blake should leave her...* She couldn't bear even to think of it. She loved him so, missed him so. Tears ran down her cheeks, blinding her. If only he could love her back....

Blake, meanwhile, was riding around New Providence in a jitney with Sarah at his side, smiling as she enthused over the beautiful flowers and the unbelievable colors of the ocean and the whiteness of the sand. If Meredith had been with them, it would truly have been paradise.

His eyes darkened at the thought. Meredith. He hadn't really given her a chance, he supposed. Her traveling made him mad and he'd pushed her out of his life because she refused to stop. In a way he was glad she had the spirit to stand up to him. But in another, he felt miserable because she was telling him he was nothing compared to her career. It hurt far more than Nina's betrayal. Because he hadn't loved Nina. And he... cared... for Meredith.

He couldn't bear to think about her. He'd come down here with Sarah to hurt her. Probably she was in tears when Amie told her they had gone. His face hardened. She was going to take a long time to forgive him for that slap in the face. He was sorry he'd done it. He'd been hurting and wanted to strike back, but now it all seemed so petty and unnecessary. Being cruel wasn't going to win Meredith back. He sighed. He didn't quite have the hang of marriage yet. But he was going to work at learning how when he got back. He had to. He couldn't bear to lose Meredith. These past few cold weeks had made his life hell, especially at night. He missed her soft body, her quiet breathing next to him. He missed her laughter and the lazy talks they'd had late at night. He missed a lot. He only hoped he hadn't left things too late.

"Sarah," he said, "how would you like to go home tomorrow?"

"I'd like that, Daddy," she said. "I miss Merry something awful!"

"Yes, so do I," he murmured under his breath.

Meredith was sitting at the computer with her reading glasses on when she heard the front door open.

"Merry!" Sarah Jane cried, and flung herself at Meredith to hug her convulsively. "Merry, why didn't you come with us? We had such fun, but it was lonely without you!"

"It was lonely without you, too, baby." Meredith sighed, hugging Sarah close.

She heard Blake's step in the hall, and her heart ran away. Her body quivered. She didn't look up because she didn't dare. He'd hurt her enough. She wasn't giving him any more openings.

"Hello, Meredith," he said quietly.

She lifted cool gray eyes to his. "Hello, Blake. I hope you had a pleasant time."

He shifted. He had a faint sunburn, but he looked almost gaunt. She realized that he'd honed down a little, too, during their cold war, and guilt made her throat constrict.

"It was all right," he said coolly. "How have you been?"

"Oh, I've had a ball," she said nervously, hiding her lack of confidence from him. She smiled at Sarah. "I went to autograph in Boston and researched a new book while I was there."

Blake's expression closed up. He'd imagined her sitting home crying, and she'd been in Boston working on another damned book. He turned on his heel without another word and left her sitting there.

"And I'm going to have a party and everything, Merry, 'cause Daddy said so!" Sarah was chattering excitedly. She looked pretty. Her hair was neatly combed and she had on a soft, lightweight cotton dress with red and beige patterns on it, obviously bought for her in the Bahamas. Blake had even put a bow in her hair.

"A party?" Meredith echoed. She hadn't been listening, because the cold look on Blake's face had hit her hard. She'd put her foot in it again by raving about her trip.

"My birthday, Merry!" Sarah said with forced patience.

"That's right," Meredith said. "It's coming up."

"And we have to have a party," Sarah said. "Dani can come, and you and Daddy, and we can have cake."

"And ice cream," Meredith said, smiling at the child's obvious excitement. "We might even have balloons and a clown. Would you like that?"

"Oh, yes!"

"When are we having the party?" Meredith asked.

"Next Saturday," Sarah said.

"Well, I'll see what I can do." She took off her reading glasses and Sarah picked them up and tried to look through them, making a face when everything was blurry.

Mrs. Jackson fixed the birthday cake with a favorite cartoon character of Sarah's on the top and Meredith arranged for a local clown to come to the party to entertain the children. She invited Dani and some of Dani's friends, anticipating bedlam. Maybe if they ate in the kitchen, it would be less messy.

"Why should they eat in the kitchen?" Blake asked icily when Meredith got up her nerve the day of the party to approach him about it. "They're children, not animals. They can eat in the dining room."

Meredith curtsied and smiled. "Yes, my lord," she said. "Anything you say, sir."

"That isn't funny," he said. He stalked out of the room and Meredith stuck out her tongue at him.

"Reverting to childhood?" Mrs. Jackson asked with a gleam in her eye as she opened the hutch to get out plates and glasses, since the party was less than two hours away.

"I guess so. He infuriates me!" She sighed. "He says we have to have it in here. Doesn't he know that cake and ice cream are terrible on carpet?"

"Not yet," Amie said with her tongue in her cheek. "But he will."

Meredith smiled conspiratorially at her. "Yes, he certainly will."

They had the party in the dining room. There were seven four-year-olds. In the middle of the cake and ice cream, they had a food fight. By the time Meredith and Elissa, who'd volunteered to help out, got them stopped, the room looked like a child's attempt at camouflage. There was ice cream on the carpet, the hutch, the tablecloth, and even tiny splatters on Blake's elegant crystal chandelier. Waterford crystal, too, Meredith mused as she studied the chocolate spots there. The chairs were smeared with vanilla cake and white frosting, and underfoot there was enough cake to feed several hungry mice.

"Isn't this fun, Merry?" Sarah Jane exclaimed with a chocolate ring around her mouth and frosting in her hair.

"Yes, darling," Meredith agreed wholeheartedly. "It's fun, indeed. I can hardly wait until your daddy gets here."

Just as she said that, Sarah Jane's daddy walked in the door and stopped as if he'd been hit in the knee with a bat. His lower lip fell a fraction of an inch and he stared at the table and children as if he'd never seen either before.

He lifted a finger and turned to Meredith to say something.

"Isn't it just such fun?" Meredith asked brightly. "We had a food fight. And then we had chocolate warfare. I'm afraid your chandelier became a casualty, but, then, you'll have *such* fun hosing it down...."

Blake's face was getting redder by the instant. He glared at Meredith and went straight through to the kitchen.

Seconds later, Meredith could hear his deep, slow voice giving Amie hell on the half-shell, and then the back door slammed hard enough to shake the room.

Elissa's twinkling blue eyes met Meredith's gray ones. "My, my, and he insisted on the dining room? Where do you think he's gone?"

"To get a hose, I expect," Meredith commented, and then broke into laughter.

"I wouldn't laugh too loud," Elissa cautioned as she helped mop Dani's face.

The clown arrived just after the children were tidied, and he kept them occupied in the living room with Elissa while Meredith and Amie began the monumental task of cleaning the dining room.

Meredith was on the floor with a wet sponge and carpet cleaner when Blake came in, followed by two rugged looking men wearing uniforms. Without a word, he tugged Meredith up by the arm, took the sponge from her hand, tossed it to one of the men and guided her into the living room.

He left her there without a word. Belatedly she realized that he'd gone to get some cleaning men to take care of the mess. Oddly, it made her want to cry. His thoughtfulness had surprised her. Or maybe it was his conscience. Either way, she thought, it had been kind of him to do that for Amie and her.

Seconds later, Amie was pulled into the living room. She stared at Meredith and shrugged. Then she smiled and sat down to enjoy the clown with the children.

It was, Sarah Jane said after the guests had gone, the best party in the whole world.

"I made five new friends, Merry," she told Meredith gaily. "And they liked me!"

"Most everyone likes you, darling," Meredith said, kneeling to hug her. Her white-and-pink dress was liberally stained with chocolate and candy, but that's what parties were for, Meredith told herself. "Especially me," she added with a big kiss.

Sarah Jane hugged her tight. "I love you, Merry." She sighed. "I just wish . . ."

"Wish what, pet?"

"I wish my daddy loved you," she said, and her big green eyes looked sadly at Meredith.

Meredith hadn't realized until then how perceptive Sarah was. Her face lost its glow. She forced a smile. "It's hard to explain about grown-ups, Sarah," she said finally. "Your daddy and I have disagreed about some things, that's all."

"Why not tell her the truth?" Blake demanded coldly from the doorway. "Why not tell her that your writing comes before she does, and before I do, and that you just don't care enough to stay home?"

"That's not true!" Meredith got to her feet, her eyes flashing. "You won't even listen to my side of it, Blake!"

"Why bother?" He laughed mockingly. "Your side isn't worth hearing."

"And yours is?"

Neither of them noticed Sarah Jane's soft gasp, or the sudden paleness of her little face. Neither of them saw the tears gather in her green eyes and start to flow down her cheeks. Neither of them knew the traumatic effect the argument was having on her, bringing back memories of fights between her mother and stepfather and the violence that had highlighted most of her young life.

She sobbed silently and suddenly turned and slipped from the room, hurrying up the staircase.

"Your pride is going to destroy our marriage," Meredith raged at Blake. "You just can't stand the idea of letting me work, or giving me any freedom at all. You want me to stay home and look after Sarah and have babies—"

"Writers don't have babies," he said curtly. "It's too demeaning and limiting."

She felt her face go pale. "I never said that, Blake," she said. "I haven't done anything to prevent a baby." She lowered her eyes to the carpet and hoped the glitter of her tears wouldn't show. "I just can't...can't seem to get pregnant."

His breath sighed out roughly. He hadn't meant to say such a cruel thing. It was cruel, too, judging by the look on her face. She seemed to really want a child, and that warmed him.

He moved forward a little, his hand going out to touch her hair. "I didn't mean that," he said awkwardly.

She looked up. There were tears in her eyes. "Blake," she whispered achingly, and lifted her arms.

He cursed his own vulnerability even as he reached for her, lifting her hard against him, holding her close. "Don't cry, little one," he said against her ear as she sobbed out the frustration and loneliness and fear of the past few weeks against his broad shoulder.

"There's something...something *wrong* with me," she wailed.

"No, there isn't." He nuzzled his cheek against hers. "Unless you count a husband with an overdose of pride. You're right. It was just feeling second best, that's all. You can't stay home all the time."

"I promised I'd go on tour," she said huskily. "I didn't want to. But then, when I kept not getting pregnant, I hated having so much time to sit and worry about it." Her arms tightened around his neck. "I wanted to give you a son...."

His arms contracted. He'd never considered that as a reason for her wandering. He'd never dreamed she wanted a child so much.

"We've been married only a few weeks," he whispered at her ear. "And the past several, I've been sleeping in another room." He smiled faintly in spite of himself. "It takes a man and a woman to make babies. You can't do it by yourself."

She laughed softly, and he felt warm all over at the sound, because she hadn't laughed in a long time.

"If you want to get pregnant, Mrs. Donavan, you'll have to have a little help."

She drew in a breath and looked into his soft green eyes. "Could you do that for me?" she whispered playfully. "I mean, I know it would be a sacrifice and all, but I'd be *sooo* grateful."

He laughed, too. The joy came back into his life again. She was beautiful, he thought, studying her face. And he cared so damned much. His eyes darkened and the smile faded. Cared. No. It was more. Far more than that. He...loved.

"Kiss me," he said, bending to her soft mouth. "It's been so long, honey. So long!"

His mouth covered hers hungrily, and she felt her body melting into him, aching for his touch, for the crush of his mouth on her soft lips. She moaned, and his kiss became suddenly ardent and demanding.

"Merry?" Mrs. Jackson called suddenly from the hall.

Blake and Meredith broke apart with breathless reluctance, but there was a strange note in Amie's usually calm voice.

Meredith moved to the closed door and opened it. "Amie, what is it?" she asked, wondering at the closed door, because it had been open when Sarah was in the room with them—"Where's Sarah!" Meredith asked suddenly.

Blake felt himself pale when he remembered the argument. Sarah Jane had heard.

Amie grimaced. "I don't know where she is. I can't find her," she said. "She isn't in her room. And it's raining outside."

It was thundering, too. And it was almost dark. Meredith and Blake didn't waste time on words. They rushed down the hall and out the back door, forgoing rain gear in their haste to find the child they'd unknowingly sent running out into the stormy night.

Eleven

Blake wanted to throw things. He searched the stable, every nook and cranny of it, and every one of the out-buildings, with Meredith quiet and worried beside him. The rain was coming down heavier now, and the last bit of light had left the sky, except for the occasional lightning.

"Where can she be?" Meredith groaned as they stood in the doorway of the barn and looked out into the night.

"I don't know," Blake said heavily. "God, I could kick myself!"

She slid her hand into his big one and held on tight. "I'm every bit as responsible as you are, Blake," she said gently. "I was being stubborn and proud, too." She went close to him, nuzzling her cheek against his broad chest. "I'm sorry for all of it. I never looked at things from your point of view."

"That goes double for me." He bent and kissed her forehead. "I wish we'd remembered that Sarah was in the room. She's had nightmares about arguments her mother and stepfather used to have. Violence upsets her. Any kind of violence. When I yelled at her about getting in the corral with the horse she—" He stopped dead, remembering. He straightened. "No," he said to himself. "No, she couldn't be. That would be too easy, wouldn't it?"

"What would?" Meredith asked as she tried to follow his train of thought.

"Come on!"

He ran toward the house, tugging her along behind him. They were both soaked. Meredith's blouse was plastered to her skin, and her hair hung in wet tangles over her face. Blake didn't look much better. His tan shirt was so wet that she could see right through it to the thick tangle of black hair on his chest.

"Did you find her?" Amie asked worriedly from the sink, where she was washing dishes.

"I'm almost sure I have," Blake said. He dragged Meredith with him and shot up the staircase.

He opened the door to Sarah's room, went straight to the closet and, with a silent prayer, opened it.

And there was Sarah Jane, sobbing silently in the very far corner of the closet floor, under all her pretty things.

"You...hate each other," Sarah sobbed, "just like my mommy and Daddy Brad. I'll have to go away...!" she wailed.

Blake eased into the closet and caught her up in his arms. He held her and hugged her and walked the floor with her while she cried. His shirt was soaked, but Sarah didn't seem to mind. She held on with all her might.

"I love you, baby girl," he whispered in her ear. "You'll never have to go away."

"But you fought!" Sarah said.

"Not the bad kind of fighting," Meredith said, smoothing the child's soft hair as she rested against Blake's wet shoulder. She smiled. "Sarah Jane, how would you like to have a brother or sister?"

Sarah stopped crying and her eyes widened. "A real live baby brother or sister?"

"A real live one," Meredith assured her. She looked up into Blake's soft, quiet eyes. "Because we're going to have one, aren't we, Blake?"

"Just as soon as we can," he agreed huskily, his eyes full of warmth and faint hunger.

"Oh, that would be so nice." Sarah sighed. "I could help you, Merry. We could make clothes for her. I can sew. I can make anything."

"Yes, darling," Meredith said with an indulgent smile.

"And Meredith isn't going anywhere," Blake added. "Neither are you, young lady." He chuckled as he put her down. "I can't do without my biggest helper. Who'll go out with me to feed the horses on weekends and help me talk to the men if you leave?"

Sarah nodded. "Yes, Daddy."

"And who'll help me eat the vanilla ice cream that Mrs. Jackson has in the freezer?" he added in a whisper.

Sarah's eyes brightened. "Vanilla?"

"That's right," he said. "Left over from your birthday party. Would you like some?"

"Blake, it's too late..." Meredith began.

"It is not," he said. "It's her birthday, and she can have more if she wants it."

"Thank you, Daddy." Sarah grinned.

"I guess birthdays do only come once a year," Meredith said, relenting. "I'll go and get it. And some cake."

"Amie will get it," Blake said, eyeing Meredith's clothes. "You and I have to change before we can join the party. We got soaked on your account, young lady," he told Sarah with a faint smile. "We thought you'd run out into the fields."

"Oh, I couldn't have done that, Daddy," Sarah said matter-of-factly. "I would have gotten my lovely party dress wet."

Blake laughed with pure delight. "I should have thought of that."

Mrs. Jackson had followed them upstairs and was sighing with relief. "Sarah, I'm so glad you're all right," she said, and smiled. "I was worried."

"You're nice, Mrs. Jackson," Sarah said.

"So are you, pet. Want to come and help me dish up some ice cream and cake while your mommy and daddy change clothes? And we could even make some cookies if you want to. It's not at all late. If your daddy doesn't mind," she added, glancing at Blake.

"Please, Daddy!" Sarah asked.

"All right," he said, relenting. "Go ahead. Your mommy and I will expect some when we get showered and changed. And they'd better be good," he added.

Sarah laughed. "Me and Mrs. Jackson will make lots," she promised. She took Mrs. Jackson's hand and went with her.

"We are a mess," Meredith said, looking down at her clothes.

"Speak for yourself," he returned. "I look great soaking wet."

She eyed him mischievously, her gaze running possessively over his hard muscles. "I'll drink to that."

He took her hand. "Well, come on. We'll get cleaned up together."

She went with him, expecting that he'd leave her at the door to the master bedroom, but he didn't. He pulled her into the bathroom with him and closed the door, locking it as an afterthought.

Meredith's heart went wild. "What are you doing?" she asked.

"We have to shower, don't we?" he said softly. His hands went to her blouse. "Don't panic," he whispered, bending to touch his mouth gently to hers. "We've seen each other before."

"Yes, but . . ."

"Hush, sweetheart," he breathed into her open mouth.

She was hungry for him. It had been so long. Too long. She gave a harsh moan, and the blood went to his head when he heard it.

"Do that again," he whispered roughly.

"Do . . . what?"

"Moan like that," he bit off against her mouth. "It drives me crazy!"

She felt his hands on her breasts when he pushed the blouse out of his way, and she did moan, not because he'd said to, but because the pleasure was so exquisite.

He reached out to turn on the shower and adjust the water, and then, his jaw set, his eyes glittering with desire, he stripped her and then himself and lifted her into the shower.

In between kisses, he soaped her and himself, and it was an adventure in exploration for Meredith, who'd never dreamed of touching and being touched so intimately. The soap made her skin like silk and the feel of his hands against her most secret places was unbearable delight.

He rinsed Meredith off, and himself, then turned off the water and reached for a towel. But he didn't dry them with it. Holding her eyes, he spread the towel on the tiles of the big bathroom floor, and catching her waist, he lifted her against him and kissed her with probing intimacy.

"We're going to make love. Here," he whispered, "on the floor."

She shuddered at the images that flashed through her mind. "Yes," she groaned, pressing hard against him so that her soft breasts flattened against the thick pelt of hair on his muscular chest.

He spread her trembling body on the thick towel and himself over her, his mouth demanding and slow, his body making the sweetest kind of contacts as he moved sensually over her.

She felt his hands on her and she shivered, but he kept on, evoking sensations she hadn't dreamed existed. She opened her eyes and looked at him and cried out, her nails digging into his shoulders as she lifted against his hand.

"I've never wanted you this badly," he whispered as he poised above her. "I don't want to hold back anything this time."

"Neither do I." She lifted her hands to his face. "I love you," she said, parting her lips as they brushed his with open sensuality. "I love you, Blake."

His hands contracted on her hips as he moved down, very slowly, his eyes holding hers so that he could see them while his body began to merge with hers. "I love you, too, honey," he whispered shakenly, jerking a little with each deepening movement. She started to lift up, but his hands held her still. "No," he murmured breathlessly, his eyes

still on hers. "No, don't . . . move. Don't rush it . . . God!"
His eyes closed suddenly and he shuddered.

She felt him, breathed him, tasted him. Her body shook
with what he was doing to it, with the exquisite slowness
of his movements, the depth . . . She clenched her teeth and
cried out in protest, her hips twisting helplessly.

"Blake . . . if you don't . . . hurry!" she wailed in anguish.

"Ride it out," he whispered at her ear. His body flowed
against hers like the tide, lazy and deliberate, despite the
sudden hot urgency that was burning them both. "It's
going to be good," he groaned. "Good . . . so good . . .
Meredith!" His body clenched. "Merry, now!"

She felt his control slip and she let go of her own, yielding totally, trusting him. And the tension all but tore her
to pieces before she felt the heat blinding her, burning her,
and she fell into it headfirst with tears streaming down her
cheeks.

His hands were in her hair, soothing her, smoothing the
wet strands away from her rosy cheeks. He was kissing her,
sipping the tears from her eyes, kissing away the faint sorrow, the fatigue, the trembling muscles.

She opened her eyes and his face came into focus. She
couldn't breathe properly. Her body felt as if it had fallen
from a great height. His eyes held hers, and there was adoration in them now, openly.

"The bed would have been better," he said, brushing her
mouth lazily with his. "But this was safer."

"She's making cookies," she told him wearily.

"She's unpredictable." He nuzzled her nose with his. "I
love you," he breathed, his eyes mirroring the statement.
"I couldn't admit it until today, but, oh, God, I feel it,
Meredith," he said huskily, his face taut with emotion that

made her heart jump with excitement. "I feel it when I look at you, when I'm with you. I didn't know what it was to love, but now I do."

"I've always felt that way about you," she whispered, smiling adoringly. "Since I was eighteen. Maybe even longer. You were the moon, and I wanted you so much."

"I wanted you, too. But I didn't understand why I wanted you so badly." He kissed her again. "You complete me," he breathed. "You make me whole."

Her arms linked around his neck, she buried her face in his throat. "I feel like that, too. Was it necessary to torture me to death?" She laughed shyly.

"It was good, though, wasn't it?" he said. "So intense that I thought I might pass out just at the last. I like losing control with you. I fly up into the sun and explode."

"Yes, so do I." She cuddled closer. "The floor is hard."

"The bed is unprotected."

She sighed. "Well, there's always tonight." She drew back a little. "Are you going to sleep with me?"

"No, I thought I'd sack out with one of the horses—oof!"

She withdrew her fist from his stomach. "Sarah Jane wants a brother or sister."

"At the rate we're going, that won't take long. There's nothing wrong with you," he added, emphasizing it. "And meanwhile, Sarah's going to have time to adjust to us and feel secure. Okay?"

"Okay. I'll stop worrying," she promised.

"Good. Now let's go get some ice cream," he said, moving away to get to his feet and pull her up with him. "I'm starving!"

She wanted to make a comment about men and their strange appetites, but she was too hungry to argue. Her eyes adored him. So much had come out of such a stormy, terrible night, she thought as he wrapped a towel around his lean hips and tossed an extra one to her. He loved her. He actually loved her. She smiled, tingling all over with the newness of hearing the words, of having the freedom to say them. It was like a dream come true. Or it would be, she thought, if she could ever give him a child. She had to force herself not to think about it. Anyway, Blake had said there was plenty of time.

Epilogue

Eight months later, little Carson Anthony Blake Donavan was born in Jack's Corner Hospital. Looking down at the small head with its thick crown of black hair, Meredith could have jumped for joy. A son, she thought, and so much like his father.

Sitting by her bed, Blake was quiet and fascinated as his first son gripped his thumb. He smiled down at the tiny child. "He's a miracle," he said softly. "Part of us. The best of us."

She smiled up at him tiredly and her hand touched the finger that was caught in the baby's grasp. "He's going to look like you," she said.

"I hope so, considering that he's a boy," he replied dryly.

She laughed. Her eyes made soft, slow love to his. "I'm so happy, Blake," she whispered. "He's the end of the rainbow. And I was so afraid that I couldn't give you a child."

"I knew you could," he said simply. "We love each other too much not to have a child together." He bent and kissed her soft mouth. "Sarah wanted to come, too. I explained that they wouldn't let her in here, but you're getting out tomorrow and she can see her brother all she wants to. She's coloring a pretty picture for him."

"She's been almost as excited as we have," Meredith said. "She'll love not being an only child. And it will give her some security. She still doesn't quite believe that she's safe and loved."

"It will take time," he said. "But she's coming around nicely."

"Yes." She smoothed her fingers lovingly over the baby's downy soft hair. "Isn't he just perfect, Blake?"

"Just perfect," he said, smiling. "Like his mother."

She searched his eyes. "No regrets?"

He shook his head. "Nobody ever loved me until you and Sarah Jane came along," he said quietly. "I can't quite get over it. I'm like Sarah—happiness takes some adjusting to. You've given me the world, Meredith."

"Only my heart, darling," she said softly. "But maybe it was enough."

He bent to kiss her again. "It was more than enough," he replied. The light in his eyes was so full of love for Meredith and his child that it was almost blinding. He smiled suddenly. "I meant to tell you—I met Elissa and Danielle in town just before I came here. They're bringing over a surprise for you." His eyes twinkled. "The store was a little crowded, full of people. I walked in, and do you know what Danielle said?"

Meredith smiled lazily. "No, what?"

"She pointed to me and said, 'Look, Mama, there's Sarah Jane's daddy!'" He grinned. "And do you know what, Merry? I think I'd rather be Daddy than president."

Meredith reached up and touched his mouth lovingly. "I'm sure Sarah Jane and little Carson will agree with that." She took his hand in hers and held it. "And so do I."

He looked down at his son, and foresaw long days ahead of playing baseball in the backyard and board games at the kitchen table. Of drying Sarah's tears and helping Meredith patch up Carson's cuts and bruises. Together, he and Meredith would raise their children and make memories to share in the autumn days. He brought Meredith's hand to his mouth and lifted his gaze to her quiet face. There, in her gray eyes, was the beginning and end of his whole world.

*   *   *   *   *

Debbie Macomber is one of America's most popular authors. In fact, her appealing characters and heart-warming stories have made her a favourite around the globe.

Debbie has always enjoyed telling stories—first to the children she baby-sat as a young teenager and later to her own children. As a full-time wife and mother and avid romance reader, she dreamed of one day sharing her stories with a wider audience. She sold her first book in 1982—and that was only the beginning! Today, there are more than 40 million copies of her books in print.

Debbie loves to hear from readers. You can reach her at: PO Box 1458, Port Orchard, Washington 98366, USA.

ALMOST AN ANGEL
by
DEBBIE MACOMBER

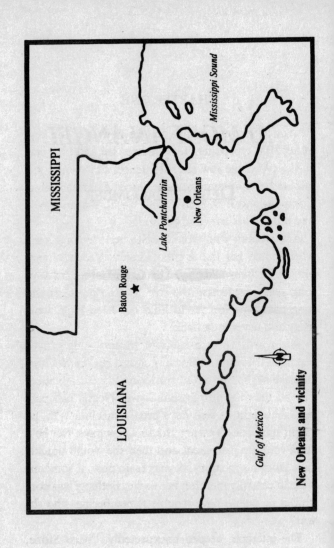

MISSISSIPPI

LOUISIANA

Baton Rouge ★

Lake Pontchartrain

New Orleans ●

Mississippi Sound

Gulf of Mexico

New Orleans and vicinity

CHAPTER ONE

BETHANY STONE'S nimble fingers flew over the keys of her IBM typewriter. Tears blurred her soft blue eyes as she typed the few short sentences that would terminate her employment with Norris Pharmaceutical Company and J. D. Norris. This was it, the end, she'd had it up to her ears and beyond!

Any woman who would waste her life for a man who treated her like a robot deserved to be unemployed. Bethany had played the part of a fool for three long years, perfecting the role. But no more! It was long past time for her to hold her head high, walk away and never look back.

The words from a militant protest song played loudly in her mind as Bethany signed her name with a flourish at the bottom of the letter. She straightened. For all the attention Joshua David Norris had paid her, she might as well have been a machine. Oh, he might miss her efficiency the first few days, but he'd soon find a replacement and then she would quickly fade from his memory. A year from now, if someone were to casually mention her name, Bethany was convinced he would have trouble remembering who she was.

The intercom beeped unexpectedly. ''Miss Stone, could I see you a moment?''

With a determination born of frustration and regret, Bethany jerked the letter of resignation from her typewriter and stood. As an afterthought, she reached for her dictation pad. Her shoulders were stiff and her back ramrod-straight as she opened the door that connected the outer office with the executive suite. She exhaled once, hard, and filled her steps with purpose as she marched into the executive office.

Joshua was scribbling notes across a yellow sheet of tablet paper in his thin spidery scrawl. He didn't bother to glance up when she entered the room, and for a few brief moments, Bethany was given the opportunity to study the man she loved—fool that she was. He was sitting, the muscles in his broad shoulders relaxed. Not for the first time, Bethany sensed the complexity of this man's character. He was strong and mature yet headstrong and obstinately blind. Often she'd been a witness to the way he buried his pain in the tight fabric of control that he wrapped around himself. In some ways, Bethany knew Joshua Norris better than he knew himself. And in others, he was a complete stranger.

His hair was dark brown with faint highlights of auburn, the result of many hours spent in the sun, sailing on Lake Pontchartrain. His brows were thick and drawn together now in concentration as he jotted down his thoughts. The smooth contours of his handsome face were broken by a square angular jaw that revealed an overabundance of male arrogance.

His eyes were a deep rich shade of brown that reminded her of bitter coffee. She knew from experience that they could reveal such anger that she was sure one look was capable of blistering paint off a wall. And then there were those rare times when she'd seen his gaze flitter over the photo of his daughter, Angie, which rested on his desk. Bethany had seldom witnessed a look more gentle. All she knew was that Angie lived somewhere in New York and was being raised by his wife's family. In all the years that Bethany had been employed by Joshua, he rarely mentioned his daughter. From everything she knew of the man, which was considerable since they spent so much time together, J. D. Norris didn't seem interested in long-term relationships and created a thick outer shell that often seemed impenetrable.

Joshua dropped the pen on top of the yellow tablet, leaned back in his chair and pinched his thumb and index finger over the bridge of his nose.

"Miss Stone, do we have any aspirin?"

"Yes, of course." His request caught her by surprise. Quickly she crossed the room to the wet bar, returning momentarily with a water glass and two tablets.

He gave her a fleeting smile of appreciation. "Thanks."

Now that she thought about it, Joshua *did* look slightly pale. "You aren't feeling well, Mr. Norris?"

He shook his head, then widened his eyes as though he regretted the action. "I've got a beast of a headache."

"If you'd like, I'll cancel your afternoon appointments."

"That won't be necessary," he informed her crisply. He tore the top sheet off the tablet and handed it to her. "Could you have these notes typed up before you leave tonight?"

"Of course." The letter of resignation remained tightly clenched in Bethany's hand. She hesitated, wondering if she should give it to him now, then quickly decided against it. The last thing Joshua needed was another problem.

His glance revealed his annoyance. "Was there something more, Miss Stone?"

"N-no." She did an abrupt about-face and left the office, her knees trembling.

Ten minutes later her best friend and roommate, Sally Livingston, stuck her head inside the door. "Well, what did he say?"

Bethany pretended to be busy, but she should have known Sally wouldn't be easily thwarted. Her friend advanced towards her desk, folded her arms and tapped her foot, waiting impatiently until Bethany had finished typing her sentence.

"Well?" Sally demanded a second time.

"He didn't say anything."

Her roommate's brow crimped into a tight frown. "Nothing? You handed J. D. Norris your two-week notice and he didn't so much as respond?"

There was nothing left to do but confess, but still Bethany avoided looking in Sally's direction. "If you must know, I didn't give it to him."

"Bethany," Sally whispered angrily. "You promised."

"I—I wrote the letter."

"That at least is a start."

"I was going to give it to him—honest, but he has a headache and he looks absolutely terrible. The timing just wasn't right, and you know how important that is in these situations."

"Beth, this is crazy! The time will *never* be right—you've got to do it today, otherwise you'll end up putting it off for God knows how long."

"I know." Defeat weighted Bethany's voice. She'd promised Sally and herself that she wasn't going to delay this unpleasant task another day, and here she was looking for an excuse to put off the inevitable. "I'll do it Friday, then."

"What do you think today is?" Sally asked, sending her dark gaze straight through her.

"Oh," she mumbled, and lowered her eyes. "Monday morning, then—first thing—you have my word on it."

Sally unfolded her arms and rolled her eyes. "I've heard that line before."

"All right," Bethany cried. "I'm a weak snivelling mass of Jell-O. I've got all the backbone of a...a worm."

"Less!"

Bethany paused and surveyed her friend through narrowed eyes. "What could be less than that?"

"You!"

"But, Sally," Beth said in self-defence, "Mr. Norris looks terrible. He's really pale and his head hurts and I think he might be coming down with some Asian virus."

"It serves him right."

"Sally!" It wasn't Joshua's fault that Bethany had fallen in love with him. The man didn't so much as guess that Bethany cared a whit about him.

It was Bethany's own fault for allowing her heart to become attached to a man who chose to live his life without emotional commitments. It wasn't that he ignored Bethany in particular. He seemed to be estranged from all women, or at least that was what Bethany had assumed. The divorce from, and later the death of, his ex-wife had left him hard and bitter towards the opposite sex. On the other hand, maybe it wasn't all women Joshua didn't like but just her. The thought was a depressing one. In the end, either way, Bethany would only be hurt. She had to leave him—it was best for everyone involved.

If only Bethany knew how to crack the thick façade Joshua had erected over the years. If she'd had a little more experience or been a bit more sophisticated, then perhaps she could have come up with a surefire plan to win his heart. But as it was, she'd simply stayed on, hoping one day Joshua Norris would look up at her and some mysterious magic would change everything. Twinkling lights would go off in the distance and little hearts would pop up around her head, and after all these years he would recognise the love she'd stored up just waiting for him to discover.

"All right," Bethany returned forcefully, her hands knotting into tight fists of steely determination. "I'll do it."

"Today?" Sally looked sceptical.

"I'll place the letter on his desk when I leave." It was a coward's way out, but when it came to standing up to Joshua Norris, no one was going to award Bethany a medal for valour.

"Good girl." Sally patted her across the back much as a general would before sending a raw recruit into battle. "Meet me at Charley's when you're through here."

Bethany nodded. Charley's was a popular New Orleans cocktail lounge. The two had taken to stopping there and relaxing with a drink on Friday nights. A reward of sorts for making it through another difficult work week.

"I'll see you there," Bethany said, and nodded once. She inhaled a steadying breath, forcing herself to accept her destiny. Once Joshua left the office, she would simply walk inside, place her resignation on his desk and be done with it. Then there wouldn't be any time for second thoughts and looming regrets. She had to forget the man and get on with her life before she woke up a disillusioned and unhappy old maid.

It was after six by the time Bethany made her way into the crowded cocktail lounge. Sally had already found a table, and when Bethany paused to glance around, she saw Sally stand up and give a short wave. Bethany forced a smile to her lips and joined her friend. When the waitress strolled by, she pointed at Sally's drink and said, "Give me whatever she's having, only make it a double."

The woman nodded and turned away.

"You actually did it," Sally murmured, her voice low and incredulous. "You finally handed J. D. Norris your notice."

The mint julep arrived and Bethany drew her wallet from inside her purse to pay for it. "Not yet, but I'm determined that I will."

"Not yet," Sally echoed, her eyes dropping to Bethany's drink in the tall frosty glass with a sprig of mint. "Then why the double?"

"Because I'm a weak, snivelling, spineless—"

Abruptly Sally stopped her, looking disgusted. "We've already determined that."

"Listen," Bethany said thoughtfully. "I've been giving some thought to my problem and I think I may be doing Joshua Norris a disservice."

"How do you mean?"

The hum of conversation and a Dixieland band playing in the distance caused Bethany to raise her voice, but only slightly. She leaned her head closer to her roommate's. "I've never given Joshua a chance." At Sally's perplexed look, she hurried to add, "He hasn't a clue to the way I feel about him ... I think I should have the courtesy to at least tell him."

"Oh, Beth," Sally muttered, and shook her head several times in a pathetic little twist. "The man has to be blind not to know how you feel. The entire company is aware you love him."

Bethany paled. She actually felt all the blood rush from her face and pool at her ankles. When she spoke, her voice came out scratchy, high-pitched and weak. "Everyone knows?"

"Maybe not janitorial."

"Oh, God." She took a long sip from her straw and nearly coughed at the potency of her drink. Tears stung her eyes and she shook her head, hoping to lessen the powerful effect.

"All right, I was just joking. Not everyone knows—but enough people do."

"Sally, don't joke about something this important. All I want is to handle J. D. Norris in my own time and in my own way."

"What do you plan to do?" Sally asked in a husky whisper. "Saunter into his office, bat your eyelashes a couple of times and suggest children?"

"No...I...I don't know yet." She pushed the short dark curls from her temple. She was twenty-five and behaving like a bungling naïve teenager.

"You've had three years to tell him the way you feel. What makes you think you can do it now?"

"I...I've never actually *told* him."

"Not outright, true, but honestly, Beth, give the matter some thought here. You're much too gentle-natured and sweet to come right out and tell J. D. Norris you've fallen in love with him. He's bound to give you one of those famous dark looks of his and send you running for cover."

"But I've been thinking..."

"The first time is always hardest," Sally joked. She reached for a handful of salted peanuts, munching on them one at a time.

Bethany's shoulders sagged with defeat as she reached for the salted nuts. "I'm hopeless."

"No," Sally answered, her look sobering. She hesitated and popped another peanut in her mouth. "But J. D. Norris is. If you were going to fall in love, why did it have to be with him?" Her elbows rested on the tabletop, and another peanut found its way between her lips. Sally's eyes narrowed with a thoughtful frown. "Beth, face it, the man's soured on women, soured on marriage, soured on life. He's the big bad wolf and you're an innocent lamb. As your best friend, I refuse to stand by and let you get your throat slit."

"But... he's wonderful." Bethany knew Joshua in ways the other employees of Norris Pharmaceutical couldn't. She'd been a silent witness to his generous contributions to charity. She admired his unwavering dedication to medicine. Bethany was sure there were times when others viewed him as harsh, but she'd never known him to be unfair or unkind. In the three years she'd worked for him, there had been enough glimpses of the real man inside to convince her that the exterior of indifference he wore was only a thin shell.

Sally chewed on the peanut as though it were rawhide, then paused, surprise widening her gaze and giving her away. "Don't look now, but..."

Instantly Bethany jerked her head around.

"I told you not to look," Sally berated her friend. "He's here."

"*Who?*"

Immediately Sally's dark eyes narrowed into thin slits, and her right eye started to twitch, a sure sign she was irritated. "I thought you said your precious Mr. Norris was coming down with some dreadful virus."

Bethany's brow knit into a thick frown. "He did have me get him aspirin." But Sally wouldn't recognise how unusual that was.

"Well," Sally said, looking properly disgusted, "he seems to have made a miraculous recovery."

"He's here?" Bethany rose halfway out of her chair before Sally jerked her back down. "But he really *did* look terrible this afternoon." She felt the muscles in her throat tighten with dread. "He's with someone, isn't he? That's the reason you don't want me to look." Already her mind was conjuring up a tall luscious blonde—someone she could never hope to compete against.

"Nope." Sally's eyes followed him. "He just sat down at the bar." The handful of nuts was positioned in front of her mouth. "You know, now that I have a chance to get a good look at him, you're right."

"About what?"

"He is... I don't know, compelling-looking. He's got a lean hardness to him that naturally attracts women. An inborn arrogance, if you will."

Sally wasn't telling Bethany anything she hadn't already known—for years. "You're sure he's alone?"

"I just told you that."

Bethany clenched her hands together in her lap. "What's he doing now?"

"Ordering a drink. You're right about something else, too. He doesn't look the least bit like himself. Not exactly sick, though."

Bethany couldn't stand it any longer. She twisted her chair around so she could get a decent look at her employer herself. The room was filled with cigarette smoke, resembling an early-morning bayou fog. She braced herself, not sure what to expect. But when her gaze skimmed over Joshua, she stiffened all the more and experienced a rush of concern. "Something's wrong," she whispered, surprised she'd spoken aloud.

"How can you tell?" Sally wanted to know, her voice barely above a whisper as though the two of them were on a top secret reconnaissance mission.

"I just can. Something's troubling him. Look at the way he's leaning over his drink . . . how his shoulders are slouched. I wonder what happened. Something's got him terribly worried—I can't remember the last time I saw him look so rejected . . . so distressed."

Sally shook her head. "I don't know where you get that. The only reason he's slouching like that is because he wants to be left alone. Didn't you ever read that book on body language? He's letting others know he isn't in the mood for company."

"Maybe." Thoughtfully Bethany gnawed at the corner of her lower lip. "But I doubt it." Without any real plan in mind, she pushed back her chair, reached for her bag and drink and stood.

"What are you doing?" Sally demanded in a tight whisper.

"I'm going to talk to him."

Sally briefly touched her arm. "Be careful, sweetie, wolves have sharp teeth."

Bethany's returning smile was weak at best. Her heart was pounding like a ramming disc against a concrete wall as she advanced towards Joshua Norris. Luckily the stool beside his was vacant. She perched her five-foot-five frame atop it and set her mint julep on the bar, folding her hands around the cool drink. She gave him a minute to notice her and comment.

He didn't.

"Hello," she said softly.

It seemed like an eternity before he twisted his head around to look at her. When he did, surprise briefly widened his intense dark eyes. "Miss Stone."

Bethany took another deep swallow of her drink, seeking the courage it would give her. But for the life of her, she couldn't think of anything profound to say. She tossed a glance over her shoulder and Sally's eyes rounded as she nodded encouragingly.

"I didn't know you frequented Charley's," Bethany managed at last, amazed at how strange her own voice sounded.

"I don't." His words were clipped, discouraging any further discussion.

"Are you feeling better?"

He turned back to her then. "Not particularly."

The bartender strolled in their direction and Joshua motioned to the tall thin man that he wanted a refill. The man poured Joshua another shot glass of Scotch, then cast Bethany a questioning glance.

She shook her head. She had a one-drink limit, and as it was, the alcohol was already rushing to her brain.

"I have aspirin in my purse if you need some."

"I don't." He answered without looking in her direction, as though he wished she would get up and walk away. He hadn't sought her company and the stiff way in which he sat told her as much.

Not knowing what else to do, Bethany took several more sips from her mint julep. The potency of each one burned a path straight to her stomach. Feeling tipsy and more than a little reckless, she lightly placed her hand on his forearm. "We've worked together all this time, I hope you feel you can trust me."

"I beg your pardon." His hard gaze cut into her.

"Won't you tell me what's wrong?"

"What makes you think anything is troubling me?"

"I've worked for you for three years. I know when something's wrong. I've seen that look in the past and I..."

"I am well aware of the length of your employment, Miss Stone—"

"Bethany," she interrupted, her unflinching gaze meeting his. "I've worked for you all these years, and I think you should know my first name is Bethany."

His eyes formed glacial slits. "And what makes you think that I care to know your first name? Because, rest assured, I don't."

Her breath felt trapped in her lungs, and scalding colour erupted in her cheeks. She'd seen Joshua be cold and insensitive before, but never anything like this. The look he gave her was more than embarrassing...it was humiliating. The edge of his mouth turned upwards in a half sneer, as though he were viewing something distasteful. His intense gaze cut her to the quick before he dropped it to her fingers, which were lightly pressing against the sleeve of his jacket.

Uncharacteristic tears pooled in Bethany's eyes. Slowly, as though in slow motion, she withdrew her hand from his arm. Her whole body went numb. The uselessness of it all hit her then, more poignantly than all the lectures Sally had given her, more cutting than her own soul-searching efforts. The message in Joshua's taut gaze was sharp, hitting its mark far more effectively than he would ever guess. He didn't know who she was; he didn't care to know. The world he'd created was his own, and he wasn't ever going to invite her or anyone else inside.

Her gaze didn't waver from his as she slid off the bar stool and took one small step in retreat. "I won't bother you again." The words managed to wrestle through the stranglehold that gripped her throat muscles. "I'm sorry... really sorry."

Bethany didn't know where she was going. All she knew was that she had to escape before she humiliated herself further and burst into hopeless tears. She walked past Sally's table without looking at her friend and manoeuvred her way through the crowded lounge and outside into the chill of the January night.

For a moment she thought she heard someone call her name, but she wasn't up to explaining what had happened to Sally or anyone else. All that mattered was escaping. Increasing her pace, she ran across the brick-lined street and down the crowded pavement on Decatur Street that bordered the popular French Quarter. The roadway was crowded, the walkways busy, but Bethany kept her head down, walking as fast as her feet would carry her. Not knowing where—not caring.

"Miss Stone. Wait."

Bethany sucked in her breath at the sound of Joshua's impatient demand, swung her bag strap over her shoulder and pushed herself to walk faster.

"Bethany."

She heard the sound of his running footsteps and jerked the heels of her hands over her eyes to wipe away any evidence of tears.

Surprisingly, once Joshua caught up with her he didn't say a word. She must have continued walking half a block with him, their steps in unison, before he spoke.

"I owe you an apology."

"I . . . was being presumptuous," she said, offering him an excuse. She'd done it so many times before that it came as second nature. "Simply because we work together doesn't mean you need confide in me."

"Perhaps, but there was little reason to be rude." Once again his words were brusque, but any anger seemed directed inwards.

Neither spoke for a minute, and when Bethany looked up, she noted they were walking past Jackson Square. Several park benches were spread across the lush green lawn in front of the statue of Andrew Jackson on horseback.

Joshua motioned towards an empty bench. "Would you care to sit for a minute?"

Bethany offered him a feeble smile and calmly took a seat, although her heart continued to beat erratically. Joshua sat down beside her. After what seemed a hundred years, he spoke. "It's Angie."

At the mention of his young daughter, alarm worked its way through Bethany and adrenalin shot into her bloodstream. She twisted her upper body so she was facing Joshua, her hands gripping his sleeve. "Is she ill? Has she had an accident?"

"No, no." Abruptly he shook his head. "As far as I know, she's in perfect health."

Bethany relaxed, dropped her hands and slumped against the iron railing that made up the back of the park bench.

Joshua sighed, his look bleak, distressed. "What do you know about children, Miss Stone?"

"Very little, actually." She was an aunt several times over, and although she dearly loved her nieces and nephews, they lived in Texas and she only saw them on summer vacations.

"I was afraid of that." Roughly he splayed his fingers through his hair. "Damn it all, I don't know what the hell I'm going to do."

Questions were popping up like fizz from a soda can in Bethany's mind, but after her earlier attempt to draw him out, she dared not drill him for information.

"Angie's mother and I were divorced shortly after she was born."

He paused as though he expected Bethany to make some wide sweeping statement. She had none to offer so kept her half-formed thoughts to herself.

"Over the years, I've visited her when I could," he went on, his brooding gaze seeking hers. "God knows, I've tried to do everything I could moneywise."

"She's a beautiful little girl," Bethany murmured, not knowing what else to say. Angie's photo was updated regularly and each time Bethany looked at it she saw the promise of rare beauty in the ten-year-old.

Joshua nodded sharply, his brow furrowed with a brooding frown. "The thing is, I don't know a damn thing about being a father."

"But you've been one for the past ten years," she couldn't help reminding him.

"Not really," he murmured, his facial features remaining tight. "Not a real father." He stood then and rubbed his hand along the back of his neck. "I've never felt more inept in my life."

Bethany was sure that the sensation was foreign to him. In all the time she'd worked for Joshua, she'd never seen him as upset or unsure.

As though forgetting his own problems for the moment, he hesitated and stared down at Bethany. His hard gaze softened perceptibly and a half smile flittered at the edges of his sensuous mouth. "You didn't deserve the treatment I gave you earlier. I truly *am* sorry."

An earthquake wouldn't have been powerful enough to tear Bethany's gaze from his. In three years, this was the most personal comment he'd ever made to her. Forgetting her earlier reluctance, she asked him softly, "Won't you tell me what's happening with Angie?"

He nodded and slumped down into the seat beside her. "I talked with my mother-in-law yesterday afternoon. It seems both my in-laws have been in poor health recently."

Bethany nodded, encouraging him to continue.

"They feel it's time for Angie to come live with me. I'm supposed to pick her up at the airport in a couple of hours." He paused and inhaled sharply. His gaze sought hers. "Miss Stone...Bethany, would you consider coming with me?"

CHAPTER TWO

THE Moisant International Airport was a beehive of activity just as Bethany had expected it would be. The first thing Joshua did once they'd entered the terminal was check the flight schedule from the television monitor positioned beside the airline reservation desk.

"The plane's on time," he announced briskly, sounding as though he'd been hoping for a short reprieve. With his hand lightly touching Bethany's elbow, he hurriedly guided her through the wide corridor to the assigned concourse, despite the fact that they'd arrived almost forty minutes before Angie's flight was scheduled to land. In all the time Bethany had known Joshua, she'd never seen him more unsettled. When it came to matters dealing with his business, he often revealed so little emotion that it had become his trademark. Bethany watched him now, amazed and pleased.

Once they found the assigned gate, Joshua paced the area, his hands buried deep in his trouser pockets. After several tense minutes, he parked himself beside Bethany at the huge floor-to-ceiling window and glared bleakly into the darkness.

"I really appreciate your coming with me," he said. "I haven't seen Angie in almost a year." He jammed his fingers through his hair and released a harsh breath. "Do you think she'll recognise me?"

"I'm sure she will." Bethany searched for something more to say that would reassure him but wasn't confident he would appreciate her efforts. Joshua Norris was a difficult man to interpret. She didn't know how far she dared tread onto this carpet of unexpected trust he'd laid before her.

A series of flashing lights glowed in the distance and Bethany felt Joshua tense beside her. She checked her wristwatch and noted the time. "It's too early for that to be Angie's plane."

Her employer nodded and seemed to relax.

"Joshua," she whispered, unable to keep herself from speaking, "everything's going to work out fine."

At the sound of his name, his troubled gaze shot in her direction, and he frowned. His eyes revealed surprise mingled with bewilderment. "No one's called me that since I was a boy."

Colour exploded in Bethany's cheeks, working its way to her ears until she was certain they glowed with the heat. She'd always thought of him as Joshua, called him that in all her thoughts. The world knew him as J. D. Norris, but she'd found the initials too abrupt for the complex man she knew him to be. "I . . . won't do it again."

"It wasn't a reprimand . . . Bethany, but a statement of fact." He said her name as though it felt awkward on his tongue, yet as though he had recognised that she had a name other than Miss Stone. When he continued to stare at her for a long moment, Bethany had the impression he was seeing her for the first time. Briefly she wondered if he liked what he saw. She knew her clear delicate features robbed her of any classic beauty. Her eyes were a pale shade of blue, but not unlike a thousand others'. Her cheekbones were slightly high, her nose firm and straight. But she didn't possess any one feature that would distinguish her as a great beauty. Friends had called her cute, but that was about the extent of it. She was neither short nor tall, just average height—a description that sounded so terribly boring. She was contemplating this fact when she noted that if Joshua were to take her in his arms—fat chance of that—but if it were to happen, the top of her head would just brush against his jawline. All he would need to do was bend his head and kiss her and her lips would meet his without...

"Are Angie's grandparents traveling with her?" she asked, purposely diverting her thoughts. With some effort, she tore her gaze from his, her composure badly shaken by the brief encounter.

"No." Joshua abruptly shook his head and turned back to stare out the window. "It couldn't be helped. She's flying in alone."

"Oh." For a ten-year-old to be placed on a plane in New York to make this long trip by herself seemed almost irresponsible to Bethany, but she kept her opinion to herself. Poor Angie. With the time difference between the two cities, the little girl would probably be exhausted—or as keyed up and as full of energy as a fresh battery.

"Has her bed been made up?"

"Bed?" Joshua echoed the word as though it were something totally foreign. "I thought I'd put her in the guest bedroom for tonight... I hadn't stopped to think beyond that. I suppose she'll need something more, won't she?'' His gaze clouded.

"I'm sure the guest room will be fine for now."

"Good."

A fresh set of wing lights blinked in the distant night. "I think that's her flight now," Bethany said.

Joshua stiffened, seeming to brace himself, and nodded. "She should be one of the first ones to disembark—I arranged for a first-class ticket."

"The flight attendant will probably escort her off."

Once again, Joshua gave a nonverbal reply, then exhaled sharply. "I can't tell you how glad I am that you're here with me."

Bethany couldn't have been more pleased herself. She'd been granted a glimpse of a whole new facet to Joshua Norris's personality. When it came to his daughter, he was a marshmallow. It seemed completely contradictory that this same man could bring a room full of board members to silence with one shattering look. She'd witnessed glares from Joshua that were colder than a tombstone in midwinter. No one would ever guess that the man who was nervously waiting for his young daughter was the driving force behind a thriving business. Bethany had trouble believing it herself.

An airline official opened the door to the jetway and two older businessmen were the first to step into the airport, carrying briefcases and garment bags. They were followed by a female flight attendant escorting a wide-eyed little girl with straight dark hair that fell to the top of her shoulders. Two pink ribbons held it away from her face, which seemed to be made up solely of round eager eyes.

"Daddy!" The girl broke away from the attendant and ran towards Joshua.

J. D. Norris looked startled, then fell to one knee as his daughter hurled herself into his waiting arms.

Two small arms flew around his neck and squeezed for all they were worth. Slowly, almost as if it were against his will, Joshua closed his eyes and returned the bear hug.

Bethany felt moisture brim in her eyes at the tender scene and bit into her bottom lip, determined not to say or do anything to disturb their reunion.

Finally Joshua released his daughter and stood, claiming her hand. "Angie," he murmured, looking down on the ten-year-old, "this is Miss Stone. She's my secretary."

"Hello." Wide dark eyes stared up at Bethany.

"Hello, Angie. Welcome to New Orleans."

"Thanks." The pre-teen grinned and let loose with an adult-sounding sigh. "I can't tell you how boring that flight was. I was beginning to think I'd never get here."

"I believe your father was feeling much the same thing."

Angie's smile grew wider. "I don't suppose there's a McDonald's around here. Grandma told me not to trust anything the airlines served and I'm absolutely starved."

"Miss Stone—a McDonald's?" Joshua was looking at her as though he expected her to wave a magic wand so one could instantly appear.

"Any hamburger will do," Angie offered next, her gaze growing wide and desperate.

"There's a McDonald's a few miles away."

"Thank goodness," the little girl sighed, shrugging her small shoulders. "I swear I could eat one of everything they have."

Come to think of it, Bethany hadn't had dinner yet, either. Her stomach growled eagerly at the mere mention of a Big Mac.

Angie prattled on about New York and her grandparents as they moved down the concourse to the baggage claim area. In addition to the travel bag the little girl had with her, there were three large suitcases.

Once they were seated inside Joshua's car, Angie leaned over the seat so her head was positioned between Bethany and Joshua.

"You're a winter, aren't you, Miss Stone?"

"A winter?" She hadn't a clue what the ten-year-old was talking about.

"Your colouring—haven't you ever been analysed?" She smothered a yawn with her palm. "It was the latest thing a few years back."

"I guess I must have missed that."

"You needn't have it done now. I have a gift for these things, and you're definitely a winter," Angie returned confidently. "You should wear more bright clothes—reds, blues, whites, those sort of colours."

"Oh." Bethany wasn't sure how to comment. As it was, her wardrobe consisted of several bold colours, but she wore more subdued ones for the office—tans and soft blues mostly.

"Cheryl Tiegs, the model, has got a wonderful programme on the Arts and Entertainment channel. You should watch that for a few fashion hints."

"Yes," Bethany said, hiding a grin. "I suppose I should."

"How's the sailing going, Dad?"

"Good," Joshua said distractedly. He seemed more concerned with getting out of the heavy airport traffic at the moment.

"I saw an interview with some guys on the sports station last night. You might think about studying tacking techniques if you want to be a really great sailor. Personally, I think the New Zealanders are the ones we're going to have to watch in the next America's Cup."

"That could very well be true." Joshua's smiling gaze bounced off Bethany's as he briefly rolled his eyes.

Angie crossed her arms over the seat and pressed her chin on top of her folded hands. She hesitated for a quick moment, then said, "We're going to get along just fine, don't you think?"

"Just fine," Joshua echoed. "What I'd like right now, though, is for you to sit back and buckle up the way you're supposed to."

Bethany sucked in her breath. His words were clipped and far more harsh than necessary. Joshua was right, but there were gentler ways of telling his daughter so.

"Oh, sure." Angie immediately obeyed, flopping back against the car seat and slipping the seatbelt

neatly into place. "You should have done this years
ago."

"Done what?" Joshua's question was absent as he
pulled to a stop to pay the attendant the parking fee.

"Sent for me," Angie said on the tail end of a yawn.

Joshua didn't answer her for what seemed like an
eternity. "You may be right," he murmured at last.

Bethany noted how his face eased into a relaxed
smile. It struck her then how rare it was for Joshua
Norris to show pleasure at something. He ran a tight
ship as the saying went. He lived his life according to
a rigid schedule, driving himself and everyone who
worked closely with him to the brink of exhaustion.
The control with which he moulded his existence was
bound to change now that his daughter had arrived.
For the better, Bethany dared to hope. For the better.

Bethany curved her fingers around the bag that
rested on her lap. The letter of resignation neatly
folded inside would stay there. Exciting things were
about to happen at Norris Pharmaceutical and with J.
D. Norris, and Bethany planned to stick around and
witness each one.

The living room curtain was pushed aside and
Sally's eager face was reflected in the glass when the
taxi deposited Bethany in front of her apartment two
hours later.

"It's about time you got home," Sally cried the
minute Bethany walked inside the door. "What happened? I've been dying to talk to you. Good grief, girl,
you should have phoned." She inhaled a huge breath

and sank onto the thick sofa cushion. "But don't worry about apologising now. Talk."

Bethany hung her jacket in the hall cupboard, biding her time. She wasn't exactly sure where to start. "Mr. Norris followed me out of Charley's..."

"I know that much. Good heavens, what did he say to you? I don't know when I've seen you look more...I don't know...stricken, I guess."

"That doesn't matter."

"He followed you, though?"

"Yes. He told me his daughter is coming to live with him."

Sally folded her pyjama-clad legs under her and leaned back, her look thoughtful. Twin brows arched speculatively as she bounced her finger over her closed lips several times. "Well, that's news."

"Angie arrived tonight, and Mr. Norris asked me to go to the airport with him."

"So that's where you've been?"

"Part of the time." Bethany slipped off her low-heeled shoes and claimed the overstuffed recliner across from her roommate. "After that we went to McDonald's."

Sally grinned at that, her smile slightly off centre. "How romantic."

Actually it had been, but she wasn't about to explain that to her friend. Bethany was convinced it was the first time Joshua had ever been to a fast-food place, and he'd looked as uncomfortable as a pond fish during a summer drought. "We went through the drive-in window because it was obvious Angie was going to conk out any minute."

"And did she?"

"The poor kid was fast asleep by the time we ar-rived at his house."

"You saw Mr. Norris's house?" Sally uncrossed her legs and leaned forward. They'd once heard that Joshua lived in a mansion.

Bethany answered with a short nod, remembering her first impression of the breathtaking beauty of the two-storey colonial building. The antebellum home was constructed of used brick in muted shades of white and red. Four white gables peeked out stately from the roof line above the second floor. The front of the house was decorated with six huge brick col-umns that were lushly covered with climbing ivy. Joshua's home was a tasteful blend of the old South and her warm traditions with the new South and her willingness to adapt to change.

"What happened there?" Sally pressed, unable to hide her curiosity.

Bethany answered with a soft shrug. "Angie was asleep by the time we arrived, so while I helped her undress and get ready for bed, Mr. Norris brought in her luggage."

"And?"

"And then he phoned for a taxi so I'd have a way home."

He'd also thanked her and apologised once more for his behaviour earlier that evening. And as he did, Bethany noted that he was closing himself off from her again. She could see it as clearly as if she were stand-ing before a huge gate that was mechanically being shut. She tried to read his features, but it was impos-

sible. She suspected that he'd regretted having confided in her once the crisis had passed, and that hurt
just a little.

Bethany didn't mention any of this to Sally, nor did
she tell her roommate how Joshua had walked her to
the cab once it arrived and paid her fare. He'd lingered outside a few moments, hands buried deep in his
trouser pockets, his face lined with a frown that left
Bethany brooding all the way home.

"That's it?" Sally asked, looking sadly disappointed. "You were gone for hours and that's the extent of what happened the entire time?"

"That's all there was." On the surface it didn't
sound like much, and really it wasn't, but far more
had been accomplished. So much more than Bethany
had ever dared to hope in a long while. For the first
time since she'd been hired as J. D. Norris's personal
secretary, her employer had seen her as something
more than an automaton. She chose to think he was
pleasantly surprised by what he'd found.

Bethany was at her desk by the time Joshua arrived
on Monday morning. She glanced up expectantly and
was disappointed when he did nothing more than offer her a crisp good-morning the way he'd done every
day of the past three years. He marched by her desk
and into his office.

Reaching for the mail, Bethany followed him inside. She'd taken his daughter's advice and chosen a
dark blue business suit with a white silk blouse and a
ribbon tie. Briefly she wondered if Joshua would no-

tice anything as mundane as the way she dressed. Probably not.

Following ritual, she poured him a mug of hot coffee and delivered it to his desk. Joshua reached for the brew and took a sip before quickly leafing through the mail. He gave brisk instructions on each piece, handed back the ones she could deal with directly and kept the rest. Once he'd finished, Bethany hesitated, standing beside his desk, uncertain.

"Yes?" he questioned crisply. "Was there something more?" He didn't so much as look up at her.

"I... wanted to ask you about Angie," she managed finally, having trouble getting the words past an uncooperative tongue. His façade was back, and from the hard look about him, it had been heavily reinforced.

"Miss Stone, in case you've forgotten, I have a business to run. My daughter is none of your concern. Now, may I be so bold as to suggest that you do the job for which I handsomely pay you?"

It took Bethany a moment to blink back the incredible hurt. "Yes, of course." Her voice was hardly more than a whisper. She found that her hands were trembling by the time she'd returned to her desk. Her legs weren't in much better shape.

By rote she managed to finish the morning's tasks, but by the time Sally arrived at noon, Bethany had worked herself into an uncharacteristic anger. She shook from the force of it, furious with herself for allowing Joshua to speak to her in that horrible tone as though she were his personal slave.

"He's impossible," she hissed when her friend stuck her head in the door.

"Mr. Norris?" Sally's gaze travelled in lazy perusal from her roommate to the closed door that connected the two rooms.

"Who else?" Bethany pushed back her chair so hard, she soared six feet from the desk.

Frowning heavily, Sally stepped into the office. "Good grief, what happened?"

"I've had it!" Bethany declared, and cringed when Sally rolled her eyes towards the ceiling. Okay, so she'd been saying the same thing for weeks, but today was different. She would show Joshua Norris that she was a woman with emotions and feelings, deserving respect. She refused to allow any man to talk to her the way J. D. Norris had. Never again. The worm had developed a backbone at last.

She reached for her bag and headed towards the door.

Open-mouthed, Sally lingered behind. "Aren't you going to let the great white hunter know you're leaving?"

"No. He'll figure it out for himself."

Sally closed her mouth, then promptly opened it again. "Okay."

Bethany was halfway out the door when she glanced over her shoulder at Joshua's office. A great sadness settled over her heart and she inhaled a soft sigh of regret. Her relationship with J. D. Norris seemed to be one step forward followed almost immediately by two giant leaps back. She'd been given a rare glimpse of the man she knew him to be and feared she was destined to wait a lifetime to be granted another peek.

Unusually quiet, Sally led the way to the company cafeteria on the third floor. They ordered their lunch, then carried the bright orange trays to the round table by the window that overlooked the rambling Mississippi River.

"You're right, you know," Bethany spoke first. "I should have quit long before now." Like a romantic schoolgirl, she'd believed that the love of a good woman would be enough to change Joshua. But she was wrong. He didn't want her love, didn't need her. Their time together with Angie was an embarrassment to him now, something he obviously regretted.

"I'm right about what? J. D. Norris?" Sally asked, watching her friend carefully. When Bethany didn't respond right away, she peeled open her turkey-on-wheat sandwich to remove the lettuce. She reached for the salt shaker in the middle of the table, then changed her mind and replaced it.

A long minute passed before Bethany nodded.

"Well?" Sally demanded. "Are you going to spill your guts or not?"

"Not," Bethany answered in a small voice that was filled with regret. She couldn't explain to Sally facts she herself had only recently faced. She had been pining away for three good years of her life, and just when she'd been given a glimmer of hope, she'd been forced to recognise how futile the whole situation was.

Eventually Sally would wear her down, Bethany realised. Her friend usually came up with some new way of drilling the information out of her. But she wasn't ready to talk yet. She lifted her pastrami sandwich from the plate and realised she might as well have been contemplating eating Mississippi mud for all the appeal her lunch held. She returned the sandwich, untouched, to the plate and pushed it aside.

"You realise I've heard all this before."

"Of course I realise that. But this time is different."

"Right," Sally said with a soft snicker.

"No, I really mean it," Bethany returned. "Listen, I recently read that the best time to find a job is when you're currently employed. I'm going to start applying for a new position first thing tomorrow morning."

Sally's narrowed gaze said that she wasn't sure if she could believe her friend or not. Bethany met that look with a determination that had been sadly absent in the past. This time she meant it—she honestly meant it. She was leaving Joshua Norris for good.

When Bethany returned to the office, the morning paper tucked under her arm, Joshua's door was open. He must have heard her because he stepped out and stood at her desk for a moment. Although she refused to meet his gaze, she could feel him assessing her. He left without a word a couple of minutes later.

The instant he was gone, Bethany spread open the newspaper to the job-ads section, carefully read the help-wanted columns and made two calls, setting up appointments.

An hour later Joshua returned, but he didn't speak to her then, either, which was just as well.

The afternoon passed quickly. Joshua requested two files and dictated a letter, which Bethany typed and returned within the half hour. No other communication passed between them, verbal or otherwise.

Once more Joshua left the office for a meeting with accounting, and fifteen minutes later Bethany walked out to meet Sally for their afternoon coffee break. Sally apparently had decided to keep her opinions to herself, because the subject of J. D. Norris didn't come up.

When Bethany returned to the office, she decided she'd ask Joshua for Thursday morning off. She would tell him she had an appointment, which was true. The appointment was to fill out job applications. And next time she accepted a job, she was going to be certain that her employer was happily married and over fifty.

"Miss Stone. Hi."

Bethany's gaze flew to her desk, where Angie sat waiting.

The youngster jumped up and smiled, looking pleased to see Bethany again. "I didn't think you'd ever get back."

"Hello, Angie." The little girl's welcoming smile would rival a Louisiana sunset. "How was your first day of school?"

The ten-year-old wrinkled up her nose. "There are a bunch of weird kids living in this town."

"Oh?"

"Not a single girl in my class has ever heard of Bobby Short."

While gnawing on her lower lip, Bethany scanned her own repertoire of famous men's names and came up blank. "What a shame," she answered, hoping Joshua's daughter wouldn't lump her in the same category as the others.

"Anyone who knows anything about music must have heard about Bobby. Why... he's world famous. Grandma and Grandpa are personally acquainted with him. Once they took me to the Carlisle so I could hear him." She crossed her arms and gave a short little pout.

At the mention of the famous New York hotel, Bethany was reassured. Bobby Short was a singer.

"I'm not going to tell Dad this," Angie continued, her voice dropping to a soft whisper, "because it would upset him, but my fellow students have no class."

Making no comment, Bethany deposited her bag in the bottom desk drawer and took her chair.

Angie came around the other side of the typewriter to face her. "Do you like Madonna?"

Containing a smile was impossible. "Quite a bit, as a matter of fact."

The youngster seemed surprised that Bethany would openly admit as much. "I do, too, but Grandma claims she's a hussy."

"And what does that mean?" The laugh worked its way up Bethany's throat but was quickly closed off when her gaze met a dark, serious pair of brown eyes.

Angie shook her head. "I'm not sure, but I think it has something to do with the fact Madonna has pierced ears."

Bethany sincerely hoped the ten-year-old hadn't noticed her ears. God only knew what she'd think of someone who had each lobe pierced *twice*. To divert the child's attention, she rolled a piece of paper into her typewriter.

Angie wheeled a chair to the side of Bethany's desk. "Dad said I'm not supposed to bother you when you're working. The new housekeeper can't come until tomorrow and so I'm here for the afternoon."

"You won't be a bother, sweetheart."

Angie looked relieved at that. "What are you doing now?"

"I'm about to type a letter for your dad."

"Can I watch?"

"If you want." Bethany's fingers dextrously flew over the keys. She finished within a few minutes.

"You're good."

"Do you want to try?"

If Bethany had thought the youngster's eyes were round before, now they resembled black orbs. "Can I really?"

In response, Bethany placed a fresh sheet of paper in the machine and moved aside. "It's all yours."

For the next hour Angie became Bethany's shadow. The little girl was a joy, and more than once Bethany was unable to hold back a laugh. Angela Norris was unlike any ten-year-old Bethany had ever known. Despite the fact that she'd been raised by her grandparents and had attended a small private school, Angie appeared utterly unspoiled. Bethany found that fact remarkable.

It was nearly five o'clock by the time Joshua returned from his meeting.

"Hi, Dad," Angie greeted. "Bethany let me use her fingernail polish. See." She held up both hands, revealing pink-tipped fingers.

The phone rang before Joshua could respond.

"I'll get that."

Bethany sucked in her breath as Angie reached for the receiver. "Mr. Norris's office, how may I help you?"

"Miss Stone?" Joshua arched his brows in a disapproving slant. "Is this your doing?"

Bethany's response was to offer him a weak guilty smile.

Angie pressed the telephone receiver to her shoulder and looked at Bethany. "It's someone named Sally asking for you."

Joshua's gaze sliced into Bethany, condensed with disapproval. "As soon as you're finished, Miss Stone, I'd like to see you in my office."

CHAPTER THREE

"You wanted to see me, Mr. Norris?" Bethany asked in a brisk businesslike tone, devoid of emotion. She trained her gaze on a point on the wall behind him so she needn't subject herself to his cool assessing eyes. No doubt she'd done something more to displease him. Again. It wasn't as though she hadn't been trying. All day she'd been finding petty ways of getting back at him for his cold treatment of her earlier in the day. Bethany didn't like to think of herself as a mean-minded person, but working with Joshua had reduced her to this level. It was more than enough reason to find other employment.

"I wanted to apologise for Angie being here," he said.

Bethany relaxed. "She hasn't been a problem, sir."

"Good. The housekeeper I hired starts tomorrow, so this will be the last time Angie will need to come to the office."

"I understand." Although it required some will, Bethany kept her gaze centred on the landscape drawing behind Joshua. "Will that be all?"

"Yes." He sounded hesitant.

Bethany did a crisp about-face and marched with military precision towards the door. She paused when she remembered her plan to look for another job. "Mr. Norris?"

"Yes?"

"I'll need Thursday off."

"This Thursday?"

"If... if it wouldn't be too much of an imposition. I've got an appointment."

"For all day?"

She straightened her shoulders. "That's correct."

He didn't sound pleased, but that wasn't Bethany's problem. "All right, Miss Stone, arrange for personnel to send me a substitute, then."

"Right away, sir."

"Miss Stone," he called out impatiently, his tone angry. "Kindly drop the 'sir,' will you? You haven't used it in the past and it's unnecessary to call me that now. Is that understood?"

"Perfectly, Mr. Norris."

Joshua expelled his breath in what sounded like a frustrated sigh. "Miss Stone, is there a problem?"

Bethany turned to him, keeping her face as devoid of emotion as possible. "What could possibly be wrong?" she asked in as much of a singsong sarcastic voice as she dared without invoking his full ire.

"That's my question!" he shouted.

"Then that's my answer."

His eyes rounded with surprise and he looked as though he wanted to say something more. But when he didn't speak immediately, Bethany turned and quickly left the room. She'd never spoken to Mr. Norris that way, never once revealed any of what she was thinking or feeling for fear she would say or do something to cause his displeasure. She hadn't dared. But she wouldn't be in Joshua Norris's employment much longer and the sense of freedom she felt amazed her.

"Miss Stone?" Angie asked, her wide eyes studying Bethany. "Is my dad mad at you?"

"No, honey, of course not."

"Good." The little girl released a long sigh that seemed to deflate her posture until her small shoulders sagged with relief. "He has a habit of saying things in this deep dark voice that scares people. It used to make me want to cry, but then I realised he talks that way most of the time, and he isn't really mad."

"I know, Angie. If you'd like, you can call me Bethany."

"I can?"

"But only if we can be friends."

The ten-year-old released another one of those balloon-whooshing sighs. "After the day I've had, believe me, I could use one."

Bethany laughed outright at that, unable to stop herself, although she could see that the little girl was dead serious.

"It's true," Angie murmured, her dark eyes round and sad. "I don't think anyone in my new class likes me. I'm not sure what I did wrong, either. But I think Grandma would say I was trying too hard."

"Give it time, sweetheart."

Angie nodded and grinned. "That's something else Grandma would say."

"By the end of the week you'll have all kinds of new friends."

"Do you honestly think so?"

Bethany gave her a reassuring nod and rolled a clean piece of paper into her typewriter. "How would you like to type a letter for me?"

"I can do that?"

"Sure. I've got some filing to do, and since you're here, you can be my personal assistant." She laid a form letter on the tabletop for the little girl to copy.

"I'll do my best, Miss Stone. I mean . . . Bethany." Angie slid the chair towards the typewriter, looking as efficient and businesslike as possible for a pre-teen.

Within a couple of minutes, Angie's brow was folded with concentration as her fingers went on a seek-and-find mission for each typewriter key. It took the girl an hour to finish the few short sentences of the letter, but when it was done, Angie looked as proud as if she'd climbed Stone Mountain unaided.

"You did a fine job, Angie," Bethany told her, glancing over the finished product.

"Oh, hi, Dad," Angie said, flew off her chair and went running towards her father. "Guess what? Bethany said I can be her personal assistant. I can come back tomorrow, can't I? You aren't really going to make me stay with that stuffy old housekeeper, are you? Bethany needs me here."

Bethany opened her mouth, then closed it. Oh, dear, she'd only been trying to amuse Joshua's daughter, and now it looked as though she'd created a problem instead of solving one.

"There may be an occasional afternoon when Miss Stone could use your help," Joshua admitted thoughtfully, his gaze resting on Bethany. "But Miss

Stone is quite efficient, so you shouldn't count on coming every day."

"But, Dad . . ."

"My secretary is usually able to handle all the work herself," Joshua said, interrupting the little girl in a voice that brooked no argument.

"I *want* to help her, though. As often as I can, and I should be able to come every afternoon, don't you think, Bethany?"

"I said you may come occasionally," Joshua reiterated, "and that's all the argument I'm willing to listen to, Angela."

"Yes, Daddy." She didn't look pleased, but she wasn't completely deflated, either.

Considering everything, Bethany felt Joshua had offered a decent compromise. When she left the office that night, Bethany realised she was actually pleased with the way her employer had handled the situation with his daughter. He might not have had a lot of opportunity to do much parenting, but he seemed to be adapting nicely. Angie and Joshua would get along fine without her. At least, that was what Bethany kept telling herself.

Thursday afternoon, Bethany was sitting in front of the television, her feet propped up on the coffee table and a hot drink cupped in her hand, when her roommate let herself into the apartment.

"You look like you had a rough day," Sally commented.

"It's a jungle out there," Bethany said forcefully. Her feet ached, her spirits sagged, and she wondered if there would ever be a job that would free her heart from Joshua Norris.

"I take it a fantastic job didn't plop itself down in your lap?"

"The woman's a mind reader."

"What happened?"

"Nothing, unfortunately," Bethany admitted with a soft moan of discouragement. "I left my application in with ten different companies and was interviewed for positions with two others. I got the old 'don't call us, we'll call you' routine."

"What are you going to do?" Sally asked, the concern in her voice evident with each syllable.

"What else can I do?" Bethany answered. "I'll stick it out with Joshua Norris until I find something suitable."

Her friend plunked herself onto the sofa beside Bethany and raised her feet onto the coffee table. "Well, I've got news for you, too."

"What?" Bethany was in the mood for something uplifting.

"Apparently Mr. Norris didn't have a good day without you."

"Oh?"

"He went through two substitutes before noon."

"Good grief, who did personnel send him?"

"I don't know, but the word was, Mr. Norris was in a foul mood all day."

Bethany tugged at the corner of her lower lip with her teeth. "I wonder why?"

"So does everyone else. I'll tell you one thing, though. There isn't a secretary in the entire company who isn't glad you're coming back tomorrow morning. Every one of them spent an anxious afternoon fearing they were going to be sent to work in Mr. Norris's office. It's like ordering a vestal virgin to walk into the dragon's den."

"He's not that bad!" Joshua might have faults, but he certainly wasn't a tyrant. Bethany wouldn't have fallen in love with a slave driver.

"Mr. Norris isn't bad? Wanna bet?" Sally returned forcefully. "Rumour has it that J. D. Norris told the first secretary she was a complete ninny."

Bethany gritted her teeth to keep from defending Joshua. It was apparent to her, if not to her roommate, that if her employer called her replacement a ninny it was highly probable that the woman had done something stupid. Bethany didn't know who personnel had sent up to replace her, but it seemed the problem lay with them and not her employer.

"You are planning to go back tomorrow, aren't you?" Sally asked expectantly.

Bethany nodded; she didn't have any choice but to return. She'd envisioned walking into his office and slapping down her two-week notice, all the while smiling smugly at J. D. Norris. But that wouldn't be impossible.

"Having you return in the morning is going to save me a good deal of telephoning."

"Telephoning?"

"Yeah," her roommate said, looking pleased. "I promised I'd call the others and let them know if you weren't going to work, because in that case, every secretary in the company was planning to call in sick."

"But that's ridiculous."

"You weren't at the office today, Beth. You couldn't possibly know what rumours have been circulating. I swear there isn't a woman in all Norris Pharmaceutical who doesn't think you should be nominated for sainthood."

Bethany grinned at that. It did her ego a world of good to have others think of her as irreplaceable. Unfortunately, Joshua was the only one who mattered, and he didn't seem to care one way or the other what happened to her.

The following morning proved her wrong.

Bethany was at her desk when Joshua strolled into the office. He paused just inside the door and looked relieved when he saw her sitting there. It might have been the lighting, but Bethany thought she saw his gaze soften. A brief smile touched his mouth; of that, she was sure.

"Good morning, Bethany."

"Mr. Norris." She stood and was halfway into his office when she realised he'd called her by her first name. Her heart ping-ponged against her breast in glad reaction. For the first time in years she was a real person to Joshua and not some kind of motor-driven robot.

By the time she delivered a cup of freshly brewed coffee to his desk and handed him the mail, she'd managed to compose herself and wipe the last traces of jubilation from her face, but not from her heart. Never from her heart.

Joshua leafed through the correspondence and gave his instructions the way he did each weekday morning. When he was finished, however, he paused.

"Miss Stone?"

She'd already stood when he gestured for her to sit down again.

"Yes?"

"How long have you been working for me now? Three years?"

Bethany nodded.

"When was the last time I gave you a raise?"

"Four months ago." Her generous salary was part of the problem in finding another suitable position. Once she listed her current wages, most places were unwilling to meet or match her price. At least that was what Bethany surmised from her experiences the day before.

"You've done an excellent job for me, Miss Stone."

"Thank you."

"I tend not to tell you that often enough."

As Bethany recalled, he'd never said it, certainly not directly.

"We seem to work well together. Until you were gone yesterday I didn't realise how much you do to keep this office running smoothly."

"Thank you." She knew she sounded as if her vocabulary were limited to those two words, but he'd taken her by complete surprise and she couldn't find anything else to say that made any sense. There must have been some truth to what Sally had told her about her replacements, but Bethany had been absent from work more than once. Not often, but a day or two now and again.

"You anticipate my needs," Joshua went on to say, looking slightly embarrassed. "You seem to know what I'm thinking and act on it without my having to comment. I'm coming to realise that's a rare quality in an employee."

"Thank you." Her lack of ability to make brilliant or any other kind of conversation greatly chagrined her.

"I feel it would only be fair to compensate you for a job well done." He paused and looked pleased with himself.

"I beg your pardon." Bethany wasn't sure what he meant.

"I'm giving you another raise."

He mentioned a sum that made Bethany gasp. The amount was nearly twenty-five percent of her already more than adequate salary. "But I just received a wage increase last October."

Joshua arched his brows speculatively. "Does that mean you don't want this one?"

"Of course I want it."

"Good," he said briskly, turning his attention to the papers on his desk, dismissing her. "That will be all, then."

"Thank...you, Mr....Norris," she said, coming awkwardly to a stand. A couple of the envelopes she was holding nearly slipped from her fingers, but she managed to grab them before they fell to the floor.

He grinned, and his look was almost boyish. "I believe you've adequately thanked me, Miss Stone."

Bethany couldn't return to her desk fast enough. The first thing she did was call Sally, who worked in the accounting department.

"Sally," she cried under her breath. "Meet me for coffee, okay?"

"Now? Bethany, dear, in case you haven't noticed, it's barely after eight."

"Not now, at ten, like always."

"Bethany?" her friend muttered, sounding vaguely concerned. "We've been meeting for coffee every day at ten for three years. Why would today be any different?"

"I got a raise!" Bethany cried, unable to hold the information inside any longer.

"Another one?"

To her way of thinking, Sally didn't sound nearly as pleased as she should have been. "What you said about yesterday must have been true, because Mr. Norris seemed more than pleased to see me this morning."

"Beth, does this mean you won't be looking for another job?"

"Are you nuts? Where else would I ever make this kind of money?"

"Where else would you risk breaking your heart?" Sally asked.

The question echoed through Bethany's mind like shouts bouncing off canyon walls. The reply was equally clear: nowhere else but with Joshua Norris.

Two weeks passed, and although nothing had actually changed, everything was different. There didn't seem to be any one thing that Bethany could pin down, but she felt more at ease with Joshua. Their routine remained exactly as it had been for three years, but Bethany intuitively recognised that Joshua felt more content. He was less formal, less austere. She guessed that the changes had come about as a result of having Angie come live with him. The ten-year-old was such a precious child that Bethany knew Joshua couldn't be around his daughter and not be affected.

Bethany was hungry for news of the little girl, but she dared not topple this fragile peace between her and her employer after that first morning when Joshua had made it clear that he didn't wish to discuss his daughter.

"Miss Stone?" Joshua called for her when she returned from her lunch break Friday afternoon.

Bethany reached for a pad and pencil and stepped into his office.

Joshua was leaning back in his chair, his hands forming a steeple that held up his chin; his look was thoughtful. "How much do you know about teen fashions?"

"Teen fashions?" she repeated, not certain she'd heard him correctly.

"Yes. Angela recently informed me she's 'out of it' and seemed quite concerned. Apparently not wearing the latest fad is a fate worse than death."

Bethany smiled and nodded, remembering her own teen years. Ten seemed a bit young, but she could understand Angie's wanting to fit in with the other girls her age.

"Short of dying her hair orange and piercing her nose, I have few objections to the way my daughter dresses."

Bethany nodded. She didn't particularly agree with that statement, but it wasn't her place to share her opinions on the matter with Joshua.

He straightened and looked uncomfortable. "I was wondering if it would be possible for you to take Angie shopping. She specifically asked for you, and I don't mind admitting I know next to nothing about how kids dress these days. Naturally I'd pay you for your time. It would mean a good deal to Angie."

"I'd enjoy it immensely."

He sighed then and actually grinned. "You don't know how relieved I am to hear that. I had visions of Angela dragging me through the women's lingerie department."

The following morning, Bethany met Angie and Joshua in a local shopping mall. The minute Angie saw Bethany approach, she broke loose of her father's hand and came running towards her as though they hadn't seen each other in years.

"Bethany, hi. I didn't think you'd ever get here."

Surprised, Bethany glanced at her wrist. "Am I late?" According to her watch, she was a full five minutes early.

"It seemed to take you forever," the ten-year-old said.

"We've been here ten minutes," Joshua admitted with an off-centre grin that took away five years.

He looked so good that Bethany had to force her gaze back to Angie. "I take it you're excited?"

"Do the Saints play football?" Joshua asked, referring to the New Orleans football team, which had just finished an exceptionally good season.

"Dad said the sky's the limit. Are you ready?" she asked, her face a study in eagerness. "I know I am."

"Good luck," Joshua said, and paused to look at his gold watch. "I'll meet you for lunch. Where would you suggest?"

Before Bethany could answer, Angie called out, "McDonald's."

"You game?" Joshua asked her, looking more amused by the minute. Bethany had trouble recognising him as the same man she worked with five days a week. For the first time in memory, he wasn't wearing a suit but was dressed casually in trousers and a light sweater that accentuated his china-blue eyes.

"McDonald's? Sure!" The last time she'd visited the fast-food restaurant had been the night they'd picked up Angie from the airport. If Joshua was game, then so was she.

By one o'clock that same afternoon, Bethany was exhausted, and Angie was just hitting her second wind. The child seemed tireless—a born shopper. It amazed Bethany how selective the ten-year-old was about her clothes. Although they'd been in at least fifteen different shops, Angie had only chosen a handful of items. Mostly sweatshirts and acid-washed jeans and a couple of pairs of white tennis shoes. Bethany did manage to talk her into one dress and a pair of patent leather shoes, but anything frilly simply wasn't her, as Angie put it.

Joshua was sitting in a booth in McDonald's munching on a french fry when Angie and Bethany joined him.

"How's it going?"

"Bethany really knows her stuff," Angie announced, already reaching for her Big Mac. "I knew the minute you told me she was going to take me shopping that this day would be special, and it has been."

Bethany felt her heart constrict at the little girl's praise. If anyone was special, it was Joshua's precocious daughter.

Angie dabbed her french fry in the ketchup and lowered her gaze to the tabletop. "I just wish I could see Bethany more often."

Neither adult spoke. Bethany gave her attention to her own hamburger, staring at it, knowing she couldn't have swallowed a bite had her life depended on it. Joshua became unusually quiet, as well.

"Miss Stone is busy, Angie. She has other friends."

"Why do you call her Miss Stone, Dad?"

"I don't have that many other friends," Bethany said quickly. "I'd enjoy seeing Angie more often."

Joshua's eyes drifted from one female to the next, his gaze bewildered, as though he weren't certain who he should answer first. It was clear from the way he looked that he felt outnumbered.

"I call her Bethany and I bet you could, too," Angie added. "Grandma told me it was all right to call an adult by their first name if they said it was okay. I bet Bethany wouldn't mind if you called her by her name instead of Miss Stone all the time. Gee whiz, you see each other every day.''

''Yes, well, I suppose I could if Miss Stone didn't object.''

''Of course I don't mind.''

''And you should call Dad J.D. like everyone else,'' Angie continued, speaking to Bethany.

''She prefers Joshua,'' he explained, his eyes holding Bethany's briefly. He grinned.

''Joshua.'' Angie rolled the name over the end of her tongue as if the sound of it were something rich and rare. ''I like that, too. When I was born, if I'd been a boy, what would you and Mom have named me?''

''David. It's my middle name.''

''Not Joshua?'' Angie sounded disappointed.

''Too confusing,'' her father explained.

''What made you decide on something like Angela?'' the little girl asked, closely studying her father. She was so intent that she stopped eating, and a french fry hung limply in her hand, halfway to her mouth.

''You looked like a tiny angel when the doctor first showed you to me,'' Joshua explained, and his gaze softened as it rested on his daughter. ''I suggested the name Angela Catherine to your mother.''

Angie nodded, not looking overly pleased. ''I wish you'd thought I looked like a Millicent.''

''Millicent?''

''Perhaps a Guinevere.''

''Guinevere?'' It was Bethany's turn to become an echo.

"Or even better a Charmaine." Dramatically the ten-year-old placed her hand over her heart, gazed into the distance and heaved an expressive sigh.

"Charmaine?" Bethany and Joshua repeated, and glanced at each other.

"Oh, yes. Those names sound pretty and smart. Angie sounds . . . I don't know . . . ordinary."

"Trust me, sweetheart, the last thing you are is conventional."

From the way Angie's eyes darted down to the table, it was apparent she didn't understand Joshua's meaning.

"That's another way of saying ordinary," Bethany explained.

"I knew that!"

Once more, Bethany and Joshua shared a brief smile.

"Bethany is such a pretty name. I wouldn't have minded that name, either."

"Thank you. My father named me, too."

"He did?"

"Yes, and when I was ten I wanted to be called Dominique because it sounded sophisticated and mysterious. I used to make up stories where I was the heroine who saved all my friends from certain death."

"You did?" Angie's eyes were growing rounder by the minute. "What about you, Dad? Did you ever want to be called something else when you were ten?"

"No."

Bethany resisted the urge to kick him under the table. Even if it was true, there wasn't any need to squelch the game.

"I believe I was closer to eleven at the time," he answered thoughtfully. "I wanted everyone to call me Mordecai. I felt it was a name that revealed character. When I said it, I felt stronger."

"Mordecai," Angie repeated slowly. "I like that almost as much as Joshua. Oh, Dad, this is the most fun I've had since moving to New Orleans."

Joshua grinned, and the smile Bethany had felt was so rare only hours before looked almost natural.

"Dad, can Bethany come home with us? Please? I want to show her my bedroom and my new television set and everything. You don't mind, do you?"

CHAPTER FOUR

"COME see my bedroom next," Angie insisted, dragging Bethany by the hand down the long hallway. "Dad had a lady come in and decide on my colours and everything... only, I wish..." She paused and glanced over her shoulder before adding, "I like lavender much better than this lemon yellow she wanted me to have."

Bethany paused in the doorway of the ten-year-old's room and swallowed a soft gasp. The bedroom was elaborately decorated with ornate French-provincial-style furniture. A huge canopy bed dominated the room, with a matching desk and armoire close by. Thick canary-yellow carpeting covered the floor and was used to accent a lighter shade of sheer priscilla curtains. The bedspread was crafted from the same flowery pattern as the window covering.

"Don't you think it's simply divine?" Angie asked in a falsetto voice that Bethany was sure was a mimic of the designer. Angie's wide gaze studied her father's secretary for a response.

It was all Bethany could do to nod. Yes, the room was lovely, but it didn't typify Joshua's daughter. The little girl who preferred acid-washed jeans and sweatshirts hadn't once been consulted regarding what she wanted in her bedroom. Bethany would stake her career on the fact. This room belonged to a soft, feminine, demure child, and Angie was direct, tomboyish and full of vitality and life.

"Look at this," Angie said, stepping around her to the armoire. She opened the top doors and revealed a television with a twenty-six-inch screen. "I can sit on my bed and watch TV as late as I want."

"What about bedtime?" Bethany wished she hadn't asked that. She may be curious, but it was better that she not know, realising already that she was going to disapprove. And if she did, she was powerless to say or do anything about it.

"Dad claims I'll go to sleep when I'm tired, and I do." She flopped down across the mattress on her stomach, legs raised and crossed at the ankles. She reached for the remote control, held it out like a laser gun and pressed a button. "Sometimes I fall asleep, and then Dad turns it off for me before he goes to bed."

Bethany managed a weak nod.

"He's real busy after dinner," the little girl informed Bethany, her eyes round and a little sad. "He has a lot of work to do...reading papers and stuff like that. You know."

Bethany did. "What do you do while your father's busy working?"

"Oh, nothing much. I come to my room and watch TV. Sometimes I read."

"What about homework?"

"Oh, Mrs. Larson, the housekeeper, has me do that as soon as I get home from school," she said, and sighed expressively, working her shoulders. "Mrs. Larson's all right, but I wish she'd let me play with the other kids, and after class is the only time I can do that.''

"Have you made new friends?''

"Sure, lots—just like you said I would.''

Bethany patted the top of the little girl's head, pleased. At least that adjustment had seemed to come easily enough.

"As soon as I admitted I like Madonna all the girls knew I was with-it.'' She paused, pressed a button on the remote control and turned off the television. "The afternoon you let me paint my fingernails helped, too, I think.'' Her gaze dropped suggestively to her clear nails, and she let loose with a hopeful sigh and raised pleading eyes to Bethany.

"I think I just may have a bottle of that same polish in my purse. If it's all right with your father, we'll coat your nails again before I leave.''

"Oh, Dad won't care,'' Angie said, flying off the bed and throwing her arms around Bethany's waist for a bear hug.

"What won't I care about?'' Joshua asked, leaning against the doorjamb, looking relaxed and amused.

His eyes sought out his daughter then drifted, almost reluctantly, to Bethany. The dark warm look in his gaze did funny things to her equilibrium and she reached out to steady herself against the bedpost.

"You won't care, will you, Dad?''

"About what, sweetheart?''

"If Bethany paints my fingernails again.''

"No,'' he murmured, his gaze continuing to hold Bethany's. "I think that would be just fine.''

"Do you want to come outside and look at the patio next?" Joshua's daughter wanted to know, her voice raised and eager. "Dad wanted to buy me a swing set, but I told him I was too old for that kind of kid stuff." She rolled her eyes for effect, and it took all Bethany's self-control not to laugh outright.

Joshua led them to the patio off the family room and gestured towards the white wicker furniture for Bethany to take a seat.

"Would you care for something to drink, Miss Stone?"

Angie slapped her hands against her thighs in a small display of disgust. "Honestly, Dad, I thought you were going to call her Bethany."

"Old habits die hard," he said, clearly trying to appease his young daughter.

"I'll take a cola," Angie said, sitting beside Bethany, swinging her stubby legs.

"Bethany?"

"Iced tea, if you have it. Thanks."

He cocked one brow and grinned broadly, his eyes alight with mischief. "What, no mint julep?"

Bethany quickly averted her gaze to Lake Pontchartrain, whose waters lapped lazily against the sandy shore only a few yards away. Joshua was teasing her about the Friday night she'd approached him at Charley's, and she didn't know how to respond.

"I'll be back in a minute."

"Do you want to walk down to the water?" Angie offered, jumping to her feet and holding out her hand to Bethany.

Bethany nodded eagerly. She'd always loved the lake, and she was more than willing to escape Joshua for a few moments. Questions were pounding against the edges of her mind like children beating against a locked door. She'd hungered for so long to know Joshua better. She was just as anxious for him to like her. It was happening and suddenly she was afraid. Terrified.

Sally would be furious with her for not having a witty comeback when he'd suggested the mint julep. He was accustomed to sophisticated women who knew how to spar verbally. All Bethany did was blush uncontrollably and look away, fearing what he would read in her gaze. At this rate, Joshua would never think of her as a mature woman and with good reason. Every time he looked at her with those warm lazy eyes, Bethany felt light-headed and dizzy.

Angie slipped off her trainers and socks and tested the water with her big toe. "It's really warm."

The day itself was almost balmy, even though it was only a few days into February.

"Do you think it would be all right if we waded a little bit? I think it would," Angie answered her own question and stepped out into the water until she was up to her calves.

Bethany slipped out of her sandals and followed, letting the cool lake lap at her toes. It was probably a silly thing to do, but she didn't care. The impulse to enjoy the water was too strong to resist.

"I love this lake," Angie said wistfully. "Dad says we'll be able to swim in a couple of months if the weather is nice, and it should be. I only wish Dad would let me swim alone, but he says I can't unless he's with me."

"He's right," Bethany said forcefully, a little frightened by the thought of Angie in the lake without an adult close by. "Don't ever go in the water alone. It's much too dangerous."

"Oh, I won't, but I don't think Dad will ever want to go. He has too much work to do. All he does is work, work, work. I tried to talk him into reading his papers on the patio so I could play by the water, but he said no to that, too."

Bethany agreed. It would be much too easy to become involved in whatever he was studying and to forget about Angie.

"Your dad's right, honey."

"I knew you'd say that," she answered with a soft pout.

Bethany laughed, enjoying the warm breeze that mussed her hair about her face. The water felt cool and refreshing, and before she knew it, she had lifted the skirt of her soft pink dress and was almost knee-deep.

"Hey, look," Angie called excitedly, waving frantically towards the house. "Dad's watching us."

Bethany twisted around and answered Joshua's wave with one of her own. In her dreams she'd often pictured a scene where they stood together by the lake with the wind whispering gently around them. She wished he would come down by the waterside and make her dream a reality. If she hadn't known better, Bethany would have thought Joshua was thinking the same thing, because the smile left his face and his gaze captured hers, holding it, refusing to let it go. The tender look was enough to cause her pulse rate to soar.

Bethany wasn't sure what happened next, or how she lost her footing, but suddenly, unexpectedly, she was slipping. Her arms flew out in a desperate effort to maintain her balance and remain upright. She should have known if she was going to make a complete fool of herself it would be in front of Joshua Norris. By the time she hit the water, she'd accepted her fate.

"Bethany, Bethany, are you all right?"

Mortified beyond all reasoning, Bethany sat in the chest-deep water and buried her red-hot face in her hands, unable to answer Joshua's daughter.

"Daddy, Daddy, I think Bethany's hurt!"

Bethany heard Angie's shouts as the little girl ran towards the house. Knowing there was nothing to do but face Joshua, she stood, awkwardly at best, and walked out of the water. Her once pretty dress was plastered over her torso and thighs, the ends of her hair dripped water onto the tops of her shoulders. Bethany didn't question how her hair could be wet and her shoulders dry, but they were.

Joshua stood on the shore, his hands braced against his hips, and did an admirable job, Bethany thought, of not laughing. She was convinced if he so much as snickered, she would burst into tears.

"Well, Miss Stone, how's the water?"

"Fine, thanks," she said, and her voice came out an octave higher than normal.

"I've sent Angela for a towel."

Bethany nodded her thanks and rubbed her hands up and down her chilled arms. A puddle of water pooled at her feet, and if it had been in her power to disappear, Bethany would have done so gladly.

"Here, Dad," Angie said breathlessly, rushing onto the scene, her arms loaded with a drawerful of soft thick towels.

Joshua draped one across Bethany's shoulders and held it there momentarily. "Whatever possessed you to wade in the lake?" he asked in a low growl. "For heaven's sake, it's February."

"The water was warm." The excuse sounded weak even to her own ears. The women Joshua knew didn't give in to impulses like that; they were too mature for something so silly, she thought with self-derision.

"Bethany, honestly." He pressed his forehead against hers. "Come in the house before you catch your death of a cold."

"I . . . I think it'd be best if I just went home," she whispered, utterly miserable.

"Like this? Wet? You can't do that. I refuse to allow it."

She was willing to suffer any discomfort in order to flee, even if it sounded completely nonsensical. But Bethany knew better than to argue with Joshua, and she nodded obediently.

With his arm cupping her shoulder, he directed her towards the house. At loose ends and wanting to help in some way, Angie ran circles around the two like a frolicking puppy.

"Are you all right, Bethany?"

"She's fine, sweetheart."

"It's all my fault."

"Bethany doesn't blame you. It was an accident, and those sometimes happen." Again Joshua answered for her.

Not knowing what to say or do to calm the distraught child, Bethany held out her hand. It was immediately clasped by a much smaller one.

Joshua led her through a set of sliding glass doors at the other end of the house into what was obviously the master bedroom. Bethany hesitated, not wanting to drip water all over his pearl-grey carpet, but he urged her forward and into the large master bathroom.

"Take a warm shower," he ordered, but not unkindly or in the harsh voice she was accustomed to hearing from him. "Give Angie your wet things and I'll have Mrs. Larson put them in the drier."

Nodding seemed a monumental task, but Bethany managed.

"When you've finished, slip into my robe." He pointed to the thick navy blue one that hung on the back of the door. "I'll have a hot drink waiting for you."

Again she answered him with a short nod. He left her then and closed the door.

"I feel just terrible," Angie wailed, close to tears. "You'd never have gone into the water if it hadn't been for me."

"Sweetheart, don't worry about it. I stumbled over my own two feet." She didn't mention that she'd been looking at Joshua at the time and daydreaming about things that were never meant to be.

Angie slumped down on the edge of the bathtub, looking mournfully sad. "I will always blame myself for this."

"I refuse to let you," Bethany said, her teeth starting to chatter. "If you do, then I'll be forced to keep my nail polish in my purse."

"Well, actually, now that you mention it," the ten-year-old said as she nonchalantly stood and walked to the door, "it really *was* all your own fault. Are you normally this clumsy?"

"Always," Bethany muttered, and turned on the shower.

When she was finished, both Angie and Joshua were sitting in the living room waiting for her. Bethany tightened the cinch on the thick robe which was so long on her that the hem dragged across the carpet. Her hair hung in limp strands about her face, and she felt as if she should stand on a street corner and beg for alms.

Joshua stood when he saw her coming and made an admirable effort not to smile.

"Don't you dare laugh," Bethany warned him under her breath, and at the same time reassured Angie with a grin. She didn't know what she would do to Joshua if he did, but she'd find a way to make him regret it.

"I wouldn't *dream* of laughing."

"Ha!"

"I'll pour you a cup of coffee."

She sat in a velvet wingback chair and accepted the cup and saucer from Joshua when he brought them to her. "Thank you."

"You're quite welcome."

Bethany had the distinct feeling he was showing his appreciation for giving him the single biggest laugh of his life.

The first sip of coffee seared its way down her throat and caused Bethany's eyes to widen at its potency. It was apparent the moment the liquid passed her lips that the brew had been liberally laced with whiskey.

"This is ... Irish ... coffee?" she stammered on a breathless whisper, having trouble finding her voice.

"I didn't want you to catch a chill."

"Dad was real worried about you," Angie piped in. "He said you were lucky you didn't swallow a fish."

Bethany's narrowed gaze sliced through her employer. How she wished she could say exactly what she was thinking!

"I've instructed Mrs. Larson to set the table for three this evening," Joshua added.

Bethany had no idea it was this close to dinnertime. "I can't stay," she said hurriedly. "Really, I must be getting home."

"You can't just leave," Angie said, her young voice tight with disappointment. "We're having pork roast and homemade applesauce and fresh peas. But you don't have to eat the peas if you don't want. Dad makes me, but he won't make you ... at least, I don't think he will."

Joshua stiffened and strolled to his daughter's side, resting his hand on her small shoulder. When he looked at Bethany, his gaze was guarded. "Miss Stone might have a date this evening, Angie. We shouldn't detain her."

"I ... I'm not meeting anyone," Bethany said quickly. She shouldn't have been so eager to let Joshua know that, but the truth was she rarely dated anymore. There was no reason to when she was already in love.

"Then you'll stay for dinner?"

Bethany's gaze fell to the steaming coffee. "All right," she said. She couldn't find an excuse not to, except that she'd hoped to salvage what remained of her pride. Not that there was much left—most of it had drowned in Lake Pontchartrain earlier in the day. What little she'd managed to hold on to had been shredded by Joshua's comment about her swallowing a fish!

"Oh good, you'll stay," Angie said gleefully. "Mrs. Larson's a terrific cook."

By the time the meal was served, Bethany's clothes were back from Mrs. Larson and she'd had time to blow-dry and curl her hair. She felt infinitely better.

"I'm starved," Angie announced, claiming the chair beside Bethany and carefully unfolding the linen napkin across her lap.

"Swimming does that to me, too," Bethany added.

The corners of Joshua's mouth quivered before he burst into a full rich laugh. Soon they were all laughing.

"Rare is the woman who can find humour in her own misadventures," Joshua announced, and his face was transformed by a careless smile.

Flustered, Bethany looked away, unable to hold his gaze any longer.

Before their meal was served, Joshua poured Bethany a glass of wine. She wasn't sure she should drink it on top of the laced coffee, but she didn't feel it would hurt. A second glass followed at the end of the meal.

Angie fell asleep on the sofa while Bethany and Joshua lingered over their second glass of wine in the living room. Candles cast flickering shadows across the wall and the light in the room was muted, creating an intimate feeling.

"I've enjoyed today," Joshua said.

"I did, too."

"I'm grateful, Bethany, that you were willing to take Angie shopping. It meant a good deal to us both. I want you to know I was serious about paying you for your time."

"Oh, don't, please. Being with Angie is a delight." She didn't add that spending her day with Joshua had been equally thrilling. He was a completely different person away from the office. Having his daughter move in with him had sanded away the rough edges of Joshua's personality. Bethany's gaze shifted lovingly onto the sleeping child. Knowing Angie had opened a door for Bethany that she thought would be forever closed to her. She was eternally grateful to the little girl.

"Angie really seems taken with you."

He said it as though he couldn't understand why, and Bethany darted her eyes to her glass of wine as the pain rippled over her in widening waves, like a pebble tossed in a pond. It hurt so much that she didn't breathe until her lungs ached and an uncomfortable feeling took control.

"That surprises you, doesn't it?" she asked, and her voice wobbled a little, although she struggled to steady it.

"What?"

"That . . . that anyone could be taken with me."

Joshua looked completely shocked. "Not in the least."

Bethany decided it was the wine that had given her the courage to talk to Joshua that way, question him. God knew she never had before . . . wouldn't have dared.

"You certainly can be a prickly thing," he added, frowning.

"Me?" That just went to prove how much attention he'd paid her over the years.

"I meant to compliment you when I said how much Angie liked you."

"I apologise, then."

"Fine."

A throbbing silence followed, during which Bethany was convinced they were both searching for ways to bring the conversation back to an amicable keel.

"I suppose I should think about driving home," Bethany murmured, discouraged and distressed. The day had held such promise, and the evening had been a disaster. She should never drink wine. It went straight to her head and disassociated her tongue from her brain.

"Before you do, I'd like to ask another favour of you, if I may," Joshua said.

Once more Bethany could feel his reluctance, as though he didn't like to be in her debt. "I'd be happy to do anything for you...for Angie," she hurried to add.

"It's about Mardi Gras next week. Angie is looking forward to attending the festivities, and, well, you know my schedule better than anyone. Would you be willing to take her to the parade? I could meet you afterwards, and we could have dinner, the three of us. That is, of course, unless you've got other plans. I certainly wouldn't want you to cancel a date with someone special."

"I'd love to take Angie to the parade."

Joshua nodded and grinned. "Bethany?"

"Yes?"

"*Is* there someone special?"

To tell him the only one who mattered in her life was her employer would have been ludicrous and Bethany had the good sense to resist.

"No...not lately." She didn't know why she tagged that comment on, but she did, for better or worse.

"I see."

Bethany wasn't sure what he read into her answer—or what there was to read. "You don't have to meet us for dinner if you'd prefer to make other plans," she blurted out, then snapped her mouth closed, hardly able to believe she'd made that offer. "I mean . . . well, if you'd rather meet 'someone special,' I'll understand.''

Joshua rotated the stem of his wineglass between his open palms. ''There hasn't been anyone for me, either,'' he said in a low, well-modulated voice. ''Not lately, anyway.'' He raised his eyes to hers and grinned.

Bethany relaxed against the back of the chair and smiled, more relaxed with Joshua than she could ever remember being. She'd often imagined quiet romantic moments such as these with him. But she'd always felt it would have been impossible.

''More wine?''

''No,'' she answered, and shook her head. ''I'd better not since I have to drive home yet.''

''I'll take you.''

Although the thought was tempting, it would only be an inconvenience for Joshua, and she would need to have Sally drive her over to pick up her car later. Knowing Sally, and what her friend would read into the action . . . no, that just wouldn't work.

''Thank you, but no, I'll drive myself.''

''What do you think of Angela's room?'' Joshua asked, and glanced proudly towards the hallway that led to the bedrooms.

Bethany wasn't sure how to comment. ''It's very . . . yellow, isn't it?''

''You don't like yellow?''

''Oh, yes, it's a favourite colour of mine.'' When it came to Joshua Norris, a wide streak of it ran down the middle of her back!

"Then why do I hear derision in your voice?"

"No reason." She hated to lie, but it wasn't her place to tell him Angela would have preferred lavender.

"You know, Miss Stone, you don't lie the least bit convincingly."

"No, I suppose I don't."

"Now, tell me what you find so offensive about the very expensive bedroom I had made up for my daughter."

"You've certainly made it appealing with the television and the stereo." Bethany hoped that would appease him, but one look at his frowning gaze told her differently.

"Yes. I realise she may be a bit young to appreciate some of that equipment."

"I just think—" Bethany stopped herself in time, silently cursing the wine for loosening her tongue.

"You think what?"

"Never mind." She shook her head so hard the hair whipped across her face. She brushed her index finger across her cheek to free a maverick strand.

"Bethany, I wouldn't ask your opinion unless I wanted it." His eyes were unusually dark and solemn.

"I worry about her, that's all," Bethany said, scooting forward a little in her chair. "You've created her own world for her and I don't know that that's the best thing for a ten-year-old who's recently left the only home she's ever known."

"You think because I can afford to give her a television and a stereo—"

"That's not my objection," she interrupted heatedly. Now that she'd started, the floodgate of opinion couldn't be held back. "Angie needs to be introduced to *your* world. She's got to spend time with you—not by herself in front of her own television while you watch yours. When you come home at night, she has to feel that she's more important to you than reading some report."

Joshua looked shocked. "I see."

"I don't mean to criticise you, Joshua, really I don't. It's just that I care so much about...about Angie." Dear lord, if she didn't shut up soon, she would give him more than one reason to fire her.

"Well, you've certainly given me something to think about."

Bethany stood. It would be better if she left, before she said something to embarrass them both.

"I'll walk you to your car," Joshua murmured thoughtfully when she reached for her bag.

He escorted her outside and opened the driver's door for her. Scant inches separated them, and Bethany moistened her dry lips, feeling the night air fill with tension. The silence seemed to vibrate between them.

"There's more to you than I ever realised," Joshua admitted. He reached out and touched her cheek, gently gliding his finger down the side of her jaw as though he were touching the most valuable thing in the world.

Bethany closed her eyes to the delicious sensation that overtook her like an unexpected weakness. Her pulse began to beat wildly. He was so close, so wonderfully close, she could feel the heat radiate from his body. She knew her lips had parted with expectation. She wanted him to kiss her more than she had ever desired anything in her life. With her eyes still closed, she raised herself on tiptoe.

With a groan, Joshua settled his mouth hungrily over hers. He kissed her until she was flushed and trembling, sliding his mouth back and forth lazily across her own, soaking in her softness, savouring her gentleness. And yet, he gripped her shoulders as though he wanted to push her away and couldn't find the will to do so. If it were up to Bethany he would go on holding and kissing her forever. It was as she'd always imagined it would be in Joshua's arms. Her whole body felt as though it were convulsing in shock waves of pleasure. If a kiss did this to her, she could only dream what making love would do.

With an indrawn breath and a shudder, Joshua dragged his lips from hers and took a step back. "Bethany," he whispered in a voice she barely recognised. "You'd better go."

She wanted to argue with him, lock her arms around his neck and tell him she didn't ever want to leave him, but that would be impossible.

"Thank you," he whispered, his voice still husky.

For one wild second, Bethany didn't know why he should thank her for anything. Then her mind cleared, and she realised he was talking about helping with Angie. If anyone should be grateful, it was her.

Joshua had just proven that dreams actually *do* come true. He'd proven it by taking her in his arms.

CHAPTER FIVE

MONDAY morning Bethany sat at her desk, her stomach a mass of nerves. The wine, she told herself, it had been the wine that had done all the talking to Joshua Saturday night. In retrospect it astonished her that she could actually have told her employer how to raise his daughter. Who in heaven's name did she think she was? Dr. Benjamin Spock?

She was a secretary. Good grief, the closest she'd ever come to mothering was burping her three-month-old niece. Sure she liked kids, got along well with them, but that didn't give her the right to wade into another family and start issuing decrees.

If the wine had been talking for Bethany, it had done the kissing for Joshua. She knew Joshua well enough to believe that when he walked into the office this morning, he would pretend Saturday night had never happened. He'd crossed the line, no doubt regretted it and would immediately step back, hoping she hadn't noticed—or had the good sense to forget.

Only Bethany would never forget being in Joshua's arms. It felt so wonderfully right and good. But instead of fulfilling a need, it had created an ever greater one. The innocent emotion she'd held against her breast and nurtured had blossomed, leaving her craving so much more.

The door opened and Bethany held her breath as Joshua stepped into the office. He didn't so much as glance in her direction, and Bethany felt as if someone had dropped a sledgehammer over her head. She was right. He regretted everything.

"Good morning, Miss Stone," he said tersely on his way past her.

Bethany closed her eyes and firmly gritted her teeth. It was worse than she'd thought. Not only did Joshua wish he hadn't kissed her, he was sorry she was in his employment.

Picking up the mail, Bethany reluctantly followed him into the executive suite, pausing long enough to place the sorted correspondence on his desk and bring him a cup of freshly brewed coffee.

Joshua leafed through the stack of letters, paused and glanced in her direction. "How are you feeling, Miss Stone?"

"Fine." From the way the one word slipped the tight constriction in her throat, it was a wonder he didn't call for a paramedic.

"Good. Then there were no lingering effects from your...swim the other night?"

"No...none—" she dropped her gaze so fast she nearly dislocated a disc in her neck "—except for a loose tongue. Mr. Norris, I feel positively terrible that I could have spoken to you in such a manner. How you raise your daughter is none of my concern, and I sincerely hope that—"

"Miss Stone, kindly sit down."

Bethany nearly missed the chair in her eagerness to do as he asked. Her hold on the pencil was so tense it was a credit to American craftsmanship that the wood didn't snap in two.

Joshua held the coffee mug in both hands and leaned back in his chair, his look contemplative. "Ah, yes, your advice regarding Angela had slipped my mind."

Oh, brother. He'd forgotten, and she'd gone out of her way to remind him! "It was the wine, you see," she said hurriedly. "I should never drink more than one glass and I'd had two when we spoke. If you'll remember, I drank the Irish coffee earlier...and I can honestly say I wasn't quite myself Saturday evening."

"I see," Joshua said with a frown. "So you have regrets? Well, that's understandable."

"Mr. Norris, you have to understand that under those circumstances...like on Saturday...sometimes my tongue murmurs things I have no intention of saying aloud."

The frown grew darker, his brows crowding together until the ledge over his eyes formed a straight narrow line. He stiffened, seeming to close her off completely.

Bethany hated it when he did that, but she was powerless to do anything more than react. "I truly am sorry, Mr. Norris," she finished weakly, utterly defeated.

"I believe you've apologised sufficiently. Shall we deal with the mail now, or is there anything else you care to confess before we get down to business?"

"The mail...of course."

Fifteen minutes later, Bethany stood, her head buzzing. She didn't exactly know where matters had gone wrong, but nothing seemed right. Joshua was terse and impatient, issuing orders faster than she could write down his instructions. When he did look at her, his handsome face was devoid of expression.

Bethany stood in front of the door that connected their two offices. Gathering her courage, she hesitated and turned around. She held the dictation pad to her breast like a shield of armour, her eyes infinitely sad. "Mr. Norris . . . one last thing."

"Yes. What is it now, Miss Stone?" he barked impatiently.

"I don't regret *everything* about Saturday night," she admitted in a raspy whisper, wanting to clear away one misconception, even at the cost of her own pride. "I can understand why *you* would prefer to forget what happened, but I don't. I . . . I promise not to embarrass either of us by ever mentioning it again."

She hurried to escape then, not waiting for a response, but several minutes later, Bethany was stunned to hear her employer whistling.

At lunchtime, Bethany pressed the button of her intercom. "Mr. Norris, I'm leaving now."

"Miss Stone," he said hurriedly, "last year . . . did I do anything special for you for Secretary's Day?"

Bethany had to think about it. "I'm not sure. You had flowers delivered, I believe."

A soft snicker followed. "As I recall you ordered the roses on your own. I had little to do with it."

"We . . . we did discuss it. Briefly."

"It seems to me most employers take their secretaries to lunch? Is that right?"

"I'm not sure."

"Lunch appears to be the proper protocol. If that's the case, it seems I owe you a lunch. Are you free this afternoon?"

Bethany's mouth made troutlike movements, opening and closing several times.

"Miss Stone?"

"Yes, I'm free."

"Good, I'll be finished here in about ten minutes."

She released the intercom and sat there with her mouth gaping open for a full minute before reality settled in. Joshua Norris had requested her company for lunch.

Sally stuck her head in the door. "Hey, are you coming or not? I'm hungry!"

Words square-danced on the tip of Bethany's tongue, and when she couldn't get them to co-operate with her brain, she jerked around and pointed her thumb towards Joshua's door.

"You mean the jerk won't let you leave to eat lunch?"

Bethany shook her head wildly.

"What, then? Good grief, woman, you look like you're about to keel over. What did that monster do to you this time?" Sally walked into the room and planted her hands on Bethany's desk, her eyes afire with outrage.

"I'm taking Miss Stone to lunch," Joshua announced, standing in the open doorway. "Is that a problem, Ms. Livingston?"

Sally leaped back from Bethany's desk as though she'd been struck by lightning. "No problem. Not for me. Well, I guess I should be getting along now. Do enjoy your lunch, Bethany. It was good to see you again, Mr. Norris...sir."

"Good day, Ms. Livingston."

Bethany's friend couldn't get out of the office fast enough. "See you later," she said weakly, and waved, all but trotting across the floor.

Joshua leaned against the doorjamb, indolently crossed his arms and legs, his face amused. "So I'm a monster. I wonder who could have given Ms. Livingston that impression?"

Bethany stood and tightly clenched her eelskin bag to her side. "There have been times in the past, Mr. Norris, when the description was more than apt."

"Is that a fact?" He seemed to find the information more humorous than offensive. "Then I'd best repent my obnoxious ways. I made reservations at Brennan's."

"Brennan's," Bethany repeated in an excited whisper. She'd lived in New Orleans most of her life and had never eaten at the world-famous restaurant.

"You approve?"

"Oh, Joshua...Mr. Norris, I'm...I'm very pleased. Thank you."

Their table was waiting for them when they arrived. If Joshua thought she was going to order a dainty shrimp salad and a glass of iced tea, then he was in for a surprise. Her appetite had always been healthy and she started off by ordering an appetiser plate, a Cobb salad, and, for the main course, Buster Crabs Béarnaise, a Brennan's specialty.

"You don't mind, do you?" she thought to ask, after the waiter had left their table.

"Of course I don't. I can see you plan to make up for all the years I didn't take you to lunch."

He was teasing her, but Bethany didn't mind. "That's not it."

"My dear Bethany, just where do you plan to put all that food?"

"Oh, don't worry. None of it will go to waste. I've never had a problem with my weight. None of the women in my family do until after they get pregnant, or so my mother and sisters tell me. From then on, keeping their figures is a constant battle. So I plan to enjoy all the goodies while I can." Bethany knew she was chattering, but she couldn't stop herself. Already she felt light-headed and the wine hadn't been poured yet.

"So you want children?" Joshua asked, watching her with smiling eyes.

Bethany spread a thick layer of butter over the top of the crisp French roll. "Of course."

"You're not afraid it'll ruin your figure?"

Bethany shrugged, pleased he hadn't noticed how thin she was. "Actually, I'm pretty much of a toothpick. I'm looking forward to adding a few curves. I'm just hoping they'll form in the right places. However, with my luck, my thirty-six-inch bust is likely to sink to my waistline." She paused in shock, amazed at what she'd just said and hoping that Joshua wasn't affronted by her loose tongue.

Joshua chuckled at that, then his eyes grew warm and serious. "I don't think you need worry, Bethany."

"I hope not," she said, and paid close attention to her roll in an attempt to calm her heart rate. She knew she shouldn't try to read anything into their conversation, but she couldn't help it. Her guess was that Angie's mother hadn't wanted children, and consequently Joshua thought all women felt the same way. It took everything within Bethany not to announce that she would gladly bear his child. At her errant thoughts she decided to forgo the wine.

"I told Angie you'd be escorting her to the Mardi Gras festivities, and she's excited, to say the least," Joshua went on to say.

"I'm looking forward to it myself."

"You honestly enjoy my daughter, don't you?"

Bethany found that a strange question. "Yes. She's delightful."

Joshua added a teaspoon of sugar in his coffee and stirred it vigorously. "I gave some consideration to what you said Saturday night. You may be right about me shutting Angie out of my life. It isn't easy after living all these years alone. But I wanted to tell you that I appreciate your insight."

"You do?" Bethany fingered the tassel on the wine list. Maybe alcohol wasn't such a detriment to her thought processes after all. Maybe it was just the thing needed to burst this romance wide open.

"I'm making an effort to spend more time with Angie, and find myself enjoying her. I have you to thank for that."

Bethany nodded, more pleased than she could remember being about anything in a long while.

"Unfortunately, time is something of a premium in my life," Joshua added in thoughtful tones. "These next six months are crucial to the future of Norris Pharmaceutical. There's a great deal at stake."

Bethany watched him carefully. She knew there had been a takeover effort made by another pharmaceutical firm several months back and that it had taken everything Joshua had to hold off the other company. His business was small yet, but the potential for growth was good if managed properly.

"What I'm trying to say is that I'm not going to have the opportunity to be a proper father to my daughter. There just isn't going to be the time for it."

Bethany opened her mouth to tell him "time" had little to do with being a good father. All Angie required was to know he loved her and that she was important to him. She needed him to listen to her problems and occasionally to laugh with her.

"Angie hasn't stopped asking about you since that first afternoon she spent at the office before Mrs. Larson, the housekeeper, arrived. She seems to like you better than anyone."

Bethany's smile grew more forced by the minute. So their luncheon date hadn't been an excuse to get to know each other better, as she'd imagined. It was a bribe—pure and simple. Joshua wanted her to baby-sit his daughter. No doubt he was willing to pay her handsomely to become a lonely ten-year-old's surrogate parent.

"I'm going to be busy for the next several weekends," Joshua continued. "And I was wondering if you'd be willing to entertain Angela for me. Naturally I'd be more than happy to pay you for your time.''

"Naturally," Bethany repeated.

The waiter delivered the appetiser tray and Bethany knew she wasn't going to be able to down a single bite.

"I'm such a fool," Bethany sobbed, holding her index finger under each eye in a fruitless effort to stop the flow of tears. Joshua had started asking her about children and keeping her figure, and like an idiot, Bethany had thought . . . had hoped that he'd become so enamoured with her that he had marriage in mind. In her lovesick mind she'd pictured the two of them starting their own family. The humiliation of her silly, childish assumptions was almost more than she could bear.

"I can't believe I'd be so stupid," she wailed to Sally, who stood faithfully close by, a box of tissues firmly clenched in her hand. Bethany hadn't told her friend what had happened, couldn't bring herself to repeat what Joshua had asked of her over lunch, because it showed what a romantic fool she really was.

"Honestly, Beth, no amount of money is worth this agony," Sally said, handing her yet another tissue.

Bethany hiccuped a sob. "But I can't quit now."

"Why not?"

"Angie needs me."

"J. D. Norris is using his daughter to blackmail you into remaining his secretary? No wonder you're so upset!"

Bethany wiped her face free of moisture. "It isn't exactly blackmail," she said miserably. But the one who would suffer if she were to refuse to look after his daughter would be Angie. The ten-year-old had endured enough turmoil in the past few weeks. Okay, if Joshua was planning on using her to keep his daughter occupied and out of his hair, Bethany would do it. But she had learned her lesson when it came to her employer. She was going to guard her heart well. She was completely unwilling to be made a fool a second time.

"At least tell me what horrible things he did," Sally cried, growing more impatient when it became obvious that Bethany wasn't going to let her know anything but the basics. "If you tell me what he said, then I can hate him, too."

Bethany shook her head forcefully, then changed her mind and wildly shook her hand in front of her friend a couple of times. "The raise..."

"Yes?"

"The lunch..."

"Yes," Sally said, and took a step forward. "Go on."

"They weren't because Joshua is interested in me. He wants a b-a-b-y-s-i-t-t-e-r."

"What?" Sally exploded.

"He was buttering me up so I'd be his weekend baby-sitter for Angie."

Sally's eyes narrowed, and she plopped herself down on the davenport and crossed her long legs, looking more furious by the moment.

Bethany reached for a tissue and blew her nose. "I should have known he'd never be interested in a woman with small breasts,'' she bellowed, burying her face in the tissue.

A loyal friend, Sally sat at her side and gently patted Bethany's back. "You're not standing still for this,'' her roommate announced with grim determination. "I won't let you.''

"Just what do 'I' plan to do?''

Sally tapped her finger over her closed lips as she mused things over. "*You're* going to find yourself a man, a real man, someone who will give J. D. Norris an inferiority complex.''

"And just where am I supposed to meet this fictitious male?''

Sally's gaze narrowed all the more. "I think you already have. In fact, we've both met him.''

"Oh, sure,'' Bethany muttered. If Sally had met someone so fabulous, then she would want him for herself. "What makes you think Joshua Norris would care if I dated a hundred men?''

"He'll care,'' Sally said, nodding her head. "Trust me, by the time you're through with him, he'll care.''

"Bethany, look,'' Angie cried, pointing towards the flambeaux carriers that lined both sides of the wide cobblestone street. A golden arch of flame shot from one torch to the other. In the background, a blast of music from a jazz saxophone pierced the night, followed by the unmistakable sounds of a Dixieland band.

"This is the most exciting night of my life," Angie shouted, and dramatically placed her hand over her heart.

Even the blue funk that Bethany had been in since her luncheon date with Joshua had evaporated under the excitement of New Orleans during Mardi Gras.

"I've never seen so many people in my life," Angie shouted to be heard above the heavy noise of the milling crowd. "How's Dad ever going to find us?"

"Don't worry," Bethany answered, her voice equally loud.

"Do you think he'll like my costume?"

Bethany nodded. "He'll love it." She paused and adjusted the halo on top of the little girl's head. After hearing the story of how she'd got her name, Angela Catherine had insisted on dressing up like an angel, with elaborate feather wings and a golden halo. Bethany's own masquerade was far less eloquent. She'd rented an antebellum-style gown, intent on playing the role of Scarlett O'Hara. She was going to flirt and flitter and play the part of a vamp and a tease. Not in front of Angie, of course; this would all be accomplished much later for Joshua's benefit. That was, if she could find the courage to do it.

Just thinking about Sally's plan to make him jealous was enough to cause Bethany to peel open the fancy lace fan and cool her flushed face.

"Oh, look," Angie cried next, pointing towards the street once more. "There's a man on stilts."

"I certainly hope those are stilts," Bethany answered with a soft laugh. "He must be all of eight feet tall.'' She checked the pendant watch pinned to the bodice of her gown and reached for Angie's hand. It was time to leave their position on the pavement if they were going to meet Joshua on time. ''We'd better start working our way towards the restaurant.''

''But the parade isn't over.''

''It won't be for hours yet, but I don't want to keep your father waiting.''

''OK,'' Angie agreed, although reluctantly.

''We'll still be able to see most of it.'' Bethany wasn't eager to leave, either. There was so much to see and do. Excitement arced like static electricity through the air. People were singing and dancing in the streets. Strangers were hugging and kissing one another. Laughter echoed all the way from the French Quarter to the exclusive Garden District.

Tightly gripping Angie's hand so not to lose the little girl, Bethany wove her way through the milling mass of humanity.

''Bethany, Bethany, stop,'' Angie shouted, her young voice filled with panic. ''I lost my halo.''

By the time Bethany turned around to investigate, the headpiece was gone.

''Oh, dear.'' There was nothing Bethany could do. The halo had apparently come loose and had been quickly carted off by a masquerader who had considered the golden circle fair game.

''Now I can't be an angel,'' Angie said, looking as if she was ready to resort to tears if something wasn't done quickly.

"I'm sure this happens all the time," Bethany said, thinking on her feet. "Most real angels must have a difficult time holding on to their halos, too, don't you think? I know I would."

"What happens then?"

"Then they're considered almost angels, and they have to work hard to regain their status as full angels."

"Oh, I don't mind that because it must be difficult to be perfect all the time."

"Then we'll consider Angie Norris to be almost an angel."

"Right," Angie answered, somewhat appeased.

Bethany couldn't remember ever being in a larger crowd in her life. Making progress down the people-filled streets was laborious and difficult, and the restaurant wasn't even within sight.

"Look, Bethany, there's Prince Charming."

Bethany looked up in time to see a tall handsome male astride a huge white stallion trotting down the side of Bourbon Street.

"He's stopping," Angie cried, her voice shrill with excitement.

Just as Angie claimed, the handsome prince pulled back on the reins of the powerful stallion and came to a halt in the street beside them. Bethany watched in amazed wonder as the man gave the beast over to a stranger, jumped down into the crowd and worked his way through the throng of partygoers until he stood in front of Bethany and Angie.

"Madam," he said softly, "your loveliness has captured my heart."

He wore a mask so Bethany couldn't see the upper half of his face, but she would have recognised that mouth anywhere. Joshua. It had to be Joshua Norris. It looked like him. But Joshua was tied up in a conference and wouldn't be meeting them for another half hour. It couldn't possibly be him. In addition, he would never do anything this wildly romantic.

"Oh, Bethany, he's so handsome. Don't you think so?"

The prince laid out his palm, silently requesting her hand. By this time, several people had formed a circle and gathered around them, watching the unfolding scene.

"Are you going to stand there all night or are you going to kiss her?" a gruff male voice shouted.

"If he wants a kiss, I'm willing," a boisterous female voice added, and the crowd laughed.

Clearly trying to appease the fickle group of merrymakers, the handsome prince took Bethany in his arms, swung her around with a flair that drew a round of applause and draped her over his forearm. Bethany's eyes went as round as satellite dishes when he lowered his mouth to claim hers. She had half a mind to object. After all, she wasn't in the habit of kissing strange men. But this was Mardi Gras, a special once-a-year time to let down one's hair and participate in the unconventional.

The prince's mouth took hers in a warm moist kiss that was as soul-stirring as a religious revival and as deep as a bottomless sea. The kiss gentled as the fierce hunger was satisfied, and his lips moved over hers like the gentle brush of a spring sun on a hungry earth.

The crowd approved heartily.

When the prince released Bethany it was a wonder she didn't melt onto the pavement. Breathless and weak, she placed her hand over her heart, heedless to anything but the man who had held her in his arms. She blinked and took a step back.

"Wow," Angie said, her eyes round and wide. "I thought he was going to suck your lips off."

Had Bethany been any less affected, she might have laughed, but even breathing was difficult... laughing would have been impossible.

Three or four women formed an impromptu line. "We've got dibs next," the first one called out, waving her fingers.

The prince, clearly being a true gentleman, kissed the hand of each woman in turn and, before they could object, gracefully remounted his white stallion and rode off.

"Bethany, why did he kiss you?" Angie wanted to know.

"I...I don't know." She continued to watch him long after he rode out of sight. "Angie—" she paused and looked down at the ten-year-old "—did that man...the one who kissed me...did he remind you of anyone?"

"Oh, yes," Angie admitted. "He looked like the guy in *Cinderella*. The one who kept trying the glass slipper on all the women's feet. I always thought that was a little silly, you know. What woman buys glass shoes these days?''

"Oh." Bethany couldn't help being disappointed. It was nonsensical to think it could have been Joshua when it simply wasn't possible. The logistics were all wrong.

And yet...

CHAPTER SIX

THE noise level decreased by several decibels when Bethany and Angie left the street and entered the restaurant where they were supposed to meet Joshua. Antoine's was probably the most famous restaurant in New Orleans, having been in operation close to 150 years. Bethany secretly hoped her employer wouldn't be there. If the prince who'd kissed her *had* been Joshua, then it would have been close to impossible for him to have changed outfits so quickly and got to Antoine's before them.

Her gaze searched the plush interior, and to Bethany's bitter disappointment, she found Joshua casually sitting at a table awaiting their arrival.

"Dad, Dad, guess what I saw!" Angie went running past the maître d', weaving her way between tables to her father, then hurling her arms around his neck and squeezing for all she was worth.

The maître d' offered Bethany a strained smile and formally escorted her to Joshua's table. He paused and elegantly held out a shield-back chair for her to take a seat.

"There was a man eight feet tall," Angie was telling Joshua, the words running together, she was speaking so fast. "And other men who tossed fire at each other and then, oh, then we met a handsome prince on a big white horse who kissed Bethany. It was so-o romantic."

Joshua's eyes widened, and when he glanced towards his secretary, the edges of his mouth were quivering with the effort to hold back a smile. "It sounds like you've had quite an evening."

"Oh, yes, and, Dad, there are so many people here, and everyone dresses like it's Hallowe'en." Angie paused and her hand flew to her hair. "I lost my halo. I was going to surprise you by being an angel because you said I looked like one, and then I lost the most important part, but Bethany said it was all right because I could be almost an angel and that's really better, because angels are supposed to be perfect, and well, you know me."

"I do indeed know you." Joshua looked up and grinned in Bethany's direction. "I'm pleased to see you made it safely."

She managed a nod, still watching him closely, hoping to prove, if only to herself, that the prince who kissed her had been Joshua. She so desperately wanted it to be him and would always choose to believe that it had been.

"Do you usually kiss strange men on the street, Miss Stone?" he asked, seeming to read her thoughts.

"I...I..." she stammered. She couldn't very well announce that she thought the man had been him, had dreamed it was Joshua, and that was the only reason she'd allowed the prince to take her in his arms.

"It wasn't like Bethany had much choice, Dad," Angie inserted, climbing off her father's lap and taking her own seat.

"So the brute forced you?"

Bethany kept her gaze lowered to her lap while she smoothed a linen napkin over the top of her thighs. "Not exactly."

Joshua leaned forward, rested his elbows on the table and clasped his fingers together. "I'm curious why you would allow a complete stranger to sweep you into his arms and kiss you in front of an onlooking crowd."

Hope fired through Bethany's blood like running water shooting off the edge of a cliff. It had been Joshua! It must have been, because no one had told him about the prince taking her in his arms or that a crowd had gathered around and had been watching.

Boldly she raised her gaze to his. "He didn't seem the least bit dangerous," she said softly. "I . . . I felt that I knew him."

Joshua cocked his thick eyebrows. "I see."

Bethany certainly hoped he did because her heart was pounding like a crazed pogo stick.

"Dad, is Bethany coming over Friday night?" Angie asked, sticking her head around the side of the huge oblong menu. "You said she was."

"Bethany?" Joshua fielded the question to her. From the way he studied the menu it appeared that her answer was of little consequence to him.

This piece of news frustrated Bethany. Joshua hadn't said anything to her about needing her Friday night. He'd taken it for granted that she didn't have any other plans, which fortunately she didn't, but his blatant assumption irked her.

"I suppose I could be there Friday night," she mumbled somewhat ungraciously.

"Mrs. Larson would be more than willing to stay," Joshua announced in a flat emotionless voice. "There's no need to feel obligated, especially if you have other plans."

"I'm not doing anything special." Bethany's admission took some of the bite out of her irritation.

"Oh, good," Angie said with an elaborate sigh. "Weekends are a dead bore, and being with Bethany is always such fun."

"Have you thought about inviting a school friend to spend the night?" Bethany asked. "We could order pizza and rent movies."

Angie slammed the menu down on top of the table, her eyes round and excited. "We could do all that?"

"Mr. Norris ... Joshua?" It gave Bethany a small amount of pleasure to toss the question back into his court.

"Pizza and rented movies and a friend for the night?" He didn't sound overly enthused by any of Bethany's suggestions. "I suppose that won't be any problem."

"I think I'll ask Melissa over," Angie murmured thoughtfully, nibbling on her lower lip. "No, I like Wendy Miller better. She wants to be a writer, like me, and when we get tired of watching videos, we could make up our own stories."

"That sounds like an excellent plan," Bethany said, pleased. "Don't you think so, Joshua?"

He mumbled something under his breath about pizza and little girls running around the house at six in the morning and left it at that.

*   *   *

The remainder of the week passed quickly. What Joshua had said about the next few months being especially busy for him and the company was true. Rarely could Bethany remember a time when Joshua had more meetings and appointments scheduled. He was working too hard and it showed. Bethany wished there were some way she could lessen his load.

"Do you have the Harrison report typed for me yet?" he asked on Thursday at quitting time.

"Not yet," Bethany admitted reluctantly, feeling guilty. The report was nearly two hundred pages in length and highly complicated. "I can stay late tonight if you want."

"No." He shook his head. "But give it top priority first thing in the morning."

"Of course. I apologise, Joshua, but there were a thousand interruptions the past couple of days." She felt obliged to explain why it was taking so long, although he didn't appear to be upset with her.

"Don't worry about it, Bethany, I understand."

Friday, Bethany skipped her lunch hour to work on the report so Joshua would have it for his meeting that evening. It was on his desk when he returned late that afternoon.

He called her into his office soon afterwards and motioned for her to sit down.

"You did an excellent job with this," he told her, granting her a rare office-hour smile.

"Thank you." She was rather proud of it herself.

Joshua hesitated and leaned back in his chair, looking anxious. "The dinner meeting is with a group of financiers this evening. I don't know what time I'll be getting back to the house. I'm afraid it could be quite late.''

"Don't worry. I can stay with Angie and her friend until you're home.''

"I really appreciate your help, Bethany.''

She nodded, unable to voice the emotion that ran like a river deep within her heart. Helping Joshua, sharing his joys and dividing his worries was something she yearned to do every day. Since Angie's arrival their relationship had changed drastically, and yet she wanted so much more.

It was after eleven by the time Bethany heard Joshua let himself into the house. She'd been sitting in the family room reading. Both Angie and Wendy had fallen asleep at ten, exhausted from a busy school week. The pair of pre-teens were sleeping in Angie's bedroom and the house had been joyfully quiet.

Bethany set her book aside and stood, eager to talk to Joshua about this important meeting. She knew that the future of Norris Pharmaceutical rested on the decision of the financiers, although Joshua had never directly told her as much. She would have had to be blind not to know the problems his company was currently facing.

Bethany met Joshua in the living room and greeted him with a warm smile. "Welcome home,'' she said softly, not wanting to wake the girls.

"It's good to be here.'' He set his briefcase down, peeled off his suit jacket and folded it over the top of the sofa. "How did everything go?''

"Great, what about you?''

Joshua shrugged. "I won't know their decision until next week sometime."

So Joshua and Norris Pharmaceutical were going to be forced to play a waiting game.

"Are you hungry?" Bethany asked.

Joshua nodded, looking slightly chagrined. "Starved, as a matter of fact. I didn't have much of an appetite earlier."

Understanding the importance of this meeting, Bethany could well believe that. She'd eaten sparingly herself. "There's plenty of pizza left."

"You'll join me?" he asked. When she nodded, he looked pleased and led the way into the kitchen. "I think I've got a couple of cold beers. Do you want one?"

"Please."

While Joshua was searching through the refrigerator for the bottles of beer, Bethany placed several slices of cold pizza on a plate and warmed them in the microwave. By the time they were heated, Joshua had brought down paper napkins and set those and the two bottles of beer on the small kitchen table.

The pepperoni pizza was excellent, better than the first time around, she decided. They didn't talk much at first. Joshua asked her a couple of questions about how her evening had gone with Angie and her bosom buddy, Wendy, and she told him how the two had been far too keen to make up their own stories to be interested in watching the movie Bethany had rented.

"Since they didn't view it earlier, I've set up the television and VCR so all Angie has to do is turn them on first thing in the morning. Hopefully that'll give you an extra hour or two of peace so you can sleep in a little." She worried that Joshua wasn't getting enough rest. Lord knew he worked long enough hours, especially lately.

"That was thoughtful of you."

A short silence followed before Joshua spoke again. It was clear that the gathering with the financiers continued to weigh on his mind. He told her his general feelings about how the reception to his proposal had gone, the vibes he'd felt, the mood that had persisted throughout the long dinner meeting.

Bethany leaned back and listened attentively while he rummaged through and sorted out his thoughts. He finished, sat quietly for a moment, then downed the last of his beer.

"I suppose I should be getting home," Bethany said, standing.

Joshua's gaze flew to his gold watch. He looked surprised when he noted the time. "I didn't mean to keep you so long, Beth."

She stopped in front of the dishwasher, turned back to him and smiled.

"Does something amuse you?"

She opened the kitchen appliance and set their dirty plates inside. "There was a time not so long ago when you didn't know my first name."

"I knew," he whispered. He was so close behind her that she could feel his warm breath against the side of her neck. "I've always known."

A shiver of awareness scooted down Bethany's spine and she braced her hands against the counter as Joshua gently cupped her shoulders, his touch so light that she thought, at first, she might have imagined it. His fingers gently stroked her skin as he ran his hands down the length of her arms. At the same time, he tenderly drew her back so her body fitted against his full height. His movements were slow, deliberate, as though he expected her to object and was granting her ample opportunity to pull away if she wanted.

Bethany went completely immobile. She couldn't have moved had her life depended on it.

Joshua rested his chin on top of her head for a short moment before he paused and lowered his mouth to the slender curve of her neck. The instant his lips touched her sensitised skin and located the pulsing vein there, heat erupted like a fiery volcano throughout Bethany's trembling body.

She didn't know who moved first. She might have initiated the action by turning and slipping her arms around his waist, or Joshua's hands could have directed her. Bethany didn't know which. It didn't matter, though, nothing did except that she was in Joshua's arms and his mouth was hungrily locked over hers. He was kissing her as if he'd thought of doing nothing else for endless hours. Again and again he dragged his lips over hers, as though the thought of releasing her so soon was too much to bear.

A helpless moan escaped Bethany. To have Joshua kiss her was almost like drowning, she thought, then bursting through the water's clear surface and feeling more alive than at any other time in her life.

Still holding her, Joshua buried his face in the curve of her neck and exhaled a deep unsteady breath.

"The most important meeting of my life," he whispered, his voice husky and moist against her flushed skin. "And all I could think about was you."

"Oh, Joshua." She tucked her hands under his arms and leaned against him for support, bracing her forehead against his hard chest.

"This shouldn't be happening," he complained, but there was no regret in his voice.

"I wanted it, too," she admitted. "Joshua," she whispered, hiding her face in his chest and closing her eyes to the warm happy feeling that enveloped her.

"You've been so good for Angie," he whispered.

Some of the good feelings left Bethany and she stiffened, fearing he was going to use her love for him to keep her as a willing baby-sitter. "I see," she whispered in a soft broken voice.

Her hold relaxed and she tried to break away, but Joshua wouldn't let her. "What's wrong?" he asked anxiously. "Bethany, you've gone all cold on me. What did I say?"

"Nothing."

"You're angry because I appreciate what a good friend you are to my daughter?"

He lovingly caressed the side of her jaw and lifted her chin so that she couldn't avoid meeting his gaze. "No, of course not. I love Angie."

"And she loves you." He bent forward and brushed his mouth over hers, his lips settling naturally onto hers for another swift sample.

She kept her eyes closed, still trapped in the lingering sensation, and yet her heart felt as if it were weighted down with bricks. It wasn't right that she should be in his arms and feel so terribly insecure. Joshua should know her feelings. "I sometimes think Angie's the only reason you...you want to be around me."

The room went suspiciously quiet. The smallest noise would have sounded like a sonic boom in the silence that stretched between them. Bethany's eyes fluttered open, but she dared not look at Joshua, dared not meet the fiery anger she could feel radiating from him.

"You don't honestly believe that, do you?"

"What else am I to think?"

He freed her arms and took a step back from her. His eyes were dark and solemn. Sad. "If you don't know the answer to that by now, then I've failed us both."

"Failed us both?" She tossed his own words back at him. "The only time you ever want me around is to...to baby-sit for Angie."

The muscles in his jaw leaped with the effort to control his anger. "I can't see where you'd ever think that."

Bethany felt miserable. Only a minute before he'd been holding and kissing her and now he looked as though he couldn't wait for her to get out of his home.

Trembling from the inside out, she returned to the kitchen table and removed their crumpled napkins.

"Leave those," he barked.

"I...I was just going to put them in the garbage."

"I don't want to be accused of using you as my personal maid sometime later. Believe me, I'd prefer to do the task myself."

If he'd struck her, he couldn't have hurt Bethany any more. Tears bled out of her eyes and she jerked her head away, not wanting him to know how sensitive she was to his cruel barbs. The words to tell him she was leaving didn't make it past the tight constriction in her throat. The only thing left for her to do was walk away. She collected her bag and her book and was almost to the front door when Joshua reached out and stopped her.

Still she didn't turn to look back at him.

"Beth," he said starkly. "I'm sorry."

Her head whirled around and she saw the regret written boldly across his face.

"I'm sorry, too, Joshua." Sorry to have doubted him, sorry to have been so willing to believe the worst of him, but she couldn't help it. She might have done him a grave injustice . . . but she doubted it.

He kissed her again, but this one lacked the urgency or the hunger of the others. With his arm wrapped around her waist, he walked her out to her car. As she drove away, Bethany could see Joshua's image in her rearview mirror, standing alone in the night, watching her long after she pulled away.

"Okay, everything's all set," Sally announced, standing in front of Bethany's desk. She wore that off-centre silly smile that told Bethany her roommate was up to something.

Bethany paused with her fingers poised over the typewriter keyboard. She would play along with Sally's game for a while, until she recognised what card Sally was hiding up her sleeve, but that wouldn't take too long. "What's all set?" she asked.

"Your hot date."

"What?" Bethany exploded, and jerked her gaze towards the connecting door, grateful it was closed so Joshua wouldn't overhear their conversation. "A hot date with who?"

"Whom," her roommate corrected with a mischievous grin.

"Whom, then!"

"You honestly don't remember, do you?" Sally looked surprised, then stunned, then impatient. Watching each emotion was like viewing the flickering movements of an old-time silent film. "You really don't!"

"Obviously not," Bethany answered. "What are you talking about?"

With a look of disgusted dismay, Sally crossed her arms and aimed her chin towards the ceiling fixture. "Does the name Jerry Johnson ring a bell?"

Bethany mulled it over in her mind. She knew Sally had been up to something the past couple of days, but she hadn't a clue what. "I find the name vaguely familiar."

"Well, you *should*, since you've agreed to a date with him."

"I've what?" This nightmare was growing more vivid by the minute. "When?" Bethany demanded.

"I've arranged everything for Thursday night."

"Not that when," Bethany bellowed. "When did I ever say I'd have anything to do with the man?"

Sally cast a suspicious glance towards Joshua's door. "The afternoon you sat in our living room going through tissues like they were chocolate bunnies at Easter. We made plans, you and I."

The image jarred Bethany's memory. She could remember her friend telling her what a fool she was being and that she would be an ever bigger one if she continued to let Joshua Norris take advantage of her. Sally had prattled on about finding a man to make Joshua jealous, but Bethany had been too miserable to listen carefully. Now she realised her mistake.

"I seem to remember you making a suggestion or two," Bethany admitted reluctantly.

"I did more than suggest," Sally said righteously, and lowered her voice to a hissing whisper. "I *acted*, which is more than I can say for you."

"But everything is progressing nicely between me and Joshua," Bethany answered in like tones, keeping her voice as low as possible. "I don't want to do anything to topple the cart."

"Sure, it's going just wonderful between you and the great white hunter," Sally scoffed. "You're taking care of his little girl every free moment. You don't have time for anything else."

"But..."

"Just answer me one thing, Beth. Has your precious Mr. J. D. Norris ever taken *you* out without dragging Angie along? Has it ever been just the two of you alone? Well?"

Her roommate knocked away Bethany's argument as easily as if she'd toppled a stack of children's building blocks. Bethany lowered her gaze, feeling miserable and lost. Even their one luncheon date alone had been an excuse to get her to watch Angie.

"See what I mean?" Sally muttered. "Mr. Norris is using you. He has been from the first, and as your best friend I refuse to stand by and let it happen. You've got to start circulating again. I'm going to introduce you to the *right* kind of men, and I won't let you stop me."

"But, Sally..."

"I refuse to hear any more arguments. Thursday night, understand."

"All right," Bethany agreed, but she couldn't have cared less about Jerry Johnson or Jerry anyone. She was in love with Joshua, and nothing would change the way she felt about her employer.

When Joshua called for her to take some dictation an hour later, Bethany briskly stepped into his office.

He smiled when he saw her, but her returning smile was strained.

"Is the Hanson report finished yet?" he asked.

"Almost, I'll have it on your desk in a few minutes."

"Good." He handed her a stack of papers. "Collate and get me fifteen copies of each of these at your convenience. There isn't any big rush."

"Is tomorrow morning soon enough?"

"That'll be fine."

Bethany would have returned to the reception area, but Joshua stopped her. "One minute, Miss Stone." He paused to write across the top of a yellow legal tablet, and when he glanced up, he looked pleased about something, relaxed in a way she hadn't ever seen in him. "Would you happen to be free tomorrow night, Beth?"

Bethany felt as if a loaded logging truck had parked on top of her chest. "Thursday night?"

"That's tomorrow. I realise it's short notice. Is there a problem?"

Her palms felt unexpectedly moist and she hoisted the papers she was holding to get a better grip on them. The small stack felt as though it weighed thirty pounds. "I'm sorry, Joshua...Mr. Norris, but I've already got plans."

"There's no problem. I should have asked you earlier." He frowned and went back to his task, scratching notes across the top of the pad.

"If...I'm sure Mrs. Larson will be able to stay with Angie, but if she can't—"

"Mrs. Larson can, so don't worry about it."

Bethany was trembling by the time she made it to her desk. Her knees were actually knocking against each other when she sat down. She could feel her heart's thundering beat all the way to her toes.

"Bethany..." Sally stuck her head around the door. "Have you got a moment?"

"Sally!" She groaned. "What is it now?"

Her friend strolled into the office. "I've got his picture."

"Whose?"

"Jerry Johnson's." She looked as pleased as if she'd managed to smuggle secret papers out of the Kremlin. "It was in the bottom of my purse. I forgot I had it."

"Sally, honestly, I don't even want to go out with this guy."

"Don't say that until you've seen his picture." She waved the photograph under Bethany's nose, as though the blurred image would be enough to convince her how lucky she was to be dating such a hunk.

Bethany grabbed the small glossy picture from her friend's hands and studied the handsome smiling face. Jerry Johnson was attractive—okay, he was downright showstopping.

Sally leaned her hip against the side of Bethany's desk, crossed her arms and looked exceedingly proud of herself. "He knows you, too."

"Why don't I remember him?" She frowned because he *did* look vaguely familiar.

"You only met him once," Sally said, and studied the length of her fingernails on her right hand. "Christmas, last year, at the Dawsons' party."

Bethany could hardly remember who the Dawsons were until she recalled they were family friends of Sally's.

"Trust me, Beth. Thursday night with Jerry Johnson is a date you won't soon forget."

"Ms. Livingston," Joshua said in a cold hard voice from the open doorway. "Seeing that you have nothing to do but traipse in and out of my office at all times of the day, I'm wondering just how much your work efforts contribute to my company."

Sally bounced away from the desk as though she'd been sitting on a hot plate. Her eyes filled with shock as she glanced to Bethany, silently pleading for help.

"Sally was making a delivery," Bethany said, stretching the truth as far as she dared.

"Yes, I heard. The photo of your hot date."

Bethany's face flushed with brilliant colour.

"I trust you two have more important business to see to on company time?"

"Yes, sir," Sally mumbled, and was gone.

"Are those papers copied for me yet?" Joshua demanded of Bethany.

"I...no. I'll take care of that first thing in the morning."

"I need them now."

"But you said—"

"Don't argue with me, Miss Stone. I want those papers copied and collated before you leave tonight. Is that clear?"

"Perfectly, Mr. Norris."

"Good. And the next time I see Ms. Livingston in my office talking to you on company time instead of being where she should be, she'll be looking for another job."

"If Sally leaves, then I'm going, as well."

"That decision is your own, Miss Stone." With that he spun around and returned to his office, soundly closing the door.

CHAPTER SEVEN

"Have aliens captured your brain?" Bethany demanded of her roommate. "Of all the crazy things you've pulled over the years, I—"

"I know...I know," Sally cut her off, still pale from her brief confrontation with J. D. Norris. Her hands went to her throat. "Honestly, I thought he was going to ask for my head."

"He damn near did." She didn't mention that hers would have rolled with her friend's. Joshua had been in such an ill temper that even hours after their confrontation, talking to him would have been impossible. Not that Bethany had tried. She knew her employer well enough to recognise his mood. And honour it.

"You're still going Thursday night, aren't you?" Sally asked, glancing surreptitiously towards her good friend.

"Of course I'm going." But Bethany didn't feel nearly as confident as she sounded. This whole idea of dating a man she'd briefly met at a Christmas party months earlier didn't suit her, especially since she'd been drinking eggnog at the time. Eggnog and wine were synonymous with trouble as far as Bethany was concerned.

Friday morning, Joshua was already at his desk when Bethany arrived. She paused between the doorway that connected their two offices, surprised to see him and dismayed at the sight he made. Joshua looked terrible. Even from where she was standing, Bethany could see and feel his fatigue. Dark smudges circled his eyes. His jacket had long since been discarded, his tie loosened and the top two buttons of his wrinkled shirt unfastened. One glance convinced Bethany he hadn't bothered to go home the night before.

"Joshua," she whispered, the concern chugging through her blood, "how long have you been here?"

Deliberately he set his pencil aside but continued to hold on to it. "When we're at the office, Miss Stone, kindly refer to me as Mr. Norris."

"As you wish," she returned stiffly, and proceeded into the room. So that was the way it was to be. Fine. Holding her back as rigid as possible, she put on a fresh pot of coffee and went back to her own desk to sort through the morning mail. When she'd finished, she returned, poured Joshua a cup of coffee and delivered it to him the way she had every morning for the past three years.

"So, Miss Stone," he said sardonically, "how did your 'hot date' go?"

His voice was so thick with sarcasm that Bethany had to bite down on her bottom lip to keep from responding in like tones.

"Fine, thank you." She handed him the sorted mail. "The letter you've been looking for from Charles Youngblood arrived."

"Good." Joshua picked through the stack until he located it. "Are you planning on seeing him again?" he demanded.

"Charles Youngblood?"

"You're being deliberately obtuse. I was referring to your... date," he said with a sneer.

"I hardly think that's any of your business," she snapped, her own patience a slender thread. "What happens outside this office isn't your concern."

"When your action directly affects the productivity of this company, I'd damn well say it's my business."

Icy fingers wrapped themselves around Bethany's vocal cords. She couldn't have answered Joshua had her job depended on it, and considering the horrible mood he was in, it very well could be.

"Miss Stone, I asked you a question. I expect an answer."

It was in her mind to shout that he was a monster and that she refused to discuss details of her dates with any employer. Instead, she squarely met his gaze and said, "My personal life is my own." Following that, she turned and walked out of the office.

An hour later, her hands were still trembling, and she remained on the verge of tears. The door to Joshua's office opened and just the sound was enough to cause Bethany to stiffen her spine, readying herself for another confrontation.

He walked over to her desk and set down the mail. A list of handwritten instructions accompanied the large stack of letters.

"Cancel my appointments for the day, Miss Stone," he said in a raspy whisper.

Bethany refused to look at him, but with her peripheral vision she saw him lean momentarily against the edge of her desk and pinch the bridge of his nose. He paused and wiped his hand down his face.

"I'm going home," he announced.

She nodded her head in quick jerky movements.

Joshua hesitated once more. "I apologise for my earlier behaviour. You're absolutely right—your personal life is your own. I had no business flying into you that way."

Again she remained silent.

"If there's anything that requires my attention, you can contact me at the house. Good day, Miss Stone."

"Mr. Norris."

"J. D. Norris said all that," Sally murmured, her eyes narrowed and thoughtful.

"I've never seen him so angry and unreasonable. I'm just glad he left because I couldn't have stood another minute . . . I think I would have quit on the spot if he'd said one more thing."

Sally broke off a part of her sugar-coated doughnut and poised it in front of her mouth. "I think he could be falling in love with you, Beth."

The sip of coffee Bethany had just swallowed jammed halfway down her throat and refused to budge. She slapped her hand over her chest and gasped. Once she'd composed herself enough to speak, she murmured, "Oh, hardly."

"I mean it," Sally countered with that thoughtful contemplative look of hers. "He's acting like a jealous little boy, which is exactly what I thought might happen. The extent of his reaction confirms my suspicions."

"A more likely scenario is that I was a convenient scapegoat for him to vent his troubles." Bethany wasn't blind to the financial problems in which Norris Pharmaceutical was currently involved. Having recently held off one takeover effort, Joshua had been hit almost immediately by another. His resources had been depleted by the first attempt and he was holding on to the control of the company by the thinnest of threads. Naturally, most of the information had been privileged, and she wasn't at liberty to discuss it with anyone, including her best friend. A good deal of what transpired had been between Joshua and other business leaders without Bethany being present. But she'd garnered enough information of what was going on from the numerous transcripts she'd typed. Unfortunately, she didn't have a clue how Joshua was surviving this latest takeover bid.

"I don't know," Sally muttered with the same piece of doughnut still level with her lips. "I've been doing a lot of thinking about the way Mr. Norris has been acting these past few weeks, and it's obvious he's enthralled with you."

"Sure he is," Bethany muttered scornfully. "Angie thinks I'm great fun and Joshua Norris knows I'm a soft touch when it comes to his daughter."

"Well, aren't you?"

Bethany was reluctantly forced to agree. "I...won't be able to meet you at Charley's after work," she informed her friend, almost as an afterthought.

"How come?"

"I...I've got to take some papers over to Mr. Norris's house for him to sign."

"Ah." Sally's eyes brightened, then were quickly lowered as she pretended an interest in her paper napkin. "Listen..." She paused, placed the half-eaten doughnut back on her plate and brushed the sugar granules from her fingertips. "Since you weren't really all that interested in Jerry Johnson, I was wondering..."

"Go ahead," Bethany said, having trouble disguising a smile, almost enjoying her friend's discomfort. "Go ahead and what?"

"Date Jerry yourself. Do you honestly think I didn't know you're crazy about him? Sally, you drool every time someone mentions his name."

"I do?"

"Either that, or your eyes start to water. I can't believe you'd fix *me* up with a date with him when you're so obviously taken with him yourself." Actually, knowing Sally's twisted way of planning things, this scheme of hers was probably the only way she could come up with to talk to him again.

"You knew?" Sally demanded.

"Not at first," Bethany was slow to admit. She'd been so caught up with what was going on between her and Joshua that she hadn't been paying attention to her friend until the obvious practically hit her over the head. After all, how many women carried a picture of a man they'd only met once in their bag for an entire year? Not many, she would bet. Only someone as sentimental and romantic as Sally.

"So you don't mind if I—"

"Not in the least. Jerry Johnson is all yours, with my blessing."

*   *   *

Bethany finished the last of her duties at five and left the office to drive directly to Joshua's home on Lake Pontchartrain. Her excuse to stop at the house was flimsy at best, but she felt terrible about what had happened that morning and longed to straighten things out—even if it meant admitting she wouldn't be seeing Jerry again.

Mrs. Larson opened the front door. "Miss Stone, how are you this afternoon?"

The portly widow with thick silver hair wore a black uniform and a large white apron. She was kind and gentle-hearted, and on the few occasions that Bethany had met her, she'd been impressed with the older woman.

"I'm fine, thank you," Bethany answered. "How's Mr. Norris?"

Mrs. Larson's lips thinned with worry as she shook her head. "I swear it's a miracle that man hasn't worked himself into an early grave."

"I know," Bethany said miserably. "Has he slept at all?" The more she thought about their argument that morning, the more guilty she felt for her part in it. Joshua was obviously exhausted beyond reason.

"He slept an hour or two early this morning, and then he was at his desk in the den, working. Would you like me to take you to him?"

"Please." Bethany followed Mrs. Larson to the large den, which was built off the living room and faced the lake.

The older woman knocked politely, then opened the door. "Miss Stone is here to see you," she announced, and stepped aside.

Joshua half rose from his sitting position. "Bethany." His eyes widened with surprise. "Were there problems? You should have phoned."

"I apologise for interrupting you..."

"It's no problem. Sit down."

She lowered herself into a huge overstuffed leather chair and folded her hands on her lap, watching him expectantly. If she didn't know better, she would have sworn he was pleased to see her, and that made her feel good about her unscheduled visit.

He returned her look, his gaze expectant, and she suddenly remembered the excuse she'd invented to come to the house. "There are some letters for you to sign... I seem to have left them in the car." She rushed to her feet. "I'll get them and be right back."

She was such an idiot! Bethany all but jumped out of the chair and hurried back outside. Instead of troubling Mrs. Larson a second time, she let herself into the house and Joshua's den.

"Taking the time to bring these over was thoughtful," he said, scribbling his name across the bottom of the first letter without bothering to read it.

"Yes... well, I felt badly about this morning," she murmured. Her face was growing warm and she knew she was blushing. "You'd obviously been up all night and, although it really wasn't any of your concern, it wouldn't have hurt me any to let you know about Jerry and me."

"Yes?" he coaxed when she didn't immediately continue. "So you've decided to continue dating Ms. Livingston's friend?" Some of the pleasure drained from his eyes. "Well, that's understandable."

"No, Joshua... I mean, Mr. Norris. I won't be seeing Jerry again."

"You won't?" Five years were peeled off his face as his expression lightened considerably. "Well, that's certainly your business."

"Yes, I know," she countered softly. With no excuse to linger any longer, Bethany stood, wishing she could find a plausible reason to stay. "How's Angie?" she asked with a flash of brilliance, and reclaimed her chair.

"She's doing just fine," Joshua answered eagerly. "Good. She's spending the night with her friend Wendy."

Silence followed.

Bethany stood once more.

"She seems to have made the adjustment from New York to New Orleans rather well."

Bethany sat back down, almost gleeful with relief to stay. "Yes, I thought so."

Another moment of silence fell between them.

"I know this is spur-of-the-moment, but would you care to have dinner with me?" Joshua asked.

"Yes." Bethany felt excited enough about the prospect to stand up and do cheers, and she had to restrain herself. "I'd like that a lot."

The smile he tossed her was almost boyish. He paused and glanced her way, eyeing her clothes, and frowned slightly.

"I can go home and change if you want." She was wearing a dark blue business suit with a straight skirt and short double-breasted jacket.

"No, you're perfect just the way you are."

"You're sure?" She was curious to know where he was taking her. When he'd asked her to dinner, she'd assumed at first that he meant for her to eat with him here at the house.

"I'm positive," he answered, although he was dressed far more casually than usual himself, in trousers and a thick Irish cable-knit sweater the colour of winter wheat.

After pausing to let Mrs. Larson know he was leaving, Joshua reached for Bethany's hand and led her out of the house. He drove into the heart of the city and parked on a side street a few blocks off the French Quarter.

"Do you like beans and rice?" he asked.

Bethany nodded eagerly. The popular New Orleans dish had been elevated with the recent interest in Cajun and Creole cooking. The recipe had originated in the slave quarters and many a Southerner had grown up in a time when each day's menu revolved around rice and beans.

"A friend of mine operates a café that serves the best Louisiana cooking in the world." He hesitated and smiled. "But be warned, the food is fantastic, but the place rates low on atmosphere."

"You needn't worry about that with me." She wondered what he would think if he were ever to join her large family for a Sunday dinner. How would he fit in with mismatched place settings, gas-station handout water glasses and an ever-flowing stream of conversation?

Joshua slipped his arm around her waist, holding her close to his side. "I wasn't worried that you'd disapprove, I just wanted to warn you."

"Okay, I consider myself properly warned," she told him, her eyes smiling. This was the man she was just beginning to know, the man she'd been granted rare glimpses of over the years. Excitement fired through her blood.

Joshua directed her down a narrow alleyway. Bethany had been up and down the streets in the French Quarter most of her life, but she didn't recognise this one.

"Are you sure there's a restaurant back here?" she asked.

"Positive."

The place was small and cramped, with only a handful of tables. The chairs were mismatched and the Formica on the tabletops was chipped, but the smells wafting from the kitchen were enough to convince Bethany that Joshua knew what he was talking about.

"What you doin' bringing that skinny chil' in my kitchen, J. D. Norris?" A huge black woman stepped out from behind an old-fashioned cash register.

"Bethany, meet Cleo."

The woman wiped her hands dry on the smudged apron that was tucked into the folds of her skirt. "You looks like a strong wind would blow you away," Cleo announced, cocking her head to one side as she studied Bethany through dark narrowed eyes.

"Then I sincerely hope you intend to feed me."

Cleo chuckled and her whole torso shook with the action. "Honey chil', you have no idea how Cleo can feed a soul." She ambled across the room and pulled back two chairs. "Sit," she ordered. With that she started towards the kitchen, paused and looked over her shoulder. "You bring your horn?"

Joshua nodded. "It's in the car."

"It's been too long, Dizzy, much too long."

"Your horn? Dizzy?" Bethany asked, once Cleo was out of sight.

"I play saxophone now and then, when the spirit moves me."

Shocked speechless, Bethany studied him for a moment, astonished at this side of this complex man that she'd never known existed. There was nothing in her experiences with Joshua that had so much as hinted at any musical interest or talent. "I had no idea," she managed to say after a moment.

He grinned, as if to say there was a lot about him she didn't know, and Bethany couldn't doubt it.

Cleo returned with plates piled high with rice and smothered with rich beans in a red sauce. "This is just for openers," Cleo warned, setting down the two plates. She returned a minute later with a third stacked high with warm squares of corn bread oozing with melted butter.

"She doesn't honestly expect us to eat all this?" Bethany asked between bites. She'd tasted beans and rice in any number of restaurants but never anything that could compare with this unusual blend of spices, vegetables and meat. Nothing had ever tasted any-where near this delicious.

"She'd be insulted if we left a crumb."

Bethany didn't know how she managed it, but her plate was clean when Cleo returned. The black woman gave her a broad grin and nodded approvingly.

"Maybe you be all right after all," the massive woman said with a sparkle in her dark eyes.

"Maybe you be, too," Bethany returned, holding in a laugh.

The huge woman let loose with a loud burst of laughter and slapped Joshua across the back. "I like her."

Joshua grinned, sharing a look with Bethany. "So do I."

"You got room for my special sweet-potato-pecan pie?" Cleo eyed them both speculatively, as if to say these skinny white folks didn't know nothin' about good food.

Joshua leaned back, splayed his fingers over his stomach and sighed. "I think you better count me out. I'm stuffed to the gills. Bethany?"

"Bring me a piece."

Cleo nodded several times. "You done yourself proud, Dizzy. She don't look like much, but there's more to her than meets the eye."

The pie was thick, sweet and delicious.

Joshua sat back and watched, eyes wide, as Bethany finished off the last bite.

"You amaze me."

Bethany licked the ends of her fingers. "I told you before, I've got a healthy appetite."

Cleo returned, carrying two steaming mugs of coffee. "You takin' this honey chil' to St. Peter's?"

Joshua nodded, and Cleo looked pleased.

After Joshua paid for their meal, he led Bethany out of the café and further down the narrow alley to another set of doors. "I hope you like jazz because you're about to get an earful."

"I love any kind of music," Bethany was quick to tell him, feeling closer to Joshua than ever before. He opened the door off the alley and a cloud of smoke as thick as a bayou fog covered them as they walked through the door. It took Bethany a second to adjust her eyesight to the dim interior. She couldn't see much as Joshua led her to a vacant table and pulled out a chair for her. The sounds of clicking ice, the tinny tones of an old piano and the hum of conversation surrounded her like the familiar greetings of old friends.

"What would you like to drink?" Joshua asked, and had to lean close in order for Bethany to hear him above the conversational hum. "A mint julep?"

She answered him with a shake of her head. "A beer, please."

Joshua turned to leave her. He must have forgotten something because he hadn't gone more than a couple of steps when he turned back. Bethany looked up expectantly and he leaned down to press his mouth over hers in a kiss so fleeting that Bethany had no time to describe it even to herself.

In the front of the room was a small platform stage. A man was playing the piano and another was setting up a drum set. Bethany watched Joshua weave a path between tables to get to the bar. He was waylaid several times as friends stopped to greet him. Within a few minutes he returned with two frosty mugs of cold beer.

Bethany had barely had time to taste the brew when Joshua stood and offered her his hand. She didn't understand at first, then realised he was asking her to dance. The small dance floor was crowded when they moved to the edge of it. Joshua wrapped her in his arms, and they soon melted in with the others.

The minute Joshua had pulled her into his embrace, a wave of warmth had coursed through Bethany. She leaned her head back and looked up at him, realising anew how much she loved this man.

He touched her cheek and his fingers felt like velvet against her cool skin. His lips were only a few inches away, and she longed with everything in her for him to kiss her again.

"Beth," he whispered urgently, "don't look at me like that."

Embarrassed, she lowered her gaze, all too aware of what he must be reading in her eyes.

"What the hell," he said, and moved ever so slightly to lift her chin and direct her mouth to his.

Bethany felt as if her bones were melting. She tasted the malt flavour of his beer as she opened her mouth to his. If his first kiss had been a sample, this second one was a feast. He slid his hands down her spine, moulding her body intimately to his as he gave her a ruthless and plundering kiss. He moved his lips in eager exploration over hers until Bethany was convinced she would faint from the undiluted pleasure of it.

When he broke off the kiss, Bethany sagged against him, too weak to do anything but cling to the only solid thing in a world that was spinning out of control. She'd never wanted a man to make love to her more in her life. She shook with the urgent need that was building up inside her. Joshua nuzzled the side of her neck and then investigated the hollow of her throat with his tongue. She was gathered as close as humanly possible against him. When he kissed her again, his mouth was so hot it burned a trail all across her face.

"Let's get out of here," he whispered in a voice so thick and raspy she could hardly understand him.

She answered with a nod.

He kept her close to his side as he led them back to their table. They were about to leave when a tall dark man with a huge potbelly and a thick dark beard stopped him.

"You can't leave this place, Dizzy, without playing the blues."

"He's right, Dizzy," Bethany murmured, looking up at Joshua.

"Good to see you again, Fats." Joshua shook hands with the other man.

"You got your horn, brother?"

Joshua nodded reluctantly. "It's in the car."

"Get it."

Joshua looked almost apologetic as he led Bethany back to their table. "I'm sorry, sweetheart," he whispered.

She pressed her hands onto his shoulders and was so bold as to reach up and brush her lips across his. "I'm not. I want to hear you play."

The man Joshua had called Fats jumped onto the stage when Joshua reappeared. He carried his saxophone with him and Fats brought a bass trombone. The man who'd been playing the drums reappeared carrying a trumpet. The first couple of minutes were spent attaching reeds, checking valves and tooting a few notes. No one seemed to mind that the dancing had come to an abrupt halt. The room seemed to vibrate with a charged sense of anticipation.

Bethany sat back, watching Joshua and loving him more each minute. He stepped to the front of the stage and his gaze sought hers. The look he sent her way cut straight through her, and then he smiled and placed the instrument between his lips.

The blast of music split the air and was followed by shouts of encouragement from the audience. Soon the sounds of the other instruments joined Joshua: the piano, the trumpet, the trombone, each in turn.

Bethany couldn't have named the tune, didn't know that it had a title—the players weren't even following any sheet music. The sounds appeared improvisational as each player in his own time bent the notes his own way, twisting and turning, soaring and landing again. Bethany flew with them and she wasn't alone. Every patron in the club joined the flight, ascending with the music. The men played as if they were one, yet each separate. Bethany soaked in every note of Joshua's music, as if her heart had become a sponge meant only to take in this man and his love. She experienced the bright tension of the score as though each bar of music were meant for her and her alone. When they were finished, her eyes burned with unshed tears.

She remained in an almost dreamlike state when Joshua rejoined her. His face was close to hers and she could see the beads of perspiration that wetted his upper lip and brow. She raised her fingertip to his face, needing to touch him, needing to say what was inside her and unable to find the words to explain how his music had marked her soul.

Joshua gripped her hand with his own and kissed her fingertips.

"You like it?" he asked her, his gaze holding hers.

She nodded, and a tear escaped and ran down the side of her face. "Very much," she whispered.

"Bethany, listen." His hand continued to squeeze hers. "I'm going out of town next week."

She already knew about his trip to California.

"I haven't any right to ask this of you." He stopped and tangled his fingers in her hair. "I want you to come with me."

If he'd asked for her soul at that moment, she couldn't have refused him. "I'll come," she replied.

His eyes ate her up, seeming almost to ask her forgiveness. "Angie will be with me. She wants you to come and so do I."

CHAPTER EIGHT

"WHEN we're in California," Angie said thought-fully, sitting beside Bethany in the first-class section of the Boeing 737, "will you call me Millicent?"

"If you like."

The little girl nodded eagerly. "At least for the first day or two. I might want to change to Guinevere or Charmaine after that."

"I may slip up now and again," Bethany admitted, doing her utmost to remain serious. There were days she couldn't keep track of who *she* was, let alone a fun-loving ten-year-old.

"That's all right," Angie said, and went back to flipping through the pages of the flight magazine. She paused abruptly and looked back to Bethany. "Do you want me to call you Dominique? I could."

Bethany hesitated as if to give the child's offer se-rious consideration, then shook her head. "No thanks, sweetheart."

Joshua sat across the aisle from Angie and Bethany. His briefcase was open and he was busy reviewing some papers. His brow was creased in thick folds of concentration, his gaze intent. Bethany was con-vinced he'd long forgotten his daughter and his sec-retary, and her heart ached a little with the realisation.

Inhaling a deep breath, Bethany pulled her eyes away from her employer and tried to involve herself in the plot of the murder mystery she was reading. It didn't work, although the author was one of her favourites. Instead, Sally's dire warning played back in her mind like a stubborn cassette tape that refused to shut off. It was happening again, her roommate had warned. Bethany was allowing Joshua to use her as a convenient baby-sitter. Bethany didn't want to believe that.

After Friday night, when Joshua had taken her to meet Cleo and she'd heard him play the saxophone at St. Peter's, Bethany had been convinced he felt something deep and meaningful for her. She wasn't so naïve as to believe he loved her—that would have been too much to hope for so soon. But she couldn't deny that Joshua had shared a deep personal part of himself with her and that went a long way towards making her forget she would be left solely in charge of Angie while Joshua tended to his business meetings.

"Daddy." Angie leaned across Bethany and called to her father. When he didn't immediately respond, his daughter took to waving her hand.

Joshua obviously didn't hear her or see her movements, or, if he did, he was too wrapped up in the report he was reading to break his concentration.

"What is it, Angie?" Bethany asked.

The ten-year-old leaned back in her seat. "How much longer? Will we be able to go to Disneyland today? I can hardly wait to see Mickey Mouse and Snow White."

Bethany checked her watch. "It'll be another couple of hours yet before we land."

"Oh." The small shoulders sagged with disappointment. "That long?"

"I'm afraid so."

"What about Disneyland?"

"There just won't be enough time after we leave the airport and check into the hotel."

"But Dad said we—"

"We'll see Mickey and Minnie first thing in the morning. I promise."

It looked for a moment as though Angie was going to argue with her, but the child apparently changed her mind and quietly settled back in her seat for a while. Then she squirmed once more.

"Is Dad going to be in meetings the whole time we're in California?"

Bethany nodded. She didn't like the idea of Joshua being constantly busy any better than Angie. When she'd originally made the arrangements for this trip, Joshua had requested that she schedule in a couple of days' free time so he could spend it with Angie, sightseeing. However, once Bethany had agreed to accompany him, the days he'd set aside to vacation had quickly filled up with appointments and business meetings. Now Joshua would be occupied the entire five days of their visit.

Their flight landed at LAX at five that evening, but by the time their luggage had been collected and the limousine had driven them into Anaheim, it was much later. Because of the time difference, Angie was overly tired, hungry and more than a little cranky.

Bethany hadn't fared much better during the long trip. Keeping Angie occupied had drained her completely. When Joshua had first asked her to accompany him, she'd been thrilled. Now she felt abused and sorely disappointed at the role she would be playing during the next few days. Her back was stiff, she was hungry, and she felt like Cinderella two nights after the ball, when her hair needed washing and there was a run in her tights.

Joshua had requested a suite for them close to the amusement park, where Bethany and Angie planned to spend a good deal of their stay. By the time they were settled in the hotel room, Angie was close to tears. Cranky because she was overly hungry, rummy because she was so tired and yet too excited to sleep.

It took Bethany the better part of an hour to convince the little girl to eat the hamburger Joshua ordered from room service. More time was spent persuading Angie that although it was still daylight, she really needed to rest. Angie was a little more cooperative once she took a bath. The ten-year-old climbed into bed with hardly a complaint and was asleep within five minutes.

Bethany felt as if she'd worked straight through a double shift when she joined Joshua in the suite's living room. She plopped herself down beside him on the davenport, slipped off her shoes and sagged against the back of the sofa, more exhausted than she could ever remember being in a long while.

Joshua set aside his papers and reached for her hand. His gaze revealed his appreciation. It was obvious from the moment Angie had started to whine in the airport when they'd landed that he wasn't going to be able to deal with his daughter patiently. He raised

Bethany's hand to his mouth and brushed his lips over her knuckles. "I don't know what I'd do without you," he murmured.

A polite nod and a weak smile were all the response she could manage.

"I don't mean for you to work while we're here." He scooted closer to her and wrapped his arm around her, cupping her shoulder. "My intention had been to make this a vacation for you, as well . . . I didn't realise Angie would be such a handful."

"She was just tired and cranky."

Joshua kissed the top of her head. "I know it was completely selfish of me to ask you to make this trip."

She didn't answer. Couldn't. Sally had been telling her what a fool she was from the minute Bethany had told her friend she would be travelling to California with Joshua and his daughter.

"The thought of spending five days without seeing you was more than I could bear."

Bethany so desperately wanted to believe him. She tucked her head under his chin and snuggled closer, almost too exhausted to appreciate the comfort his arms offered.

"I'm being unfair to you."

Bethany's eyes drifted shut when Joshua raised her chin and kissed her, his mouth brushing over hers in a swift sampling. She sighed and smiled contentedly. Tenderly Joshua smoothed wisps of hair away from her face and slowly glided his fingertips over her features.

"Such smooth skin," he whispered. "So warm and silky."

Bethany felt as if she'd gone ten rounds with Sugar Ray, but one kiss from Joshua wiped out everything but the cosy tranquil feeling of being held in his embrace. She slipped her left arm around his middle and tipped her head back, seeking more of his special brand of comforting.

When he didn't immediately kiss her again, Bethany's lashes fluttered open. What she saw in his eyes made her heart go still. Joshua was staring at her with such naked longing that she felt she would break out in a fever just looking at him. The words to tell him that she loved him burned on her lips, but she held them inside for fear of what voicing them would do to their relationship.

"Oh, Bethany, you are so beautiful." He whispered the words with such an intensity of emotion that she felt her heart melt like butter sitting too long in the hot sun. She wanted to tell him that it wasn't necessary for him to say those kind of things to her. He owned her heart, and had possessed it for three years.

His gaze held her a willing prisoner for what seemed like an eternity as he slowly slid his hand from the curve of her shoulder upwards to her warm nape. He wove his fingers into her thick dark hair, and with his hand cupping the back of her head, he directed her mouth towards his. The kiss was full and lush. Rich. The man who was kissing her wasn't the arrogant man she worked with in the office. This was the same man who'd revealed a part of himself to her she was sure few others knew existed. The same man who had soared to unknown heights on the wings of a song he'd played just for her. The same man who gazed into her

eyes and revealed such need, such longing that she
would spend a lifetime remembering the pure desire
she viewed there.

The shaking inside Bethany became so fierce that
she raised her hand to grip Joshua's collar in a futile
effort to maintain her equilibrium. Her flesh felt both
hot and cold at the same time.

When he lifted his mouth from hers, Joshua drew
in several ragged breaths. "Having you with me could
end up being the biggest temptation of my life," he
whispered in a raspy hoarse-sounding voice. He captured her hand and flattened her palm over his heart.
"Feel what you do to me."

"I don't need to feel . . . I know, because you're doing the same thing to me."

"Bethany . . . listen, this isn't the right time for either of us and—"

She cut him off, not willing to listen to his arguments. All she longed to do was savour the sweet sensations he'd aroused in her with a single kiss. She
slipped her hands around the thick cord of his neck
and she offered him a slow seductive smile as she gently tugged at him and directed his mouth back to her
own.

Joshua's eyes momentarily widened with surprise.

Bethany answered him with her own smile. Her lips
parted, deepening the kiss. Joshua groaned and kissed
her back as though he couldn't get enough of her.
Bethany's breasts throbbed with the need for his
touch, her nipples aching with anticipation. He didn't
disappoint her and his hand lifted her sweater away
from her abdomen. His fingers felt hot against her al-

ready flushed, heated skin. He sought her breast and when he found it, she sighed.

Joshua sighed, too. He circled her nipple lazily with his thumb until it grew so hard it ached almost painfully. She must have made some kind of sound, because Joshua reluctantly slid his mouth from hers.

Bethany protested with a soft moan, and when her lashes fluttered open she recognised his look of concern.

"Did I hurt you?"

"No." Embarrassed, she dropped her gaze. "It feels too good to have you touch me."

He closed his eyes like a man enduring the worst kind of torture. "Don't tell me that, Bethany."

"I can't help it."

He reached around and unclasped her bra. Bethany sank her teeth into her bottom lip as he lifted her sweater and pressed her back against the sofa. He kissed her once. Twice. Again. And while he kissed her, he worked magic with his hands on her breasts. Soon his mouth, moist and warm, replaced his fingers, and Bethany gasped as he closed his lips around her taut nipple, sucking and teasing. She arched her spine and felt herself slowly slipping beneath the waterline once more, willingly drowning in a deluge of naked desire.

The ringing sound didn't penetrate her conscience at first. But Joshua reacted almost immediately, jerking his head up and groaning aloud. A muffled curse followed.

"Yes?"

It wasn't until he spoke that Bethany realised Joshua had left her to answer the telephone. She blinked a couple of times, adjusting her eyes to the glaring light. Ill at ease, she sat upright, refastened her bra and pulled her sweater back into place.

"The flight was on time. Yes...yes, first thing in the morning. I'm looking forward to it. I've got those figures you asked to see. I think you'll be impressed with what's been happening the past couple of months. Yes, of course, eight. I'll be there."

Joshua spoke in crisp clear tones and no one would have guessed that only a few moments before he'd been making love to Bethany. The transformation from lover to businessman was as slick as ice on a country road.

It took Bethany several minutes to gather her composure enough to stand. Her knees felt shaky, and she was sure desire lingered in her expression. She brushed the hair out of her face and her hands trembled with the action. Joshua sat with his back to her, intent on his conversation. As far as he was concerned, Bethany could have been back in New Orleans. He had completely forgotten she existed.

She didn't wait until he was finished with his phone call. With her heart pounding like a battering ram against her ribcage, she walked across the floor, opened the door to the bedroom she would be sharing with Angie and slipped inside the darkened room. The little girl was sound asleep, and Bethany didn't bother to turn on any lights. She undressed silently, found her way into the bathroom to brush her teeth and wash her face. Then she eagerly slipped between the clean sheets. Within minutes Bethany felt herself sinking into a black void of slumber, but not before she heard Joshua's footsteps outside the bedroom door. He paused, apparently thinking better of waking her, then walked away.

Angie wore Mickey Mouse ears and carried a series of colourful balloons, two huge stuffed animals and other accumulated goodies the following afternoon when Bethany opened the door to their hotel suite.

"Hi, Dad." Angie flopped down in a chair and let out a giant whoosh of air. "Boy, am I tired."

Joshua grinned and sent a flashing query to Bethany. "How did you survive the day?"

"Great, I think. Only there isn't enough money in the world to get me back on some of those rides."

"Bethany screamed all the way through the Magic Mountain," Angie announced in a tattletale voice. "I thought she had more guts than that."

"At least I didn't hide my eyes when I rode through the Matterhorn."

"High places frighten me," Angie announced, accepting the ribbing good-naturedly.

Joshua leaned back in his chair and grinned at the pair. "It looks to me like you've both had a grand time."

"Did we ever. We saw Donald Duck and Goofy and Snow White."

"Did you happen upon another Prince Charming?" Joshua asked. The gaze holding Bethany's was filled with curiosity.

"Unfortunately, no."

"A shame," he muttered, looking appropriately disappointed.

"The only white stallion I encountered was connected to an old-fashioned fire truck," she informed him, sharing his amusement. "I didn't have time to investigate further."

Joshua chuckled.

"How did your meeting go?" Bethany was all too aware that the future of Norris Pharmaceutical rested on the outcome of this business trip. She was worried for Joshua and prayed everything would go his way.

"The meeting went well." But he didn't elaborate.

"I'm starved."

Bethany nearly fell out of her chair at Angie's sudden announcement. "You just ate two hot dogs, cotton candy and a bag of peanuts."

"Can I help it?" the ten-year-old muttered. "I'm a growing child—at least that's what Mrs. Larson keeps telling me."

"And I'm one pooped adult." The thought of leaving the comfort of this hotel room on a food-seeking expedition so soon after arriving didn't exactly thrill Bethany.

"Is anybody interested in taking a swim?" Joshua asked, diverting his daughter's attention.

"Me." Instantly Angie was on her feet, eager to participate in anything that involved her father.

Bethany shook her head, too exhausted to move for the moment. "Maybe later—give me a few minutes to recuperate first." Her feet were swollen, although she'd worn a comfortable pair of old shoes. Her back ached and her head continued to spin from all the carnival rides Angie had insisted upon going on.

"I'm ready anytime you are, Dad," Angie cried out, and ran into the bedroom to change.

Joshua walked over to Bethany's side and bent down to lightly kiss her lips. "You look exhausted."

She smiled and nodded. "I'm too old to keep up with a ten-year-old."

"Go ahead and rest. I'll keep Angie occupied for the next hour or so."

"Bless you." Bethany wasn't teasing when she'd told Joshua how run-down she was. The energy level of one small girl was astonishing. They'd arrived at Disneyland when the amusement park opened first thing that morning and then had stayed for a full ten hours. On the monorail ride back to the hotel, Angie had casually announced that she intended to return to the park the following morning and then had wondered what there was to do that evening. All Bethany could think about was soaking in a hot tub and taking a long uninterrupted nap.

"We're off," Joshua said, coming out of his bedroom. He was wearing swimming trunks and had a thick white towel draped around his neck. He made such an attractive virile sight that Bethany nearly changed her mind about accompanying the pair.

"Bye, Bethany," Angie said, and waved, looking happy and excited. "Rest up, okay? Because there are a whole lot of things to do yet."

The opportunity for the little girl to spend time alone with her father was so rare. Bethany was pleased that Joshua was making the effort to fit Angie into his busy life.

The door closed and, with some effort, Bethany struggled to climb out of the chair. With her hand pressing against the small of her back, she made her way into the bedroom, deciding to forgo a soak in the tub and, instead, rest her eyes a few minutes.

The next thing she knew an hour had slipped away, and she could hear whispered voices.

Angie stuck her head in the bedroom door and announced to her father, "Bethany's asleep."

Bethany's mouth formed a soft smile as she bunched up the feather pillow beneath her head and pulled the blanket more securely over her shoulders. She'd been having such a pleasant dream that she wanted to linger in the warm bed and relive a portion of it. In her mind, Joshua had been telling her how much he loved her. The scent of orange blossoms wafted through the air, and Bethany was convinced she could hear the faint strains of the "Wedding March".

"Dad," Bethany heard the ten-year-old whisper. "Have you ever thought about getting married again?"

Bethany's eyes popped open.

"No," Joshua muttered, and the tone of his voice told her that he found the subject matter distasteful.

"I've been thinking a lot about what it would be like to have a mother," Angie continued, apparently undaunted by the lack of enthusiasm in her father's voice.

Bethany lifted herself up on one elbow, wondering what she should do. If she were to make some kind of noise, then Angie and Joshua would know she was awake and end their talk. But it would be embarrassing to both Joshua and herself, and she wasn't eager to do that. However, if she sat and listened, she was going to regret it and feel guilty about listening in when their discussion clearly wasn't meant for her ears.

"Angie, listen to me—"

"You're supposed to call me Millicent," she interrupted, impatience ringing in her young voice.

"Millicent, Guinevere, whatever it is you want to be named this hour, I don't think my remarrying is a subject you and I should be discussing."

"Why not?"

Joshua apparently seemed to have some difficulty answering because silence filtered its way into the bedroom where Bethany lay listening. Muttering under her breath, she knew she should let them know she was awake. Obeying her conscience, she made a soft little noise that apparently went undetected.

"I've been thinking about what it would be like if you married Bethany," Angie continued. "I like her a whole bunch. She's such a lot of fun."

"Bethany's too young," Joshua answered shortly. "I'm nearly eleven years older than she is and—"

"Fiddlesticks," Angie cried. "I saw you kiss her once and you didn't seem to think she was too young for that!"

"When?" Joshua demanded, obviously disturbed by the information.

"A long time ago. I forget exactly when, but you did, and I saw you with my own two eyes."

Too young! Bethany mouthed the words in astonished disbelief. It was obvious that Joshua was pulling excuses out of a hat in an effort to appease his daughter.

"You *did* kiss her, didn't you?"

"Yes," Joshua barked.

"And you liked it?"

"Angie." He paused, and Bethany could hear the sigh of frustration. "All right...Millicent, yes I *did* like it." The admission was ungracious, to say the least.

"Then I think you should marry Bethany."

"A whole lot more than liking the way someone kisses has to happen before a man considers marriage," Joshua explained with gruff impatience.

"It does?" Angie questioned. "Like what?"

"Things that a man doesn't discuss with his ten-year-old daughter."

"Oh," Angie muttered.

"Now for heaven's sake, don't say anything to Bethany about this or it'll make her uncomfortable." He paused, and from her position in the bedroom, Bethany could almost see Joshua pacing the floor. "You haven't talked to Bethany about this, have you?"

"No," Angie admitted eagerly. "I wanted to discuss it with you first. You told me I could talk to you about anything and I thought I should let you know that if you wanted to marry Bethany I'd like it real well. She'd make a great mother."

"Whatever you do, Angela, don't say anything to her!"

"I won't." Bethany heard Angie make a disparaging sound, but she wasn't sure what had prompted it. "Do you want any more children, Dad?"

"What?" The words seemed to explode from him.

"You know, another kid, like me?"

"I... I hadn't given it much thought. What makes you ask that?" It was clear from his tone of voice that Angie's questions were exasperating him.

"I don't know," Angie admitted, "except that if you and Bethany were to get married, then you'd probably have more children and I'd like that. I want a little sister and then a little brother."

"Did Bethany put you up to this?" Joshua's low voice was filled with suspicion.

Bethany was so outraged that she nearly flew out of bed to argue her own defence. How dared Joshua Norris think she would use his daughter to achieve her own ends? The very thought was despicable! If he believed for one second that she would resort to those kind of underhanded tactics, then he didn't know her at all, and that hurt more than anything else he'd said.

"Bethany doesn't know anything yet. I told you, I wanted to talk to you first."

"I see," Joshua muttered.

"You *will* think about marrying her, won't you, Dad?"

A year seemed to pass before Joshua answered. "Maybe."

Bethany's face was so hot she was sure she was running a high fever. Her heart constricted and she closed her eyes to the relentless pain that splashed over her.

After lingering in the bedroom another forty minutes, Bethany opened the door and stepped into the living area only to discover Angie and her father engrossed in a television movie.

"I didn't think you were ever going to wake up," Angie announced. "I'm starved, but Dad said we had to let you sleep."

"I'm sorry to keep you waiting," she said, having trouble keeping the hurt and resentment out of her voice. "You should have gone without me. I wouldn't have minded." The way she was feeling now, she didn't know that she could maintain her composure and not let Joshua know what she'd innocently overheard.

Angie didn't seem to notice a change in Bethany's attitude, but Joshua certainly did. He glanced her way and his gaze narrowed. "Are you feeling all right?"

"I'm fine," she lied.

"Good. I hope your healthy appetite is in place, because I've picked out an excellent Italian restaurant for dinner tonight."

"Hey, that sounds great," Angie said with a laugh, reaching out to claim Bethany's hand. "Come on, let's go, Dominique."

The remainder of their days ran together with all the different activities. Angie and Bethany visited Knott's Berry Farm, Universal Studios and several other tourist attractions. In the evenings, Joshua took charge of his daughter, finding ways of entertaining the pre-teen and relieving Bethany of the task. There were plenty of opportunities for Bethany to spend time alone with Joshua, but she avoided doing so as much as she could without being obvious about it.

The final night of their stay, Angie fell asleep in front of the television. Joshua carried the little girl into the bedroom and gently laid her on top of the mattress.

Bethany pulled the covers over the small shoulders and bent down to plant a swift kiss on the smooth brow. Joshua followed suit.

"I think I'll turn in myself," Bethany murmured, her gaze avoiding his.

Joshua arched his brows with surprise. "It's only a little after nine."

"It's ... it's been a long day."

"Come on, I'll order us some wine. We have a lot to celebrate."

"Then the meetings went well for you?"

Joshua grinned and nodded.

Bethany was relieved for his sake. Now, perhaps, his life could return to normal, and her employer could go back to keeping regular hours instead of working day and night.

Joshua had a chilled bottle of Chablis sent to their room. The waiter opened it for them and poured.

"I have a one-glass limit," Bethany said, feeling awkward.

"You had more the other night, as I recall."

"Sure, but I'd just swan dived into Lake Pontchartrain, too, if you'll remember."

A smile broke out across his handsome features. "I'm not likely to forget."

They sat in the living room with the lights dimmed, looking out over the flickering lights of the city. Neither spoke for a long time.

"I want you to know how grateful I am that you accompanied me and Angie," Joshua started off by saying.

"The pleasure was all mine."

Joshua nodded.

"Since Angie's come to live with me, things have changed between us, haven't they?"

Bethany stared into her wine and nodded.

"I always thought of you as an efficient secretary, but bit by bit I've come to learn you're a warm, caring, nurturing woman."

"Thank you."

"I know you're attracted to me, Beth, and I haven't made any secret of the way I feel about you."

A droning sound seemed to attack her from all sides. He was going to ask her to marry him. She knew it as clearly as if he'd removed a diamond ring from inside his pocket and waved it under her nose. Angie had specifically requested her for a mother and Joshua was simply complying with the little girl's wishes.

She glanced up and tried to hold back the emotion that was clamouring for release.

Joshua's intense gaze held hers.

"I know this must be rather sudden, Beth, but I'd very much like you to consider marrying me. Will you?"

CHAPTER NINE

"BETHANY?"

With deliberately calculated movements, Bethany set aside her glass of Chablis. Her mind was spinning like a child's toy top, wobbling precariously now as the momentum was slowing. Her heart was shouting for her to accept Joshua's proposal, but her head knew it would be wrong.

"For a moment there, I actually thought I could do it," she whispered, feeling miserable and elated both at once.

Joshua regarded her soberly. "I don't understand."

She raised her hand to his face and lovingly pressed her palm against the side of his jaw. "I don't expect you to. I'm honoured, Joshua, that you would ask me to be your wife, but the answer is no."

"No?" He looked positively stunned. "You didn't take time to think it over. You're turning me down? I thought . . . I'd hoped . . ."

Bethany hung her head. "I want so much more out of marriage than to be a replacement mother for a lonely little girl."

Joshua's brow folded into a deep dark frown. "What gives you the impression I'm asking you to be my wife because of Angie?"

"Joshua, please . . ."

"I want to know why," he demanded, his words as stiff and cold as frozen sheets.

If he was looking for an argument, Bethany wasn't going to provide one. She stood and offered him a sad but strong smile. "At least you didn't lie and tell me how much you love me. I've always admired that inherent streak of honesty in you. It's been ego shattering at times, but I've come to appreciate it." She swallowed at the painful lump that had formed in her throat. "Goodnight."

"Bethany." He ground out her name from between gritted teeth. "Sit down. It's obvious, if only to me, that we've got a good deal to discuss."

She shook her head. If they talked things over, she would be forced to tell him that she'd overheard his exchange with Angie, when his daughter had suggested Joshua marry her. To admit as much would be humiliating to them both.

"Goodnight, Joshua."

He clenched his jaw, and a muscle leaped at the side of his face. Bethany knew he was struggling to hold back his anger. Tears blurred her vision and she looked away, determined to leave the room with her pride, if nothing else, intact.

The return to New Orleans was as much of an ordeal for Bethany as the flight to California had been five days earlier. This time, however, Angie slept a good portion of the way. Joshua sat across the aisle from Bethany, and he might as well have been on a different aeroplane for all the attention he paid her. The silent treatment was exactly what Bethany had expected from him, but it still hurt. His protective shield was securely fastened in place, and with no apparent regret he'd shut her out of his heart and his life. Whatever possibility there had ever been for her to find happiness with Joshua Norris was now lost forever. He wouldn't ask her to marry him again and no doubt was sorry he'd done so the first time.

When they landed at Moisant International, Joshua saw to their luggage with barely more than clipped instructions to Bethany to wait with Angie for his return.

"Did you and my dad have a fight?" Angie asked, tucking her small hand in Bethany's and studying her carefully.

"Not an argument." Bethany knew it would be wrong to try to mislead Joshua's daughter into believing everything was as it had been earlier in the week.

"How come ever since we left California you look like you want to cry?"

The best answer Bethany could come up with was a delicate shrug, which she knew wasn't going to appease a curious ten-year-old.

"Dad's been acting weird, too," Angie murmured thoughtfully, glancing towards her father, who was waiting for their suitcases to circle the carousel. "He hardly talks to you anymore." She paused, as though waiting for Bethany to respond, and when she didn't, Angie added, "Dad and I had a long talk, and we decided that it would be a good idea if you two got married." She slapped her hand over her mouth. "I wasn't supposed to tell you that."

"I already know," Bethany said, feeling more miserable by the minute.

"You're going to marry Dad, aren't you?" Eyes as round as grapefruit studied her, waiting for her response.

"No." The lone word wavered and cracked on its way out of Bethany's throat. She loved Angie almost as much as she did Joshua, but she couldn't marry him to satisfy his little girl.

"You *aren't* going to marry my dad?" If Joshua had looked stunned when she'd refused his proposal, it was a minor reaction compared to the look of disbelief Angie gave her. "You really aren't?"

"No, sweetheart, I'm not."

"Why not?"

Bethany brushed the soft curls away from the distraught young face and squatted down to wrap her arms around Angie, who wanted to be called Millicent. "I love you both so much," she whispered brokenly.

"I know that." Ready tears welled in Angie's eyes. "Don't you want to be my new mom?"

"More than anything in the world."

"I don't understand..."

Bethany didn't know any way to explain it. "Your father will find someone else, and..."

"I don't want anyone else to be my mother. I only want you."

Fiercely Bethany hugged the little girl close and Angie's tears soaked through her silk blouse. "I... have to go now," Bethany whispered unevenly, watching Joshua make his way towards them, carrying their suitcases. "Goodbye, Millicent."

"But, Bethany, what about...?"

Remaining there and listening to Angie's pleas was more than Bethany could bear. She lifted the suitcase out of Joshua's hand without looking at him and hurriedly walked away.

"Bethany, don't go," the little girl cried. "Don't go... please, don't go."

The words ripped through Bethany's heart, but she didn't turn around. Couldn't. Tears streaked her face as she rushed outside the terminal and miraculously flagged down a taxi.

"You honestly refused Joshua's proposal?" Sally demanded, pacing in front of Bethany like an angry drill sergeant. "You were delirious with fever at the time and didn't know what you were saying. Right?"

"No, I knew full well what turning him down would mean."

"Are you nuts, girl?" Sally asked, slapping her hands against the side of her legs and stalking the area like a caged panther. "You've been in love with J. D. Norris for years."

"I know."

"How can you be so calm about this?" Her hands made a hitting noise against her thighs a second time.

Bethany shrugged, not exactly sure herself. "I wouldn't even mention it except I'm going to be looking for another job right away. As soon as you realised what I was doing, you'd hound me with questions until I ended up confessing everything anyway."

"He fired you!"

"No," Bethany whispered. But she couldn't continue to work with Joshua. Not now. It would be impossible for them both.

"I thought you were crazy about this guy."

"I am." Crazy enough to want the best for him. Crazy enough to want him to find his own happiness. Crazy enough to love him in spite of everything. For Joshua to marry her to provide a mother for his little girl wouldn't be right. "When he first asked me, I honestly thought I could do it. The words to tell him how much I wanted to share his life were right there on the tip of my tongue, but I had to force myself to swallow them." It had been the most difficult task of Bethany's life, but she didn't feel noble. Her emotions ran towards sad and miserable. Perhaps someday she would be able to look back and applaud her gallantry. But not now, and probably not for a long time.

"But why would you refuse him?" Sally was looking at her as though it would be a good idea to call in a psychiatrist.

"He doesn't love me."

"Are you so sure of that?" Her roommate eyed her carefully, clearly unconvinced.

"I'm positive."

"Well, big deal! He'd learn to in a year or so. Some of the greatest marriages of all time were based on something far less than true love."

"I know that, but the risk is too high. Joshua might come to love me later, but what if he doesn't? What if he woke up a year from now and realised he deeply

loved another woman? I know Joshua. I know that
he'd calmly accept his sorry fate and let the one he really loved walk out of his life.''

"What about *your* life?"

Bethany ran her hand down her skirt, smoothing
away an imaginary wrinkle. The deliberate movement
gave her time to examine her thoughts. "I'm not being completely unselfish in all this. Yes, I love him,
and yes, I love Angie, but I have a few expectations
when it comes to marriage, too. When and if I ever
marry, I want my husband to be as crazy in love with
me as I am with him. When he looks at me, I want him
to feel that his life would be incomplete without me
there to share it with him."

"So you've decided to give J.D. your two week-
notice first thing Monday morning?"

Bethany nodded. "You should be glad, Sal. You've
been after me to do it for months."

"I don't feel good about this," Sally muttered,
folding her arms over her chest, her brow furrowed
with a frown. "Not in the least bit."

Monday morning, Bethany had her letter of resignation typed before Joshua arrived at the office. The
paper was on his desk waiting for him.

She gave him a minute to find it before entering the
executive suite. Joshua was sitting at his desk reading
it when she delivered his coffee to him and handed him
the morning mail.

"I hope two weeks is sufficient notice?" she asked
politely, doing her utmost to remain outwardly calm
and composed.

"It's plenty of time," he said without looking in her direction. "I'd like you to review the applications yourself, decide upon two or three and I'll interview the ones you feel are best qualified."

"I'll contact personnel right away."

"Good."

She turned to leave, following his instructions regarding the mail, but Joshua stopped her. "Miss Stone."

"Yes?"

His gaze held hers for an agonisingly long moment. "You've been an excellent secretary... I'm sorry to lose you."

"Thank you, Mr. Norris." She hesitated before turning and walking out of his office. She longed to ask him about Angie but knew it would be impossible. She hadn't contacted the little girl, believing a clean break would be easier for them both. But Bethany hadn't counted on it being this difficult, or how much she would miss the little ray of sunshine who was Joshua's daughter.

A week passed, and Bethany was astonished that she and Joshua could continue to work together so well. They rarely spoke to each other, except for a few brief sentences that were required to accomplish the everyday business of running the office. Bethany was miserable, but she knew she was right, and however painful it was for now, the hurt would eventually go away.

At Joshua's instructions, she reviewed several applications personnel sent up. She sorted out three who she felt would nicely fill her role with Norris Pharmaceutical. Joshua interviewed all three and chose a matronly woman in her early fifties as her replacement. For the next week, Bethany worked closely with the woman so the transition would be as smooth as possible.

On her last day, Joshua called her into his office, thanked her for three years of loyal service and handed her a bonus cheque. Bethany gasped when she saw the amount, pressed her lips together and calmly said, "This is too much."

"You earned it, Miss Stone."

"But..."

"For once, Miss Stone, kindly accept something without arguing with me."

It would do little good anyway, so she nodded and whispered brokenly, "Thank you, Mr. Norris."

"Have you found other employment?" he asked her unexpectedly, delaying her departure.

She shook her head. She hadn't taken the time to look. With everything else going on in her life, another job didn't seem all that important.

"I wish you the very best, Miss Stone."

"You too, Mr. Norris." She couldn't say anything more, fearing her voice would crack. As it was, tears hovered just below the surface. "Thank you, again."

"Goodbye, Bethany."

She lowered her gaze and worried the corner of her lower lip. "Goodbye, Joshua."

With that, she turned and walked out of his life.

*   *   *

"Well, did you get the job?" Sally asked her one afternoon when she arrived home from work.

The whole day had been gorgeous and sunny and Bethany knew she should be like everyone else in the city and want to enjoy this unusual display of summerlike weather. Instead she was inside, reading a book.

"The position was offered to someone else." For emphasis, Bethany shook her head. She'd gone in for an interview and was pleased for the woman who got the job since she so obviously wanted it. Bethany couldn't have cared less.

"You don't look all that disappointed."

"Sally, I don't know what's wrong with me," she said on the tail end of a drawn-out sigh. "I don't care if I ever find another job. All that interests me is sleeping, and if I'm not doing that, I'm reading. I've read more books in the past month than I did all the year before."

"You're escaping."

"I know that." Bethany didn't need her friend to tell her the obvious. It didn't hurt as much when her face was buried in a good book—as long as it wasn't a romance—reading about true love wasn't exactly her favourite topic at the present time. Murder mysteries appealed to her far more. Bloody battered bodies—that sort of thing.

Sally looked at her watch and gasped. "I've got to change and get ready," she said, and hurried towards her bedroom.

"For what?" Bethany asked, following her friend.

Sally blushed. "Jerry and I are going on a picnic."

"You've been out with him every night for the past week."

"I know," Sally admitted, and sighed sheepishly. "I'm in love, and I'll tell you right now—if Jerry Johnson proposed to me, I'd accept."

Bethany faked a pain-filled cry at the low unexpected blow and turned away. "May your first son grow up to style women's hair."

Sally chuckled, tossed her shirt on her unmade bed and reached for her jeans. "You'll be all right, won't you?"

"I'll be fine. I stopped off at the library on my way back to the apartment. I've got enough reading material to last most people a lifetime. But at the rate I've been going I'll be done with this stuff in a week." Her small attempt at humour fell decidedly flat.

Being the true friend, Sally rolled her eyes towards the ceiling and mumbled something under her breath about misguided love and Bethany not knowing what was good for her.

The apartment felt empty with Sally gone. Bethany figured she might as well get used to it. The way her roommate's romance was progressing, Sally could well end up marrying the young attorney before the end of the summer.

About seven, the doorbell rang. Bethany climbed off the sofa to answer it, unsure who it could be.

"Joshua?" She pulled open the door and nearly sagged against it. Bethany was never more shocked to see anyone in her life.

"Is this a bad time? I know I should have phoned, but I was detained and..." He let the rest of what he was saying dwindle off.

"No, I'm not doing anything important. Please come in." She stepped aside in order for him to enter the apartment.

Bethany hurried ahead of him and picked up an empty fizzy-drink can and a banana peel, feeling embarrassed and foolish. "Sit down." She gestured towards the davenport. "Can I get you something to drink?"

"No, thank you."

She deposited the rubbish in the kitchen and rushed back into the living room, holding her hands behind her back in nervous agitation. "Is something wrong at the office? I mean... I'd be happy to help in any way I could."

"Everything's fine."

Alarm filled Bethany when she realised there would only be one reason Joshua would come to her. "It's Angie, isn't it? She's had an accident—"

"No. Angie's doing very well. She misses you, but that's to be expected."

Relief flooded through her and she sagged into the chair across from Joshua.

He sat uncomfortably close to the end of the cushion on the sofa. "The purpose of my visit is to see if you'd found another job."

"Not yet...." She couldn't very well announce that she'd taken to job hunting the way a cat does to water. If she spent the rest of her life reading and eating bananas, she would be content.

"I see." He braced his elbows against his knees and laced his fingers together. "I thought I might be able to help."

"Help?" It came to her then. The purpose behind his visit should have been as clear as Texas creek water. Anyone but a blind fool would have figured out that Joshua wanted to hire her as a baby-sitter for Angie. If he couldn't convince her to marry him then he would no doubt be willing to pay her top dollar for her child-rearing services.

"Yes, help," Joshua said, ignoring her look of outrage. "I have certain connections and I may be able to pull a few strings for you, if you'd like."

"Strings?" Bethany repeated. So he hadn't come because of Angie. She narrowed her gaze suspiciously, not knowing what to believe.

"Is something wrong?"

"No," she returned quickly.

"I understand Hal Lawrence of Holland Mills is looking for an executive secretary, and I'd be happy to put in a good word for you."

"That would be thoughtful."

"I'll call him first thing in the morning, then."

"Thank you." Bethany continued to watch him closely, unsure what to make of his offer.

Joshua stood and the action was reluctant. "I was wondering . . ." he said after an awkward moment.

"Yes?" she prompted, tilting her head back so far that she nearly toppled in her effort to look up at him.

Joshua jammed his hands inside his trouser pockets, then jerked them out again. "What makes you so certain I don't love you?"

Briefly Bethany toyed with the idea of asking him outright what he *did* feel for her but was hesitant to do so.

"Bethany," he said softly, "I asked you a question."

"I wasn't asleep," she answered weakly, her voice trapped and unstable.

"Asleep?" he demanded. "What in the hell are you talking about?"

"The first day in California," she continued, refusing to meet his impatient gaze. "I overheard Angie ask you if you'd ever thought of remarrying."

"Ah," Joshua whispered, sounding almost relieved.

Bethany didn't like his attitude. "Perhaps more important, Joshua Norris, I heard your answer."

"You're basing everything on that?"

"As I recall, Joshua, you seemed to think I'd put her up to the questioning. That was the worst of it . . . that you'd assume I would use Angie that way."

"I knew you wouldn't do that—you must have misunderstood me."

"Perhaps." She was willing to concede that much. "Even if I hadn't heard you talking to Angie . . . that night you ordered the wine . . ."

"Yes?" He was clearly growing impatient with her, shifting his weight from one foot to the other.

"You didn't tell me how you felt then, either. I may have been too willing to jump to conclusions, but it seems to me that if you honestly love me then that would've been the time to tell me as much."

"Did it ever occur to you that a man wouldn't ask a woman to marry him without feeling something for her?"

"Oh, I'm sure you do...did," she corrected stiffly. "I haven't worked with you all these years without knowing how you operate. Unfortunately, I want more."

Joshua paced back and forth a couple of times before sitting back down again. He leaned forward, braced his elbows on his knees and exhaled sharply.

"The word *love* frightens me," he said after a moment, his gaze levelled on the worn carpeting. "I loved Angie's mother, but it wasn't enough. Within a year after we were married, Camille was discontented. I thought a baby would keep her occupied, but she didn't want children. I should have listened to her, should have realised then that nothing I would ever do would be enough. But I was young and stupid and I loved her too much. Angie was unplanned and Camille had a terrible pregnancy. When she was about five months along, she moved to New York to be with her family. Camille never cared for Angie, had never wanted to be a mother. Whatever instincts women are supposed to have with a baby were missing with her. Her mother was the one who took care of Angie from the very first.

"Camille insisted she needed a vacation to recover after Angie's birth and stayed with her parents while I took what time I could to fly between the two cities.

"Angie was only a few months old when Camille asked for the divorce. She was in love with another man." He paused and wiped a hand over his face, as if the action would clean the slate of that miserable portion of his life. "Apparently Camille had been involved with him for months after she moved to New York—even before Angie was born."

The pain in his eyes was almost more than Bethany could stand. She stood, walked over to the sofa and sat beside him. Joshua clasped her hand in his.

"She died in a freak skiing accident a few months later."

"Oh, Joshua, I'm so sorry." She closed her eyes and pressed her forehead against his upper arm.

"Why?" he asked, almost brutally.

"Because . . . because she broke your heart."

"Yes, she did," he admitted reluctantly. "I'd assumed I was immune to love until Angie came to live with me. I felt safe from emotional attachments."

A tear rolled down the side of Bethany's pale face. If Joshua was hoping to convince her he loved her, he'd failed by dragging his daughter into the conversation. Everything he was saying now only went towards proving her point.

Joshua paused and gently wiped the moisture from her cheek. He gripped her shoulders then, turned her in his arms and firmly planted his mouth over hers. His kiss was unlike any they'd shared in the past. His mouth moved urgently in a ruthless plundering as if to punish her for the misery she'd caused them both. He slid his hands from her shoulders to her back, crushing her breasts into his warm sturdy chest. This was a trial by fire, and Bethany felt herself lose control, surrendering all she had, all she would ever be to

Joshua. Like a hothouse flower peeling open its petals, Bethany blossomed under Joshua's expert lovemaking.

When he'd finished, Bethany's body was aflame and trembling. He straightened and sucked in deep gulps of air. His gaze was narrowed and clouded.

"Honest to God, Bethany, if this isn't love, I don't know what is."

With that, he stood and walked out.

Bethany was too weak to do anything more than lift her hand to stop him. Her voice refused to go higher than a weak whisper when she called out to him.

The front door slammed, and Bethany sat there for a full minute, too bemused to do anything except breathe. Gradually the beginnings of a smile came. A shaky kind of hopeful happiness took control. Joshua had never been a man to express his emotions freely. Maybe, just maybe, she'd misjudged him. He'd swallowed his considerable pride and come to her, and although he hadn't admitted that he loved her, he'd come close. In thinking about their conversation, Bethany realised she hadn't given him the opportunity to tell her how he felt.

An hour later the phone rang. Bethany reached for it and was pleasantly surprised to hear Joshua answer her greeting.

"Oh, Joshua, I'm so pleased you called. I've been thinking ever since you left and—"

"Bethany, have you heard from Angie?"

"No," she admitted, a little hurt by the cutting edge of his voice.

"You're sure she hasn't called you?"

"Joshua, of course I'm sure." The implication that she would lie to him was strong and she didn't like it in the least.

"Joshua, what's going on?"

A long moment passed before he spoke. "Angie's missing. Mrs. Larson saw her after school, but she hasn't been seen by anyone since."

The memory of the little girl telling her how much she enjoyed swimming and how she wished her father would go with her more often rang in Bethany's mind like a funeral gong.

"Joshua," she whispered through her panic. The day was gorgeous. Sally and Jerry were on a picnic. "Could Angie have gone to the lake?"

CHAPTER TEN

BETHANY didn't bother to ring the doorbell to
Joshua's Lake Pontchartrain home. She barrelled
through the front door, breathless and so frightened
she could barely think clearly. Her mind continued to
echo Angie's words about wanting to swim alone in
the lake like ricocheting bullets, and the fear Bethany
experienced with each beat of her heart was debilitat-
ing.

"Joshua," she cried, stepping into the living room.

He walked out of his den, and his eyes carried a
look of agony of the damned. "She hasn't been seen
or heard from since right after school ... there's no
evidence she went down to the lake. At least none that
Mrs. Larson or I could find...."

Tears blurred Bethany's vision as she rushed across
the room and into Joshua's arms. She wasn't sure what
had driven her there—whether it was to lend comfort
or receive it, she didn't know. Perhaps both. His chest
felt warm and solid as she pressed her face into it and
breathed in deeply in an effort to regain her equilibrium.

Joshua held on to her desperately, burying his face
in the gentle slope of her throat, drinking in her
strength, her courage, her love.

The thought passed though Bethany's mind with
laser swiftness that this was perhaps the first time
Joshua had ever truly needed her.

"I think she may have run away," he confessed in a voice that rocked with emotion. "She told me once that she'd thought about it. There's no other plausible explanation."

"But why?"

Joshua dropped his arms and momentarily closed his eyes. "I'm rotten father material. From the first, I've done everything wrong. I love Angie, but I'm just not a good parent. God knows I've—"

"Joshua, no!" Bethany reached for his hand, holding it between both of her own and pressing it to her cheek. "That's not true. You've been wonderful, and if you've made mistakes, that's understandable...really. No parent is perf—" Bethany stopped speaking abruptly, cutting off the last word. Her eyes grew round as the horror of her actions struck her between the solar plexus...the consequences of refusing Joshua's proposal. "It's me, isn't it? Angie's... been upset because I haven't talked to her since...the California trip. She assumed I turned you down because of her, and, Joshua...oh, Joshua, that just isn't so." She took a step away from him and folded her hands over her middle as the reality burned through her like hot oil. "That's...that's why you came to see me today, isn't it? You were worried then that something like this would happen, and you thought..." Everything was so amazingly clear now.

"No," Joshua said gruffly, regretfully. "I'm not going to lie. Angie and I *did* discuss the matter before I proposed, but she accepted your decision..." He paused and looked away, his face tight and proud. "In fact, she took it better than I did." He turned away and raked his hand impatiently through his hair. "Telling you this no doubt confirms the worst."

"Confirms the worst," she repeated. "I don't understand."

"You chose to believe I asked you to be my wife because I was looking for a mother for Angie."

Bethany couldn't help thinking exactly that. But it wouldn't have mattered if Joshua truly loved her. She looked at him, her soul in her eyes. "That's true, isn't it, about wanting me to be a mother to Angie?"

His shoulders sagged a little, and a sad smile bounced against the edges of his mouth but didn't catch. "I can't say the way Angie loves you didn't weigh into my decision, and I suppose that condemns me all the more. But my daughter loves Mrs. Larson, too, and the thought of marrying her never once entered my mind."

Bethany's heart began to do a slow drumroll.

"I know you probably don't believe this, but I *do* love you, Bethany. I have for weeks."

His words had the most curious effect upon her. She stared at him, her blue eyes as wide as the Mississippi River. She was too stunned to react for a wild second, then she calmly, casually burst into tears.

It was clear from the way Joshua jerked forward and then quickly retreated that he didn't know what to do.

"Then why didn't you once so much as hint at the way you felt?" she wailed.

"I did," he countered. "Every way I knew how."

"But..."

"You weren't exactly a boiling pot of information yourself," he told her.

"You knew how I felt." If everyone at Norris Pharmaceutical right down to the newest member of the typing pool realised she loved Joshua Norris, it was unlikely that he'd failed to notice.

"Yes," he admitted reluctantly. "I realised it the evening we bumped into each other at Charley's... the night Angie arrived."

That soon. Bethany gulped at the information. Her thoughts were interrupted when a glimpse of colour flashed in her peripheral vision. She turned abruptly to see the tail of a flowered summer shirt disappear into Joshua's sloop. Angie.

"Joshua..." She folded her fingers around his forearm and pointed towards his sailboat moored at the end of the long dock at the edge of the lake. "I just saw Angie."

"What?" He was instantly alert. "Where?"

"She's hiding in the sailboat."

"What the bloody hell! Why?"

"I...don't know."

"Well, I intend to find out. Right now." He jerked open the French patio door hard enough to pull it off its hinges.

"Joshua..." Bethany ran after him. "Calm down."

"I will once she's been properly disciplined." Bethany was forced to run to keep up with his lengthy strides.

He marched onto the dock like an avenging warlord. "Angela Catherine," he shouted, and the sound of his anger was furious.

The top of a small brown head appeared, followed slowly by a round pair of dark eyes.

"Angie! How could you have worried us this way?" Bethany cried, and covered her mouth with her hand, both relieved and upset.

"Hi, Dad." Hesitantly Angie stood and lifted her hand to greet him. "Hi, Bethany."

"Come out of that boat this minute, young lady," Joshua demanded.

"Okay." As though she'd recently returned from a world tour, Angie retrieved a pillowcase stuffed full of her clothes and tossed that to her father. She handed Bethany a week's supply of snack foods jammed to the top in another. Joshua's daughter made a show of climbing over the side of the sailboat and onto the dock.

Bethany had to give the child credit for sheer courage.

"I suppose I'm going to get the spanking of my life," she said, calmly accepting her punishment. "I don't mind, really." She squared her shoulders and offered her father a brave smile.

"Go to your room and wait for me there," Joshua ordered.

"Okay." The ten-year-old glanced from her father to Bethany and back again. "Can I ask Bethany something first?"

Joshua expelled his breath in a burst of impatience and nodded.

"Are you going to marry my Dad and me?"

"Angela Catherine, go to your room." Joshua pointed in the direction of the house. "Now!"

The young head dropped. "All right."

The two adults followed Angie through the patio doors. Bethany deposited the pillowcase full of food onto the living room carpet and rubbed her palms back and forth as she gathered her thoughts.

"I was right," Joshua said, looking pale and greatly troubled. "Angie had decided to run away."

"I don't think she was planning to go far."

Joshua sat on the edge of the sofa and dragged his hands over his face. "But why?" He tossed the question to Bethany and seemed to expect an answer.

"I . . . I don't know."

"Angie and I have been closer than ever the past few weeks," Joshua admitted, and every feature of his handsome face revealed his bewilderment. "I can hardly believe she would do this."

Not able to understand it herself, Bethany sat beside Joshua, her legs weak with relief that they'd found the little girl.

"I'm not cut out for this parenting business. I've done everything wrong from the minute that child was born," Joshua muttered, his discouragement palpable.

"I sincerely hope you don't mean that," Bethany whispered, and rested her head against the outside curve of his shoulder.

He turned to her then, his gaze narrow and curious.

"I'd like us to have a family someday," she whispered, gladly answering the question in his eyes.

"You would?" His voice was taut, strangled and nothing like normal.

"Yes," she answered with a short nod. "Two, I think. Three, if you want."

"Bethany, oh, dear lord." His eyes went dark, the pupils dilating as he continued to stare at her with his mouth gaping open. "You mean it, don't you?"

"Of course I mean it! I love you so much."

His eyes dropped closed, as though he had paused to savour each syllable of each word. "Then you *do* plan to marry me?"

"I'd prefer to before the children are born," she answered with a soft teasing smile.

Joshua pulled her into his arms and kissed her then with a hungry desperation, rubbing his mouth back and forth over hers, sampling her lips as a man would enjoy an expensive rare delicacy.

Bethany wound her arms around his neck and leaned into him, offering him everything. He broke off the kiss, but his lips continued a series of soft nibbles down the side of her face.

"That night at Charley's," he whispered.

"Yes..."

"Having you come up to me at the bar, your eyes so full of concern, your love so open...it shook me to the core. I'd worked with you all that time, and I'd never seen you as anything more than an excellent secretary."

"I know," she said with a tinge of remembered frustration. Bethany ran her fingers through his hair and down the side of his face to his neck, revelling in the freedom to touch him. "I was ready to give you my notice then. I thought my love for you was completely useless."

"I think I realised that, too...and for a time I thought it would be for the best if you *did* find other employment. Then you were gone that one day and the office seemed so empty and dark without you. I realised that if you left, nothing would ever be the same in my life again, and I couldn't let you go."

"Oh, Joshua."

"My reasoning wasn't so selfless," he admitted. "I didn't intend to fall in love with you...that took me by surprise. The day you fell in the lake, I knew it was useless to pretend anymore. Oh, my beautiful, adorable Bethany, what a pitiful sight you made that afternoon, with water dripping at your feet."

She groaned at the memory.

"But you held your head high and walked out of that water as though drenching yourself in it had been your intention all along. I stood on the shore and knew right then and there it wasn't going to do the least bit of good to fight you any longer. I was going to love you all the days of my life."

"The prince..." She lifted her face to watch him, needing to know if the man who'd swept her into his arms at the Mardi Gras parade had been Joshua.

"Yes?"

"It was you, wasn't it?"

He looked sheepish and a little embarrassed when he nodded. "I can't believe I did anything so crazy... it's not like me, but I wanted to kiss you again, needed

to because I didn't know if I'd ever get the chance with
what was happening with the—''

"But why?" she interrupted.

He took her hand and lifted it to his mouth. "You
were aware of only a fraction of what was going on
with the company at the time. I nearly lost it, Bethany,
nearly lost everything. I was in the middle of the biggest financial struggle of my life. The timing for falling in love couldn't have been worse."

"Telling me you loved me would have gone a long
way, Joshua Norris."

He grinned. "Now perhaps . . . but not last month.
Everything I had in the world was on the line. I had to
deal with the financial hassles before I could pursue
our relationship."

"I could have helped." She wasn't sure how, but
surely there would have been some way.

"You couldn't—there wasn't anything you could
have done. I knew if I lost Norris Pharmaceutical, I'd
be losing you, too."

"How can you say that? I would never have left
you. . . ."

"I know." He bunched her face between his hands
and kissed her again. "I died a thousand deaths when
I heard Sally arrange that date for you."

"She . . . she was convinced you were using me."

Joshua leaned his forehead against hers. "As a
baby-sitter? There wasn't a single moment I needed
you to watch Angie—they were all excuses, each in-
stance, to have you close, to spend time with you. I
thanked God for the excuse. I was so afraid I was go-

ing to lose you to someone else while I was forced to deal with the second takeover bid. I invented reasons to keep you close."

"But in California, when Angie suggested you marry me, you didn't sound pleased with the prospect."

"I wish to God you'd been asleep that day," he admitted with a frown. "Everything was still up in the air—I'd only met one day with Hillard and his group. I loved you then, Bethany, but a man can't come to a woman without something to offer her."

"But you seemed to think I'd put Angie up to that conversation."

He grinned. "If I *did* suggest that, then it was with a prayer and a smile because I wanted you so much, and I was hoping you wanted me, too. I could hardly stand the wait myself. The day the negotiations were finalised, I asked you to marry me. Delaying it even a minute longer was intolerable."

"But you didn't tell me you loved me that night and..."

"Good lord, Bethany, I was a nervous wreck. Surely you noticed? I'd been as jumpy as a toad all evening, waiting to get you alone and then, when I finally managed, you didn't seem the least bit inclined to want my company. All day I'd been rehearsing what I wanted to say and instead I blurted out the question like a college freshman. You could have bowled me over with a Ping-Pong ball when you refused."

"I thought..."

He interrupted by sliding his mouth over hers. "I know exactly what twisted thoughts you'd been harbouring...and I'll admit my pride took a beating that night and all the nights that followed. It wasn't easy to come to you this afternoon, but I've realised my life isn't going to be worth a damn without you."

"Oh, Joshua." Tears of tenderness filled her eyes and a precious kind of sweetness pierced her heart. She found his mouth with hers and kissed him with all the bursting aching love stored so restlessly there.

"And then I blew everything a second time and came home to discover Angie was missing."

At the mention of his daughter, Bethany straightened. "I think we should talk to her. Together."

"All right," he agreed, standing. His hand was linked with hers as he led her down the hallway to the downstairs bedrooms.

Joshua rapped at Angie's bedroom door and then let himself inside. Angie sat on the edge of the mattress, her head bowed and her hands clasped in her lap.

"All right, young lady, what do you have to say for yourself?"

"Nothing."

The word was so low Bethany had to strain to hear it.

"Surely you realised how worried Bethany and I would be?"

Angie nodded several times, still not looking at them.

"If you knew that, then what possible reason could you have for doing something like this?"

Two small shoulders jerked up, then sagged.

"Are you unhappy, sweetheart?" Bethany asked.

The little girl shook her head. "I like living here better than anyplace in the world."

"Then why would you want to run away?" Joshua demanded.

A short pulsating silence followed.

"So Bethany would come."

"I beg your pardon?" Joshua advanced a step towards his daughter.

"So Bethany would come," Angie repeated a little louder.

"I heard you the first time, but I don't understand your reasoning . . . not in the least."

"When you talked to me last week, you said we might have been hoping for too much with Bethany, because she didn't want to marry you, and I knew that was wrong. I knew she loved you and I know she loves me, so I figured if something bad happened, then she'd come and you two would talk and then maybe she'd want to marry us."

Bethany gasped at the logic, because essentially that was what had happened.

"Your intentions may have been good, but what you did was very wrong."

"I know." For the first time Angie raised her eyes to meet her father's. "Can you let me know how many swats I'm going to get? If you tell me that, I can hold back and not cry."

Joshua seemed to be contemplating that when Angie interrupted him.

"I saw Bethany from the sailboat and she looked real worried, and then I saw you talking and I couldn't hardly wait to hear what you said, so I snuck out of the boat and came to the patio to listen." A smile as wide as the Grand Canyon broke out across the little girl's face. "I wasn't sure, but it sounded like Bethany wants us."

"Oh, sweetheart, I've always wanted you." Bethany wasn't sure if Joshua would approve of her comforting Angie, but she wrapped her arms around the little girl and hugged her close.

"You're going to marry us?"

Bethany nodded eagerly.

"Oh, good!" She beamed a smile at her father and added, "You can give me as many swats as you want, and I bet I won't even feel them."

Bethany was just preparing to move into the role of stepmother, and she didn't want to cross Joshua, but she couldn't bear the thought of Angie being spanked. She tried to tell him as much with her eyes.

He answered her with a look of his own, cleared his throat and announced, "Seeing that everything's worked out for the best, I believe we can forgo the spanking."

"We can?" Angie all but flew off the bed. Her arms groped for Joshua's waist, and she hugged him with all her might.

"However, you caused Bethany, Mrs. Larson and several others a good deal of concern. You're restricted for the next two weeks, young lady."

Some of the delight drained out of Angie's eyes. She sank her teeth into her lower lip and nodded. "I won't ever do it again, I promise. I... I thought it would be fun, but it wasn't. I was bored to tears."

"Good. I sincerely hope you've learned your lesson."

"Oh, I did." She slipped one arm around Bethany's waist, and the other around her father, and stood between the two adults. "We're going to have such a good life together."

"I think so, too," Bethany agreed.

"Especially after the other kids arrive," Angie said, looking vastly pleased with herself. "I want a sister first, okay? And then a brother."

Joshua's gaze reached out to Bethany and wrapped her in an abundance of warmth. "I'm more than willing to do my part to complete the picture."

Bethany couldn't have looked away to save the world from annihilation. Tears of joy welled up in her eyes, and she nodded. "Me, too."

Angie released a long slow sigh. "Good. Now when can I tell my friends about the wedding? I was thinking Saturday the fifteenth would be a good choice, don't you? At the reception, we'll serve Big Macs and macadamia nuts."

"Sounds good to me," Joshua said with an indulgent chuckle.

"I couldn't think of anything I'd like more," Bethany added.

"Now about the honeymoon..."

Joshua's gaze didn't leave Bethany as he spoke. "Now, that's one part I plan to take care of myself."

"Anything you say, Dad." Angie looked up at Bethany and winked. "We're going to be so happy."

And they were.

*   *   *   *   *

Ann Major's larger-than-life characters, compelling plotlines and sensual prose have touched the hearts and emotions of millions of readers all over the world. Whether she writes a simple love story or a more intricately plotted tale of romantic suspense, she always delivers. Her books have been repeatedly placed at the top of national and international bestseller lists.

Ann, who lives in Texas with her husband of many years, is the mother of three college-age children. She has a master's degree and has taught English both in high school and college. She is a frequent speaker at writers' groups.

Ann loves to write; she considers her ability to do so a gift. Her hobbies include hiking in the mountains, playing tennis, sailing, reading, playing the piano, but most of all, enjoying her family.

PASSION'S CHILD
by
ANN MAJOR

This book is dedicated to my editor, Tara Gavin. She believed in this project and continued to guide me even when I lost faith.

And to Isabel Swift for her editorial help.

And to my friend Page Dinn for sharing the details of her glamorous racing experience during Antigua Race Week.

Prologue

Death hovered like a dark angel in the closed, airless room. There was no escape. For either of them.

Her shoulders stiff with fatigue, her body numb, Amy sat huddled beside her sister's bed where Lorrie lay groaning in labor. With each contraction, Lorrie's feverish hand clamped around Amy's in a bone-crushing, death vise of agony.

Through a mist of tears, Amy watched the snow outside blowing in the field between the trees. Oh, where was Dr. Pierce? Was he really making a house call to treat an injured fisherman as his loyal nurse had sworn, a bit too fervently, hours ago? Or was he comfortably ensconced on one of the frayed red leather stools at Big John's Tavern, getting himself stumbling drunk, his frequent condition by this time most Saturday afternoons? Or was his battered Fiat stalled on the side of some bleak highway in the snow?

An icy wind swept off the Pacific, up the high, ragged-edged, barren cliffs and moaned in the forlorn grove of stunted trees outside the window of the tiny hospital.

Inside the small building, Amy bit her lip, almost welcoming the suffering as Lorrie's fingers cut into her own again. The pain in Amy's bruised and swollen hands seemed little enough compared to what Lorrie was going through—little enough since everything that had happened to Lorrie was Amy's fault.

And Nick's. One couldn't very well forget that there was always a man responsible for every baby born. Nick had taken his pleasure, and sixteen-year-old Lorrie had been left with months of nausea and waiting, with a clumsy, thickening figure, and now with this hellish pain.

Amy would hate Nicholas Browning till the day she died for what he had done to her little sister. If only they'd never met him. If only they hadn't both been foolish enough to fall in love with him.

Amy's stricken gaze flickered fearfully to Lorrie. Her still face was translucently pale. Purple shadows lay beneath her eyes. Wet gossamer strands of inky-dark hair were glued to her bloodless cheeks.

As Amy gently brushed her sister's matted hair away from her hot sticky face, Lorrie whimpered pitifully.

"Amy! Oh, Amy, it hurts!" she sobbed. "It hurts!" She tightened her grip on Amy's wrist and pulled her closer. Lorrie's eyes were wild and glazed. "Amy, am I dying?"

Amy suppressed a shudder of sheer terror. "Of course not, darling. I'm here, and I'm going to take care of you and the baby."

"How?" came a threadlike whisper.

The single word echoed in Amy's heart. "If it's the last thing I do, I'll finish school and find a way to make enough money to support us all. I promise you."

"Oh, I—I wish I was like you—brave and strong, but ever since Mama died, I've been scared of just about everything. Like now," Lorrie whispered.

Amy couldn't bear looking into her sister's terrified eyes. "Hush, darling," she murmured in a low, strangled tone.

The trees outside nearly bent in two. Snow began to swirl.

Amy was wondering why she'd ever thought this god-forsaken fishing village clinging to the ocean's edge in northern California was a haven. It seemed a hellish prison now. But six months ago, when she'd been afraid Lorrie might do something desperate if she didn't get her out of L.A., Amy had convinced Lorrie that the only solution to their problem was for them to switch identities and come here, for Lorrie to have her baby in secrecy and give it to Amy to raise. Thus Amy had bleached her own black hair platinum blonde, the same shade as Lorrie's, and Lorrie had dyed hers black. They had masqueraded as each other. When they returned to L.A. after the baby's birth, Amy, not Lorrie, would claim the child as her own and raise it.

It had been a nightmare hiding here; a nightmare keeping Lorrie from going crazy with boredom and doing something desperate again; a nightmare evading the towns-people's prying curiosity. There was one nurse who'd somehow figured out the truth, and Amy worried about Nick tracing them here and charming the nurse into confiding in him what she knew.

Lorrie's frail body tensed in a rigor of pain, and she let out a low wailing scream that seemed to be wrenched from the depths of misery. For a moment Amy was so frightened that the breath went out of her lungs with a gasp. Then she felt her bruised hand crushed even harder.

How long did it take for a baby to come? It seemed to Amy that Lorrie had been lying in that bed for days rather than hours with beads of perspiration soaking her dull black hair as she writhed.

Amy felt for Lorrie's pulse. It seemed weak and fluttery, and Amy didn't like the way her sister had begun to lie listlessly between the pains. Her face was as gray as the winter sky outside, and breathing was growing fainter. She was losing what strength she had.

If the doctor didn't come... If the baby wasn't born soon...

The blood was thudding in Amy's ears so loudly she could hardly think. Something had to be done, and quickly.

Carefully, Amy disengaged Lorrie's fingers from her wrist and made a dash toward the door. Just as she reached it, Dr. Pierce opened it and stepped inside. The nurse, who was aware of Amy's anxiety, came in with him, hovering beside him protectively.

He was thin and old. His body bent over like a crane's, and he moved with brittle birdlike motions.

"Where have you been?" Amy cried.

Dr. Pierce looked at her with faded blue eyes. "Trying to save a dying man."

Amy heard the sense of failure in his contrite tone and said nothing more as he moved past her to examine Lorrie.

Dear God, let him save Lorrie, Amy thought.

At last he turned and whispered a battery of orders to his nurse. "The baby's in breach position. Take her into the delivery room."

The faded eyes rested briefly on Amy, but she was too numb for her mind to frame a question.

Lorrie's lips quivered as she was wheeled away from Amy, but when Amy tried to follow the stretcher, the nurse gently restrained her.

Alone, Amy sank into a chair and covered her face with her hands in despair as she listened to her sister's muffled screams coming from inside the delivery room.

It seemed to Amy that she was outside the delivery room for an eternity, keeping her silent vigil, praying feverishly to God and chewing her lip until it was raw.

In the awful hell of that waiting, one thought reeled through her tired mind. If Lorrie and the baby lived, no matter how desperate Amy might become, no matter how rich he was, she would never ask Nicholas Browning for help. She would protect Lorrie and the baby from him with her own life if necessary.

Once Amy had loved him, but he had broken her heart and turned her love to desperate hate. He had nearly destroyed her sister.

Amy knew it would be hard raising a child alone, without a father, but she was determined to succeed.

She was just as determined to hate Nicholas Browning until the day she died.

One

Damn! Nick had known Amy was trouble from the first minute he'd laid eyes on her seven years ago. She was still trouble, and she always would be.

Nicholas Browning was standing in his darkened office that overlooked the marina. He stood alone, a golden colossus of a man, staring unseeingly out the floor-to-ceiling windows at the purple sky and the gray froth of wind-whipped waves on San Franciso Bay. His black mood mirrored the turbulence of the weather outside.

Although he'd shut his door, the faint sounds of Christmas music and his staff's laughter filtered into the room.

Nick was president of South Sails, a world-famous sail loft owned by his cousin, Sebastian Jacobs. Nick's office was extravagantly decorated. Sumptuous red Persian carpets lay over gleaming parquet floors. Leather chairs and sofas surrounded his immense desk. Twin Chinese statues of apple-green jade guarded the doors. It was an office meant to impress, and it did. The man to whom it belonged was rich, successful, and proud of it.

At twenty-nine Nick was equally proud of his accomplishments. Against one wall his sailing trophies gleamed from glass shelves—two Olympic silver medals in the Sailing class and his three trophies for J-24 championships occupied positions of prominence. Above them were framed photographs of several twelve-meter yachts and their colorful spinnakers. The largest picture was of Nick, at the helm of *America's Lady*, Sebastian's challenger in the last America's Cup campaign.

Nick loved sailboats and he loved racing them. He liked designing and manufacturing sails and he prided himself in being the best at everything he did. Most men with an all-consuming passion for both their work and their play were happy men.

But he had never been like most men.

Nick didn't hear the Christmas carols. He was lost in his own thoughts. He remained at the windows, his muscular body tense, his emotions quietly controlled.

"Damn!" He expelled the curse in a taut whisper. How was it possible that one woman could bring him so much pain?

It was almost Christmas and, as usual, he was running away because for him the holiday season was the loneliest time of the year. Not that he was a man who ran away from many things. Not that he would have admitted his feelings to anyone.

Nicholas Browning had been born a bastard, and he'd learned a long time ago how to conceal loneliness behind a stubborn wall of defiant pride.

Nick jammed doubled fists into his trousers and watched the white yachts straining at their dock lines as the fierce winds began to whistle through their shrouds.

Everything had been so simple until Marcie brought him his mail.

Tomorrow Nick had been planning to leave for Australia to sail Sebastian's converted twelve-meter in the six-hundred-and-thirty-mile Sydney-to-Hobart Race and in its associated Southern Cross Cup Series. That was why Marcie had organized the early "bon voyage" Christmas party next door.

Nick went back to his desk and sat down in the leather chair behind it. On the smooth, varnished surface were neat stacks of checks he'd signed as well as invoices, letters, and file folders.

He switched on his Dictaphone, then abruptly turned it off again. He couldn't work. All he could think of was Amy.

Amy! Dear God! Why couldn't he forget her and accept their separation the way she had?

Because he wasn't made of ice the way she was—damn it! Because he'd married her for the right reasons, and she'd married him for the wrong ones.

His eyes strayed to the two pieces of personal correspondence that had arrived today. Inside Sebastian's Christmas card, he'd enclosed a picture of Amy sailing her catamaran with Triple. Sebastian's brief note said that Amy had sent the photo in her Christmas card to him. Amy worked for Sebastian, too, and though she had nothing to do with the South Sails operation, she was one of Sebastian's most valuable executives.

It infuriated Nick that she treated Sebastian like family while ignoring her own husband. Amy had been Nick's wife for more than five years, and never once since their separation had she willingly corresponded with him.

Why the hell did he still care? Nick picked up the picture. He would have given anything to feel indifferent toward her, but the mere sight of her laughing, upturned face sent his pulse thudding with a violent mixture of unwanted emotions.

She hadn't smiled at him like that in years! He stared at the glossy image of a slim young woman strapped into a trapeze, hiking out with only her feet against the side of the boat. A soaked, long-sleeved white T-shirt was plastered to her body. The water made it transparent so that the lines of her bikini were clearly visible. Not that Amy usually wore a bikini in public or ever wanted herself to be photographed in one. She was prim and proper to the core.

His gaze swept over her full breasts, down her flat belly, down the curving length of her brown legs. Memories of her supple body beneath his, her arms wrapped around him, her hands clinging, her soft voice crying out assailed him.

Once she'd been his touch, to caress, to love. Once he'd made her forget how improper it was for a lady to go wild in bed. Then he'd lost her—completely, irrevocably—and he still didn't know why. Maybe that was the reason he couldn't let her go.

In the picture, her long black hair flew about her neck and face in lustrous tangles. Usually she wore it primly secured at the nape of her neck in that tight little knot he detested. He remembered the perfumed scent of her hair—the silken feel of it against his cheek as it fanned out over his white pillow. The last time he'd slept with her had been two years ago. She'd come alone to San Francisco for his younger brother Jack's funeral, and when Nick had turned to her in his uncontrollable grief, she'd ended up in his bed. But the next morning she'd left him, and her determination to have nothing to do with him had seemed even stronger than before.

Why, damn it? Why?

In the photograph, Triple was at the helm—Triple who was only six years old—and the catamaran was difficult for even a man to manage. Nick felt a surge of paternal pride as he examined the image of his sturdy little boy. Triple's jaw was squared with determination, every muscle in his small body straining as he gripped the tiller and fought to control the boat.

For all her coldness as a wife, at least Amy was a warm and dedicated mother. Triple wasn't an easy child. He was bold and precocious, and he had a peculiar penchant for bringing disaster on himself by tackling tasks too difficult for him. He'd been christened Michael John Browning. From the crib he'd been three times as much trouble as an ordinary child would be, and from a multitude of mischievous activities he'd derived his nickname, Triple Trouble, which had long since been shortened to Triple.

The hastily scrawled inscription at the bottom of the picture read:

Dear Sebastian,
    This was taken right before Triple lost hold of the tiller and we capsized. Triple got pretty mad when we landed in the water.

Love, Amy

Nick smiled. He always got mad at himself when he made mistakes sailing. Jack had been like that, too. Nick cut the painful thought short. He still found it hard to accept losing Jack.

Nick forced himself to set the picture aside. There was no use torturing himself by looking at it. He'd made a bargain to stay out of their lives for eleven months out of the year. But every July, Triple was his. Only July. The rest of the year Nick tried to forget he had a family. Of course, he sent cards and small gifts on holidays, but he'd learned he was happier if he put Amy and Triple out of his mind and concentrated on his work.

Nick knew she didn't want him. Sometimes he wondered if she ever had. Had Amy done all of it only because he was rich and she'd been after money, dropping him when she'd seen a way to make use of Sebastian instead—and have her independence, too?

Nick picked up the Christmas card that Triple had sent and studied his son's scribbled, misspelled message once more.

All I want fro Christmas is to see yuo, Dad. Love, Triple.

Every time Nick reread the brief note, he knew that he felt the same about Triple. It was hell having a son, and yet not having him. Hell, flying to the other side of the world to race a sailboat when all he really wanted to do was spend time with Triple.

The spelling mistakes pulled at something else inside Nick. Triple had inherited dyslexia from him. His case wasn't as severe as Nick's had been. Lots of first-graders mixed up letters, but Nick knew from experience how much more difficult it was going to be for Triple to learn to read and spell. More than anything Nick wished he could be there to help him.

But that simply wasn't possible. Amy would never allow it.

Anger ripped through Nick. Triple's card was a plea for love. Only someone with a heart of stone could ignore it.

Who did she think she was? Triple was his son, too, and it was Christmas.

Nick glanced at his watch. It was nearly four. Triple was probably home already for the holidays, but Amy would still be at work.

To hell with her.

Nick reached for the telephone and punched the buttons briskly. Even though he rarely called Triple, he knew the number by heart.

"Hello..." The vibrant feminine greeting was a husky caress. The unexpected sound of Amy's voice jarred his nervous system.

She had been expecting someone, someone she obviously wanted to talk to. Was it another man?

The muscles in Nick's stomach contracted sharply at the thought.

"Hello," she repeated, still sounding friendly, though a little uncertain.

He imagined her sitting rigidly at her desk in that austere little office in her Malibu home. He had bought her that house and she'd said she hated it because it was too extravagant—like him.

She was probably wearing a suit made of stiff material buttoned tightly to her throat—something she'd bought on sale somewhere. Her hair would be pulled back in that awful little bun.

"Hello," he managed at last, the low tones of his own voice oddly strained. "It's me. Nick."

Her swift intake of breath was like a gasp of pain. She expelled his name in a rush of hostility. "Nick! How dare you—" She caught herself. It was her custom to treat him with no show of emotion.

A long, hushed silence followed. It was taking her longer than usual to gain control of herself.

"We made a bargain," she said in her coolest, most businesslike tone.

"*You* made the bargain," he ground out, fighting to hold on to his temper. "I have a right to talk to my son."

"Not by the terms of our agreement."

"Your agreement," he corrected.

"Nick, this is the best possible solution."

"For whom?" His short, brittle laugh was forced. "Just get Triple on the phone," he snapped.

Nick expected her to hang up on him. To his surprise she didn't.

"He's not here right now. Dad took him Christmas shopping a while ago."

"Why didn't you say so?"

"Because—" She broke off. "Because I don't want you calling here. Ever."

"It's Christmas. Triple sent me a card and told me he wanted to see me. I thought maybe I could stop off in L.A. tomorrow on my way to Sydney. I could see Triple for an hour or so while you're at work."

"No!"

"Did it ever occur to you that maybe it would be good for Triple if I saw him more often?

"No, Nick." Her voice was losing that prim, no-nonsense quality. She sounded vulnerable, frightened. "I won't have Triple torn between us."

"Isn't that what you're doing by forcing me to stay away from him?"

"I don't want you in my life!"

"We're talking about Triple's life."

"Nick. Please . . . No."

"Triple needs me whether you believe it or not. I'll be there tomorrow. If you don't want to see me, make sure you're not around tomorrow afternoon. That shouldn't be too hard. We all know how dedicated you are to your career and making money."

He realized how harsh he sounded. When Amy tried to boss him around, no matter how he strained to hold on to his patience, his temper always got the better of him. But he didn't want to end their conversation on a hostile note. He softened his voice. "Of course, I'd rather see you, too. We haven't seen each other since the night after Jack's funeral."

If Amy hadn't come to him then and restored his faith in the sweetness of loving, he might never have made it through the darkest hour of his life, Nick thought. His own family had stayed in Texas where the real funeral and burial services had been held.

"The night . . ." Her soft voice faded away.

He imagined her brows drawing together as an unwanted blush suffused her cheeks. She would be biting her bottom lip, too. Prim and proper Amy wouldn't like remembering the long, wanton night they'd shared.

"Are you afraid to see me?" he accused huskily. "Afraid we might end up in bed again?"

She had regained control of herself. "Why, you conceited, low-down . . ." She searched for a suitable insult. "Sex maniac!" she hissed.

"Thank you," he murmured, some inner demon driving him to goad her. "It was wonderful, wasn't it?"

"You are the most insufferable egotist I've ever known. That night meant nothing." Her voice had an odd, choked sound.

"Oh, but you're wrong." His low voice was as smooth and rich as velvet. "It meant a great deal to me. Admit it, Amy. You were as starved for me as I was for you."

She made a low sputtering sound that had no translation in polite English.

"I don't think I would have made it, if you hadn't been there. I really would like to see you tomorrow," he said. "Will Sam and Lorrie be there? I'd like to see—"

"Leave Lorrie alone," Amy replied icily. "I know it never mattered much to you which one of us you dated, but—"

"You know that's not true," he said quietly.

"No, I don't."

"Amy, you're the only woman I've ever loved." His low voice was intense and sincere.

"Don't!" She sounded vulnerable, lost, not her usual composed self at all. "Don't lie to me. I can't bear it. You've had lots and lots of women. And all of them were more suitable to your nature than I was. You'll never make me believe I was special."

"You still are."

"No..." The single word was a cry of pain.

"Damn it, Amy. Would you please tell me what Lorrie's got to do with us?"

A deep chasm of emotion-charged silence seemed to separate them. Some sixth sense told him Amy was terrified.

"N-nothing! Forget I said it!" she blurted out. "I didn't mean anything."

But he knew she did.

The line went dead. She had hung up on him.

Nick set the receiver down slowly. He felt far from good about their conversation. He didn't like pushing himself on people who didn't want him. Not even his own wife.

Why the hell had she been so upset when he mentioned Lorrie?

Suddenly he was furious at the unfairness of it all. Most of all he was furious at Amy. From the first, she had refused to give him or their marriage a chance.

Nick's gaze strayed to Triple's note again. In a burst of anger and frustration he wadded it up and threw it toward the trash can, but his aim was off, and it fell soundlessly onto the plush red carpet.

A cord inside of him was beginning to unravel. He couldn't live like this much longer. It was either fight for Amy or lose her forever.

If ever a man was born to fight, it was Nick Browning. Long ago he'd been hurt so deeply and so thoroughly by both his parents that it had arrested the growth of tenderness and softness in his nature, bringing into sharp focus all those other qualities he possessed—intelligence, determination, and ruthlessness.

The one thing he was good at was fighting. And this time, with Amy, he was determined to win.

Two

The hospital waiting room, with its rows of gray vinyl chairs and couches, its little Formica-topped tables, was nearly deserted. There was only a solitary rumpled figure hunched hopelessly in a darkened corner. Beside her was a briefcase she hadn't opened and a messy pile of magazines she'd skimmed and then tossed aside. She couldn't concentrate on either the words or the pictures.

Amy Browning's long black hair was lank and uncombed. Half of it was still pinned in its neat little knot; the other half streamed down her back, a mass of tangles and pins. Her young-looking face was thin and drained of color. Circles of exhaustion ringed her haunted eyes.

No one would have recognized this frightened woman as the hard-driving businesswoman she was. She'd climbed to the top by sheer force of will. When it came to money she could be as hard as nails. But when it came to her family, she was soft.

Amy's fingers were folded together tightly in her lap over her wrinkled wool skirt. Her eyes squeezed shut as she said a desperate, silent prayer.

Dear God, Please don't let my baby die!

It was February. Outside the thick walls of the hospital, a fierce storm howled down from the Gulf of Alaska and battered the city of Los Angeles and its environs. Waves tore gaping holes in the beaches and undermined the foundations of seawalls and expensive beach houses so that they tumbled into the sea. In the hills, where there had been fires the summer before, there were floods and mud slides. Gale-force winds swept across the city, shattering windows in high rises and littering the streets with shards of glass, flattening palms along the wide boulevards, blowing Mexican tiles off the roofs, crumpling highway signs and downing power lines. In the Santa Monica Mountains a blizzard raged.

It was the storm of the century, newsmen said, but Amy was scarcely aware of it.

Behind the closed doors of the intensive care unit her son, Triple, was fighting for his life.

Viral encephalitis, the doctor had said.

Amy was alone. Utterly and forlornly alone.

Dear God, where was Lorrie? Why hadn't she come as she had promised? How could anything be more important to her than Triple's life?

As always, Amy, who'd spoiled Lorrie worse than their own mother would have, had she lived, tried to rationalize her younger sister's failure to be of support when it was Amy who was in trouble. Not once in the past two days had her sister dropped by. Although Lorrie had given other excuses, Amy guessed it was because she was too involved with her acting career.

Lorrie had never been strong enough to cope with her own problems, much less with anyone else's. She was a gentle, quiet, some might think ineffectual woman. Amy was the person everyone in the family leaned on. None of them probably had any idea how close she was to a total collapse. Amy was the rock, the foundation of their lives. Amy was always in control.

A shudder swept through her slender body.

But not now. Oh, not now!

Sam Holland, Amy's father, was at home, his own health too precarious to endure the arduous wait at the hospital. While Lorrie hadn't bothered to call, Sam had phoned faithfully every hour on the first day. Later he'd stopped. It was as though he'd sensed that his calls merely added to Amy's tension. They'd emphasized the grim fact that Triple was not getting well.

Amy glanced at the sensible quartz watch she always wore. It was still an hour until visiting hours started. Then she would have only fifteen minutes with him.

She remembered how thin Triple had been when she'd seen him last. He'd been unconscious, his little face as white and bloodless as his pillowcase, so different from the vital six-year-old of two days before.

Triple had inherited Nick's lusty temperament and untamable spirit and was a constant whirlwind of precocious curiosity and adventure. He'd gotten into more scrapes than most children twice his age. She'd given up chasing him, or worrying about him when he got himself into trouble; she'd stopped attempting to answer his endless battery of questions.

He was all boy, and no matter how much she nagged, his shoelaces remained untied; the knees were always worn out of his jeans; and an assortment of skateboards, bikes, or footballs littered the driveway. In his room he kept a treasured hoard of fearsome pets in jars and clumsily made cages. Usually Triple was impish and happy, but when he squared his jaw and scowled at whomever displeased him, he could throw a tantrum that his bullheaded father would have been proud of.

In Amy's eyes, even so terribly ill, Triple was the most beautiful little boy on earth. His dark lashes lay in little curled fringes against the bright flush of his feverish cheeks. His baby-fine, golden-brown hair fell across his forehead in wispy ringlets. Although his blue eyes were closed and not twinkling with their usual mischief, no one could have helped but admire the even perfection of his features and the baby-smooth texture of his skin. He had an adorable up-turned nose, a heart-shaped mouth and a square jaw, too much like his father's for comfort.

Unconscious, Triple seemed angelic. Awake, he was a diminutive human volcano.

Ignoring the tubes and monitors, Amy had touched her darling boy's forehead on that last visit, and his skin had been burning hot beneath her fingertips.

She wasn't used to worrying about him. When he was a baby she'd worried herself sick over him every time he'd gotten into trouble, until finally she'd been drained of every dram of anxiety in her soul, and she'd stopped. He was so fiercely independent he seemed able to get himself out of every jam.

Only this was different. This illness was beyond even his extraordinary powers of self-preservation.

A spasm of fear gripped her. "Triple, you have to get better," she whispered. "Grandpa and Mommy...and Aunt Lorrie need you. And who will catch bugs and guppies for your snake, Geronimo?"

Amy's body curled into a ball in the vinyl chair. Oh, how she longed to see Triple chasing around the house breaking things, letting lizards loose.

"Mrs. Browning..."

She looked up to see Dr. Alsop's elderly, seamed face and wondered vaguely how long he'd been standing there.

"I'm sorry," she whispered, startled, as she attempted to rise. "I didn't hear you come in."

"Don't get up, my dear. I just dropped by to let you know that I'll be in the record room for a while. But I'll be back to check on Triple before I go home."

Dr. Alsop was Triple's pediatrician, and he'd hardly left the hospital since Triple had been brought in.

"Is Triple . . ." Her voice broke.

He shook his head grimly. "There's no change. Mrs. Browning, isn't there someone who could be with you?"

"No. My sister . . ."

"I was thinking of Triple's father."

Amy's golden eyes came alive and flashed like giant bits of bold glitter against the chalk-white pallor of her face.

"We're separated," she managed to say in a tight voice. Involuntarily she twisted the gold band of her wedding ring until it cut into her flesh like a knife.

"I know. Still . . ."

She was aware of Dr. Alsop's troubled gaze studying her.

"He's the last person I'd share something like this with," she said icily. "The very last."

"Is he really so terrible?"

She dug her nails into her palms. "Some people might not think so."

"But you do?"

Her thin-lipped silence was that of a person who had a bitter distaste for the subject at hand.

"Nevertheless, he is the boy's father."

"A mere accident of birth, doctor. He doesn't deserve Triple."

"He did marry you, I remember, when Triple was a year old."

"That was no favor, I assure you." Her heart was thudding violently at that hateful memory. "Please, Dr. Alsop, I have enough to cope with just worrying about Triple."

Dr. Alsop said no more, but after he left, she felt lonelier and more miserable than before. Not that her loneliness was the doctor's fault. Nor did it have anything to do with where she was or what she was doing with her life.

Nick alone had brought her that kind of pain. She loathed him for the things he'd done in the past, but for Triple's sake she endured his occasional phone calls and gifts to his son. For her son's sake she concealed her bitter contempt and endured the one-month separation from Triple every July, when her son went to San Francisco to visit his father.

With an effort she pushed Nick from her mind, and her thoughts returned to Triple. She buried her face in her hands.

If Triple died . . .

Outside there was the confident tread of hard-soled shoes striding briskly down the length of the glossily waxed hall floor. The door to the waiting room opened softly, and then closed behind the man who barged inside. Amy was only vaguely aware of these sounds, but instinctively, as if even in that first abrupt moment she had sensed new danger, her spine stiffened to some semblance of its usual ramrod tightness. She glanced up, her eyes dazed and unfocused.

A tall, broad giant of a man silently stood across the room from her. Even in her shattered state Amy was aware of his commanding masculine aura.

Beneath the raincoat the man wore flame-red slacks and a white shirt open at the neck. His blond hair, brown skin, and the flamboyance of his dress struck an unpleasantly familiar note, but before she had time to realize who he was, his low, huskily pitched voice sent shock waves of dread through her body.

"Hello, Amy."

Although the raspy voice sounded different—deep and frighteningly cold—she recognized it instantly.

She sucked in her breath.

It couldn't be. Not him! Not here! Not now! Her nerves clamored as she desperately fought to deny Nicholas Browning's presence. *Let me be wrong!*

Her heart had begun to race. She felt both hot and cold at once as she glanced toward the bronzed giant in the dripping raincoat who was striding purposefully toward her.

But she wasn't wrong. It was Nick. Nick with that velvet-smooth, husky voice that could make every nerve ending in her body quiver. Nick, the brashly arrogant egotist she'd once loved so intensely she'd forgotten he was the very type of man she'd always heartily disapproved of—a man who was all show and no substance. Nick with his unruly, damp gold hair falling over his brow; Nick with his sharply chiseled features and aquiline nose, his attractively sun-bronzed skin. Nick with his large, well-muscled body and that intimidating self-confidence that gave him the dashingly reckless air of a buccaneer.

Nick, the very last person she wanted to see—especially now, when she felt so exposed, so vulnerable.

Amy lifted her chin defiantly and dared to meet his gaze. His narrowed eyes were very blue, darker than usual with some deep emotion. She felt them burning across her face.

Hastily she ran her hands through her hair and tried to compose her features into a cold, unfeeling mask.

She succeeded only in looking young and frightened.

"Nicholas." His name escaped her lips, not in greeting but on a faint note of whispered fear. Emotion rushed into her throat, swelling, pushing, choking off speech and breath.

She wanted him to leave, to go away at once. "I don't have the energy to fight you," she was able to murmur.

His lips parted and she could see the tips of his even white teeth, but the smile never reached his eyes.

"Good. Maybe we'll get along for a change."

There was nothing like his sarcasm to make Amy bristle. "Just go," she whispered.

He raised his eyebrows. "Darling, I've flown halfway across the world to get here. I'm damned if I'll leave before I find out what's going on."

Darling. Though he had no right to call her that, even mockingly, the mere word was an intimate caress that made something inside her melt. Soft words came so easily to a womanizer like Nick. Romance was his way—gentleness toward women, and insincere kindness. Those things meant so much to a plain, lonely woman not used to them, but they meant nothing to him.

She rose stiffly as he made his way across the room. The floor seemed to rock unsteadily beneath her feet.

"How is he?" Nick demanded.

She turned away from him, trying to ignore his bold masculine presence, but she was aware of him in every fiber of her body.

His hand closed around her arm like a vise and he whirled her to face him.

"Damn it, Amy. Don't shut me out. Is he dead or alive?"

He towered over her. His blue eyes blazed with an anguish and fear as terrible as her own. His volatile emotions were always so close to the surface, so overpowering.

"Alive," she whispered brokenly. "I haven't seen him for nearly three hours, and he was unconscious then."

"Have you checked with the nurses' station lately?"

She twisted her hands helplessly. "I've just been sitting here."

"You mean you haven't even—" He started to say something, then checked himself as he examined her face and saw the haunted guilt creep into her eyes. "You look exhausted," he said, his low voice kinder. "I've never seen you like this before, so close to the edge. Why aren't Lorrie or your father here?"

"Dad isn't up to the strain," Amy murmured.

"And Lorrie?"

Amy bit her bottom lip and stared at him sullenly without answering. It bothered her that Lorrie hadn't come. Perversely, it bothered her even more that Nick should miss her, too.

"I—I don't know."

His handsome face hardened. She could feel his eyes ruthlessly assessing the damage anxiety and two sleepless nights had wrought on her. She had never been the beautiful, glamorous type a man with Nick's lusty appetites and gaudy tastes naturally preferred, but usually she was at least school-teacher prim and impeccably neat.

"You don't look so hot yourself," she murmured defensively. That was a lie, of course. Nick couldn't look anything but dashingly attractive.

Ignoring her insult, he reached up and gently brushed a lock of black hair out of her eyes, securing the wayward tendril behind her ear. "Always the girl who has to prove she can tough it out alone, aren't you?" he said. His hand lingered caressingly against her cheek. "I know all about toughing it out alone."

Touching a woman came easily to a man like Nick, she thought. The warmth of his fingers stirred old, unwanted memories. Once she had believed in him. Once she had loved his touching her like that. Once she'd loved him.

"Amy, he's going to make it," Nick whispered softly.

She stared at him wordlessly until he let his hand fall away.

"Sorry," he said, chagrined by her look. "I forgot."

He looked tired, too, she thought. He was far from his flashy, suave self. His coat was rain drenched. His parrot-bright clothes were as untidy as hers. His golden hair was wet and lay matted against his dark brow.

Amy remembered vaguely the storm outside.

"I know I probably look a mess," he said, shrugging out of his raincoat and tossing it across the back of a vinyl chair over her own jacket. "I just got in from Holland. I've got a bad headache and a case of jet lag that won't quit. When Sebastian called I was with Hans at the lab going over the tank test results or our latest yacht design for Sebastian's next America's Cup campaign. I dropped everything and took a cab to the airport. My clothes are still in Amsterdam. The flight was hellishly bumpy."

"You always were a big sissy when it came to planes."

"Big sissy, hell," he growled. "It was a miracle we got down at all."

"You needn't have put yourself through all that. There wasn't any reason for you to come," she said woodenly.

For a long moment his fathomless blue eyes bored holes in her. She almost regretted what she'd said.

"Amy, I'm here for the duration, whether you want me or not. Is it so wrong for a father to be worried sick when he finds out his son is in the hospital? You didn't even bother to call me."

Because she hadn't wanted him to come.

"I'm your husband, Amy, despite the way you try to forget it. That gives me certain rights." His low, gravely tone was harsh with mockery.

He raised his hand to curve it possessively along her slender throat, exerting mastery as he turned her face toward his. "Amy..." His furious gaze held her eyes for an end-less moment.

What he'd meant to do or say neither of them would ever know, because suddenly his touching her changed every-thing. There had always been an inexplicable physical bond between them, and even now, when she hated him, she felt its pull. The shock of it made her shudder.

Dimly she realized she should be fighting him. Instead his unexpected gentleness mesmerized her and, when she made no effort to resist him, the anger in his gaze died. All she was conscious of was the feather-light tracery of his fingers on the soft, sensitive skin of her throat. She seemed to stop breathing as his eyes explored every inch of her face.

They were both drawn, although neither wanted to be.

He had claimed that as her husband he had certain rights. Had she been rational, she would have argued that in their marriage that wasn't true. But the words wouldn't come as she felt her body being arched toward his by powerful mus-cular arms.

His shoulders seemed to enclose her. She felt herself being molded against the hard contours of his male length.

His fingers twined into her long black hair, and he pulled her head back. His brilliantly blue eyes burned into hers for what seemed like forever, and she felt a ripple of the old unwanted excitement.

Her throat went as dry as dust. In spite of everything, she wanted him to hold her.

She closed her eyes helplessly.

For a split second Nick's warm mouth hovered over hers, so close she could almost taste him. In another moment she would have been lost.

A rush of cold air swept into the room as the waiting room door swung open. Dr. Alsop hurried toward them, his thick fingers sifting the pages of a fat chart.

Breathing erratically, Amy sprang free of Nick's arms, stumbling backward. She felt ashamed of her reaction to him. Immediately she turned this emotion into fury toward Nick.

As for Nick, he stood statue still and regarded her with equal coldness. It never occurred to her that he might be feeling just as wary, having discovered the power she still held over him.

Amy flushed under the doctor's frankly speculative gaze. It was humiliating to have been caught in Nick's arms, especially after their earlier conversation. "It's all right, Dr. Alsop. This is Nick Browning, my...er..." She met the hot, scathing brilliance of Nick's eyes, and her faltering voice failed her.

"Her husband," Nick drawled politely, offering one hand to the older man and encircling Amy's waist with his arm, as if boldly defying her to challenge his right to do so. "I was in Holland. I wanted to get here as quickly as I could, so I had to spend most of the night on a plane."

Amy's blush deepened as Nick drew her tremulous body more closely against his own. Although she was still shaking, it maddened her that his grip was rock hard, that he seemed totally unaffected by what had nearly happened between them.

Dr. Alsop's eyes gleamed with interest. After a second or two he took Nick's hand and heartily pumped it. "I'm glad you're here. She hasn't eaten or slept since we admitted Triple. You've got two patients to worry about, young man."

"How is Triple, doctor?" Amy pleaded, desperate to change the subject.

The doctor's face masked all emotion. "We have the results of his spinal tap. He's no better, but he's no worse, either. I wish I had happier news, but I'm afraid we still have a very sick little boy on our hands. At this point, it could go either way. His condition may improve or it may deteriorate. There could be permanent brain damage, but sometimes children will recover fully within two to four weeks. If he can just hold on, he still has a chance.''

"A chance..." At the thought of Triple dying, something inside Amy broke. "That's all you can promise me? A miserable chance?" She remembered the night her mother had died, and she began to sob quietly. "Doctor, if that child dies, I'll die, too."

"Mrs. Browning, we're doing everything we possibly can to save him."

But the doctors had done everything before, she thought.

"Will it be enough?" Her normally controlled voice was rising.

"Darling," Nick said gently, understanding her pain because it was his own. "Dr. Alsop wants to save Triple just as much as you do. You have to believe that." His arm tightened supportively around her, his other hand reaching up to brush her hair out of her eyes.

Nick was the last person she wanted to comfort her, especially after what had just happened between them. "Let go of me," she cried, stiffening as he pulled her even closer.

"Shhh. You're hysterical, Amy," came the low, hatefully soothing voice.

"If I'm hysterical, whose fault is that?"

His grip merely tightened.

"No," she protested.

"Amy, honey. I'm here to take care of you."

"I don't need you."

"Yes, you do. You're just too stubborn to admit it."

As she struggled to free herself, she caught glimpses of his anxious face. The skin was pale beneath his tan, but he'd set his jaw in hard, determined lines. It was in his nature to take over, to command, to subdue.

Amy twisted and bent every way against the iron grip of his arms until her frantic heart felt near to bursting. She didn't need anyone. She hadn't needed anyone in years. Not since the boating accident when she'd been a child and her mother had been drowned and her father crippled.

No, it was the other way around—everyone else needed her.

"Amy, don't fight me."

Nick's arms were a vise choking off her breath, and no matter what she did, they stayed around her. Her legs brushed against his hard thighs; his body was as tough and unyielding as steel.

It was no use. No use fighting Nick. He was too big, too powerful, too determined. At last she let herself collapse against him, panting, breathless. Her head nestled against his shirt and her scalding, bitter tears fell against his chest, spotting the white silk fabric. She could feel the warmth of him seeping into her. His hand gently stroked her mussed hair.

"Amy, he's my son, too."

She felt his great body tense with his desperate pain, and her hatred dissolved. Tenderly she reached up and brushed his rough cheek.

She relaxed in his arms, realizing how nice it was to be held, to be comforted. How drawn she was to Nick's masculine strength, how much she needed it.

Amy was aware of his palm molding itself to the curve of her throat, his long fingers sliding into the tumbled length of her hair at the back of her neck. His other hand now cupped the side of her tear-dampened face, lifting her chin with his thumb until her eyes met his.

"It's going to be all right, darling, I promise you."

A tremor of vulnerability shivered down her spine. How did he know? How could he possibly know? Yet even though believing him defied all logic, his words made those inner screaming voices of insidious doubt grow fainter.

Weakly Amy's hand fumbled for Nick's waist, and she held on to him.

Dr. Alsop said softly, "I could prescribe a sedative."

"Maybe later. Right now I want to make sure she gets something to eat." While he spoke Nick kept stroking the length of her hair, and his velvet voice and gentle touch were infinitely soothing.

"Doctor, I want to see Triple," Nick demanded.

The doctor nodded. "I'll see what I can do."

Dr. Alsop made the necessary arrangements for them to slip into the intensive care unit before visiting hours. Beneath the disapproving glare of the head nurse, whose surly expression was that of a marine drill sergeant who'd been crossed, they stared quietly at their unconscious child. Father and mother clung to one another, bound together by the terrible bond of mutual anguish. When the nurse ordered them to leave, Nick led a reluctant Amy quietly back to the waiting room, where they sat silently for a long time, holding on to each other.

As they sat together, Amy found it impossible to summon the hatred she'd felt toward Nick for years, or even her fear of him. Maybe it was only because she was so numb with terror over Triple, but she actually felt stronger because Nick was there.

Almost before Amy realized what was happening, Nick had taken command of her and of her life, precisely as he had in the past. The cynical side of her nature would have said it was just his way. He had the ruthless instincts of a predator. He always waited for the right moment—when she was most vulnerable—and then he moved in for the kill.

That was exactly the method he'd used to force her to marry him.

But at that moment she was too vulnerable and grateful for his presence to make such a cynical assessment of his character.

Revitalized, Amy felt a surge of resentment as she watched Nick wolf down two bags of chips and a ham sandwich oozing with mayonnaise.

She was reminded that he had other lusty, uncurbed appetites.

"It's positively indecent the way you enjoy your food when Triple..."

Nick looked up, surprised at the bitterness in her voice. "How would starving myself help Triple?" he demanded with infuriating male logic.

Silently Amy wadded up an empty potato-chip wrapper in disgust and tossed it onto her tray.

He glanced at the half-eaten, cold, cheese-on-rye sandwich in front of her. "And you'd better finish that," he ordered, "if you know what's good for you."

She felt a pang of guilt. Although Triple was no better, she herself felt much stronger. She hated Nick, but he had always made her feel vitally alive when he was around. It was as if battling him recharged some essential part of her.

Nick had taken charge—cajoled her into combing her hair, washing her face, putting on lipstick, resting and eating. He'd had Dr. Alsop call in a renowned pediatric neurologist, and new experimental medicines were being administered to their son.

Nick was staring at her from across the table, in that determined way of his. A flash of her usual stubbornness flared. She shoved the sandwich away.

He pushed it back. His fingertips grazed hers, and she flinched at the flash of heat contact with his skin brought to her body.

"Eat, darling," he insisted.

She jerked her hand away from his and stared hard at him. "Stop calling me that."

"Maybe I will—if you eat," he whispered.

She was aware of his coiled impatience, of her own fierce tension, and finally her gaze fell before the compelling force of his. She lifted her sandwich and took a tiny bite. The bread was stale and the cheese was cold and tasteless.

"I want to get back upstairs," Nick said, "but we're not going until you finish that sandwich. We've only got a little while until visiting hours start. I wouldn't want to miss seeing Triple because of your stubbornness."

"My stubbornness?" she demanded.

"Yes, of course, yours. I'm determined now beçause I have to be when I'm around you, that's all," he said.

"Excuse me if I don't see the difference."

"Eat, Amy." He glanced at his watch again. "If you want to see Triple, you've got five minutes."

Normally she would never have allowed him to dominate her so thoroughly, but she ate all of her sandwich—in a sullen silence that was so thick he made no attempt to interrupt it until they were back in the waiting room.

It was one minute until visiting hours.

"Triple seemed fine when I saw him at Christmas," Nick said. "You haven't told me how all this started."

"He just got sick suddenly during the night. I heard him cry out in his sleep. I went to his room, and he was burning up with fever. I rushed him to the emergency room." Her tremulous voice lowered. "I've been here ever since."

"Darling, I know it's been awful for you," he murmured.

There was that word again. It made her feel so vulnerable. Every muscle in her body stiffened.

"You said you wouldn't call me that."

His hand folded over hers, and her pulse jumped beneath his fingers. He turned her hand over in his palm and studied it thoughtfully. "I said maybe."

Through his densely curling lashes, he studied her. Amy didn't dare lift her eyes to his.

He was impossible. He always had been and always would be. But despite her fierce determination to despise him, she was reluctant to let go of the strong hand holding hers.

Why did Nick have to be the only person with whom she could share her maternal anguish?

Because he was the father of her only son.

For years she had tried to dismiss the importance of that simple biological fact. For years she had tried to convince herself that the biology of parenthood was not nearly as important as the actual parenting. For years she had tried to tell herself that Nick didn't belong in their lives, that she was capable of raising Triple alone.

Nick had told her she was wrong, but she'd refused to listen.

Now she wondered how she'd ever summon the strength to send him away again.

Her fingers tightened in his, and she held on to him.

Triple was as still and gray faced as death. There was no change, the female drill sergeant in white explained. He was holding on, but just barely.

Fresh horror gripped Amy. His eyes seemed more sunken, and beneath his white skin, his cheekbones stood out like batons in a sail.

Amy looked at all the criss-crossing tubes, Triple's IV, the oxygen mask covering his mouth and nose and the little lights blinking with bright regularity on the monitors. The room smelled faintly of antiseptic.

As Amy watched, Nick leaned over and pressed Triple's hot, limp fingers. "Triple, it's your dad. I'm here, and I'm not leaving until you're well."

Not by a flicker of an eyelash did Triple respond. Heat fairly radiated from his flushed face.

"I'm here," Nick repeated. "Can you hear me, Triple?" Amy held her breath.

There was no sound other than the metallic rattling of the air-conditioning vent.

"He doesn't hear you, Nick," Amy said hopelessly. "Oh, I'm so afraid he'll never..."

Nick sensed how close she had come again to the breaking point. "I think we'd better go," he said.

"No. I want to stay with my baby. I have to stay with him. I..." She touched Triple's forehead. "Oh, Nick, he's burning up."

"Hush, darling," Nick murmured hoarsely. He brought his fingers gently to her lips as if to seal them. "I think the crisis will come tonight," he said. "I know it's hard for you to leave him here alone, but it's just as hard for me."

Amy looked into her husband's bleak eyes and saw a pain as terrible and profound as her own. His handsome face was haggard with anxiety. Nick needed her every bit as much as she needed him.

Without thought she slowly put her arms around him, and offered him the only thing she could, the warmth and comfort of her body. She had him in her arms, her face pressed against the roughness of his cheek. When she felt his large body shudder against hers, she just hugged him until finally he let her go.

Stiffly, blindly, like two sleepwalkers they stumbled toward the waiting room.

Later in the night, it became so cold that she began to shiver. He took care of her, wrapping her snugly first in her own light jacket and then in his oversize raincoat. He stretched out on the sofa and pulled her down beside him.

"Get some sleep, Amy," he whispered, pushing her raven head down on his lap when she made a feeble show of resistance. "Forget how you feel about me. We're in this thing together." With a weary sigh he let his own head fall back against the cushion.

Sleep. She wondered vaguely if she could ever sleep again, but she lacked the strength to argue with him.

Instead she let her cheek obediently rest upon the firm warmth of his thigh. Even though she was determined to watch him warily, it wasn't long before her eyelids started to droop. His masculine profile blurred.

She forgot the danger of him and relaxed in his arms. Soon she slept the deep, still sleep of a person utterly exhausted while behind the closed doors of the intensive care unit, their son battled for his life.

Three

An icy fear knotting his stomach, Nick held Amy in his arms. Throughout the long night he was afraid as he hadn't been afraid since Jack's fatal motorcycle accident two years before. Jack had fought for his life for three days and three nights, but in the end he'd lost.

Losing the brother who'd always hero-worshiped him had devastated Nick. In many ways he loved the wild and boisterous Triple exactly as he'd loved his wild and boisterous younger brother.

It couldn't happen all over again. He couldn't lose Triple the same way he'd lost Jack. He still dreamed of Jack, still missed him.

Dear God, not Triple, too! Nick knew if he lost Triple he would lose Amy as well.

He remembered his last visit with his son right before Christmas, and he was glad that he'd gone against Amy's will and seen Triple. Brief though their visit had been, Triple had been thrilled to see him.

The little boy had taken him into the garage and shown him Amy's catamaran. He had bounded onto the twin hulls with the sprightly agility of a small monkey and precociously pointed out what everything was.

"Could you teach me how to sail her, Dad? I mean *really* sail her?"

"I thought you already knew how. Sebastian sent me a picture of you and your mother."

"'Course I know how, Dad," Triple had proclaimed with his usual lack of modesty. "Only Mom doesn't think so, and she said she's not going to let me sail her anymore 'cause she says I don't do what she says on a boat. I bet if you taught me how, she'd change her mind. And I bet pretty soon I could sail so fast I could beat every kid around here. 'Specially Elgin Ferris."

"This is a mighty tough boat for a little boy to start off with," Nick had said, laughing. But he'd promised Triple that when summer came, he'd teach him how to sail. "I might have to get you your own boat."

Triple jumped down from the boat with a single, foolhardy leap. Shining blue eyes gazed eagerly up into Nick's. "My own boat, huh? Maybe I could spend the whole summer with you instead of just July."

"Maybe..."

Nick had realized then that he should have fought Amy long ago for more time with Triple. Instead, he'd buried himself in his work and sailing races and had ignored what was really important—his son.

No more, he vowed, glancing at the sterile hospital walls. Not after coming this close to losing Triple. If Triple lived, Nick was determined to change things. He was through with letting Amy call the shots. He'd let her use him to suit her own purposes long enough.

The delicate floral scent of Amy's perfume rose to Nick's nostrils. Her fingers clutched at his arms as she whimpered in her sleep from some bad dream. He glanced down at the tousled dark head in his lap and saw pain flicker across her pale features.

Even in her sleep, she was suffering. Whatever she felt toward him, she loved their son. Nick felt a rush of protectiveness toward her. He wished he could help her get through this as she'd helped him when Jack had died.

She moaned softly, burrowing her head into his belly in an intimate way that would have deeply shamed her had she been awake. Through the thin silk of his shirt he felt her hot mouth nuzzle against his flesh.

He caught his breath at a sudden flash of unwanted desire. Again her hands clutched him, as if she were seeking to bury herself in the warmth of his body.

Almost involuntarily his hand came to rest on her head. He smoothed the wispy strands of black silk into place, touching her lightly for fear of waking her. In the dim light with her inky lashes curling against her pale cheeks, her delicate features softened by sleep, she was very lovely.

Still asleep she called his name. He felt a sudden tearing pain in his whole being. More than anything he wanted Triple to live. And he wanted his wife. It didn't matter that she'd used him and married him only when he'd forced her.

Dr. Alsop led Amy and Nick into the intensive care unit. "I know it isn't visiting hours, but Triple's so much better this morning, I knew you'd want to see him. He's been awake, and his fever's down."

"Then the crisis is past?" Nick demanded.

"Maybe not entirely, but he's definitely much improved."

Dr. Alsop knocked on Triple's door and pushed it gently ajar. "I wouldn't stay too long. After what he's been through, he'll tire easily."

As they stepped inside, a single shaft of wan sunlight streamed through a high window and touched Triple's hair. It gleamed like dark gold against his pale skin. He was no longer flushed, and a slight sheen of perspiration beaded his forehead. To Amy he looked like a sleeping angel.

"Triple," she whispered.

Triple's eyes opened drowsily. He managed a thin smile for his mother, and then a bigger one for his father, which produced a gnawing ache in Amy's stomach. "Dad, I knew you'd come," he whispered. Triple clutched Amy's hand weakly when she touched his fingers. "Didn't you just know he would, Mom?" His blue eyes were big and trusting as he gazed at her.

Only for a second did the shock of her son's eager questions register on Amy's face. She was too aware of Nick's piercing gaze.

"I should have known it," she replied evasively, letting her lashes fall to veil her eyes. She felt an uneasy prick of conscience. His father's presence meant so much to Triple, and for five years she'd done everything she could to keep them apart.

"Dad, you're going to stay for a while, aren't you? You're not leaving the minute I get better, are you? Mom, you'll make him stay, won't you."

A twinge of guilt raced through Amy. "Triple, your father's a very busy man," she said softly. "We can't expect him to stay too long when he has to run South Sails with its branches all over the United States. Not to mention all of his racing commitments."

Amy would have said more, but when she felt Nick's hard blue gaze raking her, she swallowed the words.

Nick leaned over the bed and contradicted his wife in a deceptively smooth voice. "I won't be leaving, son—not even when you're better."

"Is that a promise, Dad?"

"That's a promise, son." Nick's cutting gaze slashed up to Amy's face as he spoke, daring her to protest. "From now on, I'm not going to let anything come between us."

Amy cringed at the words that spelled her doom and at the defiant challenge she read in her husband's eyes.

Triple's need for his father was natural. It was the circumstances of her marriage that made Nick's continuing presence a frightening prospect.

"Good." The faint word died on Triple's lips as he let his eyes droop shut. "You don't have to go just 'cause I'm sleeping, either, Dad," he murmured, his voice dying away again. He had forgotten his mother completely.

Nick smiled, a slow smile that transformed his rugged features into an expression of unbelievable tenderness.

This sweet look tore Amy to pieces. Once he had reserved it for her alone. She closed her eyes against the sharp ache of longing that assailed her as she remembered the bittersweet tenderness of their brief love affair. When she opened them again, she was glad Nick had his broad back turned toward her as he leaned over the bed holding Triple's hand.

"Excuse me," Amy murmured shakily. "I'll let you spend some time alone with him." She stumbled outside.

When Nick returned to the waiting room, he found Amy tucked into one desolate corner.

"Sulking?" he demanded, not in the mood to indulge her coldness toward him.

"No," she whispered raggedly, twisting the leather strap of her purse. She couldn't look up. She was too afraid he might read the aching emptiness in her eyes. "Damn you. Why did you have to come back?"

"He's my son, too," Nick said.

"We shouldn't be fighting over him."

There was the barest tensing of his expression. "That's exactly my point."

"Nick, you shouldn't have made a promise to Triple you don't intend to keep."

Eyes as calm as a blue winter sky met hers. "Don't worry, I didn't."

"You can't mean that you really intend to stay."

"For a while." At her frown, a bitter grimace chased across his mouth. He came closer, so close that he towered menacingly over her. "Would it really be so awful having your husband home, Amy?"

His gaze swept over her, and she was too conscious of every part of her body that his eyes touched.

"I don't feel like I have a husband," she replied sharply, rising to her feet, desperate to escape.

"Then I've definitely stayed away too long." He spoke with a deadly softness that should have warned her. "I realized that last night when I held you in my arms and almost kissed you."

Disdain glittered coldly in her eyes. "No," she murmured with tight finality. "The best thing for all of us would be for you to go away and stay out of our lives completely."

"I don't believe that anymore. Last night you needed me. When I got here you were falling apart."

"Last night I would have been fine, if you hadn't come."

"Oh, you would have?" She was edging toward the door. With the swift, savage grace of a jungle cat, he seized her by the wrist and yanked her against his body. "You lying little cheat," he muttered bitterly. "You can't even say, 'thank you, Nick, for being there when I needed you.' No, you just use me and then kick me in the gut when you're through with me." His harsh grip dug into her skin. "I'm tired of that treatment, honey."

"Nick, don't . . ."

"I flew across an ocean and this entire country to get back to you, to help you, but you don't want me. All you've ever wanted is my money. Or Sebastian's, once you'd used me to get ahold of him."

Words of denial sprang to Amy's lips, but she bit them back.

He pressed her against himself until every hard muscle and bone of his body imprinted themselves on her soft curves. He was burning hot, his arms crushing steel bands. "Maybe it's time you learned what marriage really means."

Her heart raced in frantic alarm. "Nick, I don't want you," she whispered breathlessly.

His hands wound into her hair. She felt his fingers digging into her scalp as he pulled her head back. She despised him, but the hard pressure of his male body against her ignited her senses. The warmth of his breath gently wafted over her lips, and his musky scent tantalized her. Every nerve in her body was treacherously aware of him.

She pushed at his arms, struggling to break their hold.

"But I want you," he said softly. His eyes were as hard as diamonds. "And maybe I'm tired of wanting and never having. You're my wife. Maybe it's time I took what I want."

Brutally he covered her lips with his, and his rough, unshaven cheek burned against her own. He kissed her hard and insolently, not caring that he hurt her, that he humiliated her.

"You are mine," he muttered hoarsely, determined to dominate her with the emotion that dominated him. "Mine."

The fierce words branded her soul. Overpowered by his masculine strength, she didn't even try to fight him. His mouth smothered hers, and blackness whirled in a mist of stars behind her closed eyelids.

She felt faint, helpless in his arms, caught in the blaze of his passion. Only when she stopped fighting him did the furious quest for revenge cease to rule him, a gentler emotion stealing into his heart. His hold didn't slacken, but instead of hurt, his mouth exerted mastery.

Intuitively sensing this change in him, her body melted into his, and slowly some emotion, long buried in the cold tomb of her heart, flared hotly alive as his lips and tongue and hands caressed her. Against her earlobe he murmured soft, heated endearments, and she could not hold back a tiny moan of surrender. She returned his kisses, softly at first, her mouth playing sweetly beneath his, and then more feverishly.

In the white heat of passion all their differences ebbed away.

"You are mine," he whispered, and she could not deny it.

When he let her go at last, she was so thoroughly shaken she would have fallen clumsily, had he not reached out and caught her gently in his arms. Only when she had regained her balance, did he let her go.

Not a word passed between them as she turned her back on him and went to the small window that looked out on the hospital parking lot.

She heard his footsteps approaching behind her, and the tiny hairs on the back of her neck prickled in awareness of him. She didn't dare to look at him, but a fierce tremor of longing shivered down her spine.

With one kiss he'd shown her that all their years apart, all her stubborn determination to hate him were as nothing against the terrible power he held over her. She had loved him, and once he had almost destroyed not only her life but the lives of the people she loved more than anything.

"Why don't you just go?" she said in a low strangled tone. "Please..."

She was aware of his hands brushing over her hair, and she quickly sidestepped to avoid his touch. But not before her heart had betrayed her and begun to flutter wildly.

He flicked the miniblinds apart. "Storm's over," he said. His voice was distant, yet warmly ironic.

She glanced indifferently at the gray, wet world revealed through the parted blinds. All she could think of was his immense body, so burningly near her own. All she could feel was an insane urge to throw herself into his arms and let him hold her once more. No matter what he'd done in the past, he had a power over her senses no other man had ever had.

"I think it's time I drove you home," he began, "so we can both shower and change and get some rest."

His matter-of-fact suggestion created a chaos of emotion. He was closing in on her, taking over, ordering her around as if it were his right to do so.

One kiss, and he thought he owned her.

Amy whirled around.

For a numbed moment, she could only stare mutely at him.

In the gray light his blue eyes flashed with the glint of icy steel as he regarded her down the arrogant length of his aquiline nose. She noted the commanding thrust of his jaw—never a good sign—the startling prominence of his chiseled cheekbones and the cynical lines slashed on either side of his hard mouth. His was always an uncompromisingly masculine face, but at the moment, he looked so

ruthlessly determined she knew that only a fool would dare
to stand up to him.

Her own jaw squared. "No. I don't want to go home with
you," she said stubbornly.

"Look," he said, "I'm too tired to argue."

Amy felt a mild pang of unwanted sympathy for him. It
wasn't only exhaustion that had etched those lines beneath
his eyes and beside his lips.

"I can't leave Triple," she insisted. "I have to be here
when he wakes up again."

"If you don't look after yourself, you're not going to be
much use to Triple when he does get better. I've already left
your telephone number at the nurse's station in case there's
an emergency while we're gone."

"Nick!"

"There's no use arguing." He snapped the miniblinds
shut. His hand wrapped around her elbow, his fingers biting into her flesh as he propelled her across the room to the
chair where they'd left their things. He picked up her jacket
and purse and shoved them into her reluctant arms.

"You always win, don't you?" she murmured angrily as
he pulled on his raincoat and then helped her into her jacket.

She felt his touch graze the nape of her neck as he pressed
the collar of her jacket flat. Abruptly her body stiffened.

A dark flush colored his cheeks. "With you it's never
easy."

"Sunday driver!" Nick muttered fiercely, jamming his
right heel down hard on the accelerator.

Amy's heart lurched as the tires screamed around a curve
and the car shot forward on a fresh burst of speed. She
clutched the handles of her briefcase so tightly her fingers
ached as Nick caught up to a pickup and zoomed past it.

"Pretty sunset," Nick said mildly, impervious to her fear as he glanced over his left shoulder at the scarlet dazzle that splashed ocean and sky. At the same time he noted the pickup in his rearview mirror with male satisfaction.

"If you're going to drive like a maniac, you could at least keep your eyes on the road," Amy sputtered nervously. Up to this point, they had driven in tense silence ever since he'd roared out of the hospital parking lot twenty minutes ago.

A faint smile played at the edges of his mouth, and for a minute she thought he was going to make a sarcastic retort. To her surprise, Nick lazily turned his attention back to the road. His gaze slid to her, brief and sweeping. "Whatever you say, sweetheart."

Her mouth was tautly compressed, her nerves even more gratingly on edge than before.

The daylight was fading. Mud slides had carved new fissures in the Santa Monica Mountains, and several homes dangled precariously from the edge of a cliff. In places the road was blocked. Over the Pacific the sky was very high, rinsed by the storm's deluge to a pale, clear lavender. Little tufts of cloud drifted on a wet, cold wind, nestling into the pockets between the hills. A red sun hung low against the horizon, gilding the ocean's placid surface with streamers of blood-red fire.

All Amy saw was the wet asphalt whipping beneath the blue hood of her Oldsmobile, and it was too much for her. "You're not racing a twelve-meter in the Indian Ocean, you know," she said tightly.

"I know." After a deliberate pause he continued. "But, honey, I've got a hell of a lot more at stake in this contest."

He braked slightly, probably only because her driveway was in sight. Tires spun gravel as he skidded to a stop a fraction of an inch from her Wedgwood-blue garage door.

"Home at last," he murmured. A corner of his mouth lifted cynically as he eyed the charming redwood establishment nestled against a low dune.

Home. Never before had the word struck such an ominous note of doom in her heart. Just for a second her eyes darted toward him.

His chiseled profile was backlighted by golden-red light, its lines as hard and unyielding as those of a tyrannical emperor stamped on some ancient coin. Nick looked indomitable.

He was her husband. She found this fact distinctly chilling.

"Yes," she agreed. "Home. At last. I never thought I'd reach it alive."

Low, harsh laughter came from his throat. "Oh, you're very much alive." His hand reached across the distance between them and traced the soft flesh of her upper arm before she jerked it furiously away. His voice became low and sexy. "Believe me, honey, that's exactly how I want you."

She wasn't ready for the sudden softening of his tone, like a caress of velvet sliding against sensitive skin. "I thought I made it clear I didn't want you touching me," she said.

"Honey, that may be the message you thought you meant to send," came his treacherously raspy voice, "but it's not the message I got." With sickening accuracy, he continued, "You wanted a lot more than I could give you in a hospital waiting room. Maybe now that we're home..."

"Not if I can help it!" she whispered.

His eyes bored into hers. "But you can't," he said.

He let his veiled gaze glide over her face and figure in silent admiration, and he grinned broadly as if he were contemplating some delightful prospect.

"You don't know what you're talking about!"

"Wait and see." The smug half smile lingered on his lips.

Scorching waves of shame splashed her cheeks with spots of fire. She longed to think of some stinging retort that would set him properly in his place.

Instead she snatched her keys from the ignition and threw open her door. Then she sprang out of her car and rushed up the brick path to her front door. The hushed sound of his laughter followed her. Then his car door slammed.

She was sifting through her purse for her house key, when his hand closed around her wrist.

"I'll find it," he said.

A shiver of apprehension raced icily over her flesh at his touch. Swiftly he located the key. As he was pulling it out, she tried to jump away, but he caught her by the shoulders and held her against his body.

"We wouldn't want anyone to think I wasn't welcome in my own home," he murmured silkily.

"Why not, if it's the truth?"

He said nothing, but there was the barest tightening of Nick's square jaw as he inserted the key in the door. Before he could unlock it, the lock rattled from the inside, and the door was suddenly thrown open by a dark middle-aged woman, with a thick coil of iron-gray hair perched precariously on top of her head. A pair of grubby gardening gloves protruded from the pockets of the woman's worn apron.

At first Apolonia registered shock at the sight of her embarrassed mistress in the arms of her estranged husband. Then her stoic Indian face burst into the radiant smile that was normally reserved solely for Triple.

"Mr. Neecholas," she cried with uncustomary exuberance, her black eyes growing brilliant as she ignored her mistress's scowl and concentrated on the golden giant looming in the doorway. "I'm so glad you here!"

Nick released Amy and swept the short woman into his arms, giving her a hearty bear hug that lifted her off her feet. "Of course, I'm here," he said, gently mocking Apolonia's accent. "The prodigal husband has come home—where he belongs."

"Mr. Neek, we missed you so much. I go to the kitchen now, and make you something good to eat."

Although he seemed to be smiling down at Apolonia broadly, he was watching Amy too. "Now, that's the way to welcome a man home."

Amy paled at the sharp thrust of Nick's double-edged barb. Did he never miss an opportunity to bait her?

"I been using the gloves you give me for Christmas," Apolonia said proudly, patting the pocket at her thick waist as he set her down once more.

"So I see. But I hope you've been rattling those pots and pans in the kitchen."

Apolonia never liked thinking about cooking and cleaning, the job she'd been hired to do. "How is Triple, Mr. Nick," she said quickly, craftily changing the subject to the little boy they both loved.

"He's better."

"Mr. Nick, Mr. Sebastian, he send some clothes over for you."

"Great."

"I put them in Triple's room."

"Apolonia, I do believe you've lost weight."

"I been sick with the flu, but I feel better now. And, Mr. Nick, Mr. Sebastian, he wants you to call him about business...."

Amy sneaked past the effusive pair and left them babbling in the doorway as she moved on into her house, down the long hall toward her bedroom, grateful for once that the cement-headed Apolonia, who had rarely shown more than the mildest feelings of warmth toward the woman who had faithfully employed her for nearly five years, adored Nick.

Amy was about to open her door, when she heard her father's voice behind her.

Turning, she saw a frail, hump-shouldered figure step from the den into the dim hallway. Behind him rose the blare of the television.

"Is that Nick I hear?" Sam asked, his eager voice suddenly choked with emotion.

"Who else would Apolonia abandon her potted plants for and offer to cook a meal for?"

Sam smiled. "Triple must be better or you two wouldn't be here."

Amy nodded. "He's conscious now, and his fever's down."

"Honey, why didn't you tell me Nick was coming?" Her father gave her a searching look.

"Because I was hoping he would leave as soon as Triple was out of danger," she snapped truthfully.

"Sam!" Nick's voice boomed down the hall. The next second he had joined them. "I can't tell you how great it is to see you!"

Nick's white grin transformed his dark face, and just for a second Amy felt herself softening. Then her blood turned to ice as she realized how susceptible she still was to Nick's false brand of charm. If she didn't know better, she might almost have believed he cared something for Sam.

"Amy, you can go now. I'll see to Sam." Nick waved her away, dismissing her imperiously as if she were of no importance.

She had longed to escape him—until he told her to.

"Well?" Nick drawled offensively, one of his eyebrows arching in her direction when she remained.

"I'll stay, thank you," she grumbled perversely.

"Suit yourself," came his indifferent reply. He turned back to her father.

Sam's smile was almost as silly and warm as Apolonia's had been as Nick shook his father-in-law's hand affectionately. Sam's faded eyes were shining with blissful happiness, and it upset Amy to see her own father thirstily drinking in the sight of the one man who'd shattered all their lives.

Nick ignored her coldness and switched on the lights in the den. The relaxing, cozy room was decorated with African masks and furnished with Mexican rawhide chairs. A rumpled blue blanket at the foot of the couch and an untidy stack of newspapers on the floor told of Sam's lonely vigil while Amy had been at the hospital.

"This place is as dark as a tomb. I bet you haven't eaten a home-cooked meal in days," Nick said.

The answer was all too apparent, and the brief accusing glance Nick gave Amy made her squirm with guilt.

She met his gaze with a withering scowl that would have daunted a less forceful man.

"Well, now that I'm here, all that is going to change. Sam, you've endured Apolonia's bullying too long. And Amy's, too."

"Mine?" Amy shot Nick a dark look, but he just grinned boldly back at her, pretending he didn't see her anger as he marched across the den. He stopped in the middle of the room, eyeing a scarred chessboard tucked beneath a pile of magazines. He went over to the board and picked it up, studying it thoughtfully.

"Do you still play chess, Sam?"

"Not since you left." The wealth of loneliness in his reply pulled at Amy's heart. Never once had she offered to play with him.

"Me neither," Nick said with grave sincerity as he set the board down. "But that's something I'm going to change, too."

Amy drew in a deep, furious breath. Enough was enough! Watching Nick take command of her disloyal household was unendurable. "You won't be here long enough to change anything."

Nick's eyes met hers, and he smiled, though not as cordially as before. He yanked the proper cords, and the drapes danced open. "I wouldn't count on that, darling, if I were you." His voice was very quiet, but it filled the room, grating, like rough stones grinding together.

The sun had sunk below the horizon, but rich burgundy streaks painted the sky and ocean. The surf was high. The beach was littered with driftwood and other bits of broken flotsam, mute evidence of the waves that had ravaged it only hours before.

"I always forget how beautiful the view is here," Nick was saying, speaking more to himself than to them.

He could never resist the water. He opened a glass door and stepped outside into the briskly cold, salt-scented air.

He was glad to get out of the house, away from Amy. Her hostility bothered him more than he had any intention of showing her.

A gull screamed and dived toward the sparkling waves. It flapped away, something caught in its beak.

Nick shut the door and drew a deep breath to ease his tension. He felt like a knight that had just breached the walls of his enemy's castle. It didn't matter that he was exhausted from the battle. He'd fought his way inside, and he intended to stay—for as long as it took him to get what he wanted.

Nick's eyes scanned the magnificent house that spilled over its hill. The redwood beach house was mansion-size, modern and bold in design with skylights, trestled ceilings and immense windows that looked out on the ocean. He'd bought it to make Amy happy. She'd hated it and Malibu on sight.

At the bottom of the hill a vine-covered pergola curved around an immense, glassed-in swimming pool. The surrounding gardens, Apolonia's favorite domain, were perfectly groomed. There were jacaranda trees and Lebanese cedars, ivy-clad stone walls, beds of purple and red flowers, their petals battered and limp from the storm.

Nick's fingers clenched around the lightly gold-stained railing as he stared beyond the immediate grounds to the flat, rapidly darkening ocean. Amy had certainly come up in the world. Six and a half years ago she'd been a lifeguard at the yacht club, working her way through UCLA. She'd been poor but smart and awesomely ambitious. Then she'd met Nick and through him, his father's cousin Sebastian. She'd used her pregnancy to worm her way into Sebastian's heart, and more importantly his wallet. It baffled Nick that Sebastian trusted her so implicitly and wouldn't listen to a word of criticism concerning her.

Working for Sebastian, Amy had gone straight to the top. For all her softness toward her family, she could be hard when it came to business, to money. Now she lived in a colony of movie stars and wealthy international celebrities.

What a fool he'd been not to realize what she'd been after. All he'd seen was her softness, her innocence. He'd even admired her determination and ambition.

He wondered if the money and success had made Amy happy. Was she ever lonely? Did she ever ache for a man with whom to share her life as he ached for a woman? Or were her governing emotions only greed and ambition?

No matter what happened, no matter how she fought him, he wasn't leaving until he had the answers.

Four

The hot water ran through Amy's freshly lathered hair and soaked into her skin. Whorls of steam twined around her. Amy felt she could have stood forever in that tiled compartment with the sweet-scented warmth flowing over her body. If only Nick hadn't invaded her territory and upset the equilibrium of her life.

Closing her eyes, she turned her face into the nozzle and tried to forget him as shampoo bubbles rushed down the curve of her back, pooling in a soft mountain of foam at her toes.

But she couldn't forget him. Memories from the past swirled in her mind like the mists swirling around her body.

Amy had been a young and vulnerable twenty when Nick burst into her life like a tornado. She and Lorrie had had summer jobs at the Riviera Yacht Club at Newport Beach where Nick was a member. At first he was aloof, apparently too far above them to notice them.

But Amy had noticed him. Although she was proud and ambitious herself, she'd never seen anyone so brash and self-confident, so filled with purpose. She'd been instantly prejudiced against him because he was rich and handsome and because he was the cocky type all the women chased. Nevertheless, she'd watched him with an avid interest, even before he'd asked Lorrie out.

Nick had wanted to be the best sailor in the world. He wanted to win the America's Cup someday. He was nearly finished with his engineering degree, and he planned to be a great sail maker and work for his older cousin, Sebastian. At first she thought he was only bragging, but then she saw him throw himself into his sailing with an all-consuming, formidable energy as a member of the handpicked crew fine-tuning Sebastian's latest America's Cup challenger.

Amy could not help envying Nick that summer. Imagine being the son of one of the richest rancher-oilmen in the nation, even a bastard son who hadn't always felt loved and wanted as a child. Imagine being the cousin of a multimillionaire like Sebastian Jacobs, a man who thought nothing of sponsoring an America's Cup campaign.

Nick's world seemed glamorous, while hers was hard. He could have anything he wanted. Amy had had to work for everything she had. He never noticed her, but she felt curiously restless and excited whenever he was around. She found him dangerously fascinating, and she resented him because of it.

With her own mother dead, Amy had always felt responsible for her younger sister and crippled father. She felt she had to move up in the world so that she could take care of them, but it was a struggle to work, nurture her family and study.

It was one thing to observe Nick from afar; quite another when he started dating her younger, impressionable sister. After her second date with him, Lorrie had come home starry-eyed, and Amy had panicked, thinking Nick much too sophisticated and worldly for her baby sister.

The next afternoon Amy went down to his boat at the club. It had been a sparkling summer day. He was in the cabin, busy at some task, and she had interrupted him.

He'd come up through the hatch and stepped onto the deck of his gleaming white yacht, a braided coil of line dangling from his brown hand. He was shirtless and perspiring, a bronzed god of rippling golden-brown muscle. When he saw her, his expression became impatient, arrogant. Never had he seemed richer or more spoiled. Amy felt all the resentment she'd harbored against him flare up.

"Miss...er...?"

It galled her that he had forgotten her name.

"Amy Holland. Lorrie's sister."

"Oh, yes. The lifeguard. I remember."

"I know you must be busy, and I shouldn't be bothering you..." She paused, but he didn't deny her words. "It's because of Lorrie that I'm here."

"Really?" He raised his eyebrows. Brilliant blue eyes surveyed her. She had not been sure what they expressed. Disbelief—a certain cynical amusement perhaps.

Amy felt uneasy being alone with him, furious, and yet exhilarated. "Let me explain."

"Please do."

"She's only sixteen and you're twenty-two. She's a child. You're so much more sophisticated. You've had so many women. One more or less can't mean anything to you. You could date someone else. Someone older and less impressionable."

He dropped the coil of line on the deck with a thud and stepped closer, concentrating his full attention on her.

"You've obviously made quite a study of me. I hadn't realized I'd made such an impression."

"Y-you haven't."

"So you think I've had a lot of women?" There was a new note in his voice. A dangerous note. "So many that losing one could make no difference."

Amy felt numb with dismay. All she had done was make a fool of herself.

"Who told you that?" he asked.

"No one. I could just tell."

Again he raised his eyebrows. "So Lorrie's only sixteen?" Amy nodded. "She lied to me about that."

Amy believed him. Lorrie never lied about important things, but on rare occasions she had been guilty of telling little white lies when she wanted something badly enough.

He was watching Amy. "And you're the big sister?"

She nodded again. "By four years."

"Then you're older...and less...impressionable." Slowly, casually he inspected her in the insolent way she'd seen him admire other more beautiful women. He laughed and said, "It looks like I picked the wrong sister."

The way he looked at her made Amy feel funny inside. His casual attitude unnerved her. She was horrified by the way he'd twisted everything around. She was sure he was secretly laughing at her.

"I didn't come down here to flirt with you," she snapped.

He merely stepped closer and laughed again. She felt her cheeks blazing. He smiled down at her, as though he were very pleased about the way things were turning out.

"I'm not flirting, either," he said huskily.

She felt on fire with anger and with some new, inexplicable emotion. "I'm just a joke to you."

"No." There was a baffling intensity in his gaze.

Amy was near tears. Before he could say more, she turned and ran down the dock, but when she looked back, she found that he was watching her still, with the same darkly intense expression in his eyes.

Why had she gone to speak to him? He'd seen through her, seen her own secret desire for him that she hadn't even seen herself. All she'd done was make a fool of herself.

He didn't call Lorrie again, and the next week, he started asking Amy out. At first she'd refused, but he'd been very persuasive. There was an immediate affinity between them. They were both ambitious and driven to excel. They loved the water and boats. All too soon they came to love each other. Even trivial occurrences seemed to take on a special importance when she shared them with him. Nick spent every free evening at her house with her, not seeming to mind the shabbiness of her family's little home. It wasn't long before their romance blossomed into a love affair. Mutual friends began to warn Amy that she was getting in too deep, that although Nick had dated many women, he had never really been serious about any of them.

At first Lorrie hadn't seemed to be bothered about Nick's asking Amy out, but as Amy fell more and more deeply in love, Lorrie's attitude began to change. At first she was only quiet when he visited. Then one night after she stumbled upon Nick and Amy kissing, the change in her became more dramatic. She seemed to go wild and started dating Nick's younger brother, Jack. He would pick her up on his motorcycle, and she wouldn't come home for hours.

When Amy expressed her concern about Lorrie dating Jack, Nick had laughed, saying that, yes, his brother could be wild at times, but Jack really liked Lorrie. Nick had told Amy he understood her urge to constantly meddle in a younger sibling's life—he was guilty of it himself sometimes—but it was an impulse one should fight.

"But Lorrie doesn't have a mother," Amy said.

"She has you, and you care for her and spoil her more than any mother would," Nick had replied. "Lorrie's lucky. If I'd ever had someone like you to love me, I wouldn't have wanted anything else." His eyes on her had softened like his words.

Amy had forgotten her initial impression of Nick and had believed he loved her—until that last night of the summer before he was to leave L.A. for Berkeley. He had taken her out for dinner, then afterward they went out on Sebastian's boat and ended up making love on it. Nick had driven Amy home, dropping her off and saying he'd return to the apartment he and Jack shared so he could pack.

Amy had promised Nick she would transfer to Berkeley and would join him in a few weeks. That night on a sudden impulse, after he'd gone she'd driven to his apartment, just to see him one last time.

Amy bit into her bottom lip as she remembered.

When she'd gotten to his apartment, she'd heard hushed voices coming from beyond Nick's door. Nick hadn't been alone. Lorrie was there too, and as Amy stood outside the door and listened, she'd heard soft cries. Every warm emotion in her heart had turned to ice.

Finally, hoping she might have made a mistake, Amy had gone to the window and peeked inside through the half-drawn shades. There was no mistaking what she saw.

Lorrie was in Nick's arms, on his bed. She wasn't wearing much. Nick was speaking to her softly. Jack was nowhere in sight.

The scene had been too incriminating for any explanation to wipe it clean. Amy had rushed home, too hurt to confront them, but somehow, Lorrie must have seen her. Later her sister had come to her and confirmed Amy's worst suspicions. She'd begged her forgiveness.

Amy remembered Lorrie's stricken, bewildered face. "I didn't mean for it to happen! I didn't! I tried to stop loving him when you started going with him, Amy. I could see how much he meant to you. I even dated Jack—to forget Nick. But he was unforgettable."

Sweet Lorrie, always trying to help and never quite managing it. "I know," Amy whispered.

"I had to see him before he left," Lorrie had continued. "I didn't mean for anything to happen, but when he kissed me, I couldn't seem to stop him."

At this point she broke into a torrent of fresh tears, and Amy's heart twisted with the agony of her hopeless love.

"It was awful. I feel so guilty. I hate him now for what he did to me. For what he did to you. And I hate myself. He never loved...either one of us. Oh, Amy, I'm so sorry. Please say it won't matter. Please say you still love me. I don't care about him. Not after..."

Lorrie's luminous eyes were wide with horror. Amy's imagination had filled with lurid images of Nick with Lorrie.

"It wasn't what I thought it'd be," Lorrie moaned darkly. "I'll never care about him again, if only you'll love me. If you stop loving me, I swear I'll die."

For all her outward glamour and beauty, Lorrie was still a child. But she was more fragile, more easily wounded than any child, perhaps because she'd lost her mother so young, and Amy had always been fiercely protective of her.

"Of course, I love you," Amy said in spite of her own pain, stroking her hair. "I'll never stop loving you."

"You can have him. I'll never go near Nick again."

"I don't want him."

Lorrie looked up. "Then Nick won't come between us."

"Never again."

"And you won't go away with him?"

Amy could feel her sister shaking.

"No."

Slowly Lorrie had quieted down.

As time passed, although Amy felt destroyed, she had tried not to blame Lorrie. Only Nick. Sometimes Amy had wanted to kill him, not just for his betrayal of her, but for what he'd done to a mere child. Lorrie was never the same after that night. Her innocence was gone, and there was always a sadness in her eyes. She rarely dated. She became more dependent than ever on Amy.

Amy saw it all so clearly. On that first day when she'd gone to speak to Nick she had broken them up, and by doing so, she had inadvertently stolen the man Lorrie had believed she loved. Lorrie had been too immature to handle this loss. Nick had decided Lorrie was too young for him and had dated her older sister instead. But his initial attraction for the more beautiful Lorrie had lingered. When she'd come to him on that last night, even after a night of lovemaking with Amy, he hadn't been strong enough to resist the temptation. He was a man of lusty appetites—a man easily aroused, and once aroused, he could be very determined. No doubt he had even regretted what had happened. But it was too late for his regrets to make any difference. For all his appeal, he'd proven he was a man of weak character, and Amy despised him.

Maybe she could have forgotten him and that awful night if only there hadn't been the baby. But then she'd been trapped after its birth. Nick had found out about Triple and had forced her to marry him.

At least Amy couldn't be sorry about Triple, no matter how much pain his birth had brought her. She loved him too dearly.

Nick was the problem, she thought, still standing in the shower. He had to go before he started making trouble all over again.

Amy turned off the water and got out, quickly toweling herself off with a thick Turkish towel and dressing in a pair of purple slacks and a voluminous pullover sweater. She dried her gleaming hair, wound it into a knot at the nape of her neck, and put on fresh makeup. While she went about these ordinary, habitual tasks, she kept wondering about Nick.

What did he intend? It was alarming the way he knew just what to say and what to do to win the loyalty of everyone close to her. Sam and Triple had always adored him, and although at first the gloomy Apolonia had presented a challenge, Nick had hastily surmounted it by pretending an interest in her gardening. As for Lorrie, Amy couldn't bear to think about their relationship. She was relieved that her sister wasn't home.

Amy had locked both her bedroom and her bathroom doors, but she'd half expected Nick to force his way inside while she was showering.

Since he hadn't come looking for her, Amy decided to go looking for him. When no one answered her soft knocks at Triple's door, she pushed it open. In the dim light she saw a suitcase spread open across Triple's bed. Masculine toilet articles littered the navy bedcovers, along with the red slacks and silk shirt Nick had been wearing.

One step into the room, and she realized she should have waited for Nick to look for her. The bathroom door opened, bounced against the door stopper, and Nick stepped boldly into the bedroom. Though she was standing in the shadows, the dazzling white light from the bathroom played over his immense body, and she had no trouble seeing him.

He was naked. For an endless moment she could only gape in breathless surprise. She felt her cheeks grow hot, and her heart begin to hammer as she struggled to focus her attention on something besides bronzed skin and well-defined muscles. But no matter how she fought it, his virile maleness held her gaze like a magnet.

He had just showered and a sheen of dampness glistened in his golden hair. The tangy scent of masculine after-shave lotion emanated from his smooth jawline. She caught the pleasant smell of fresh soap.

Black slacks and a long-sleeved blue dress shirt lay carelessly over one muscular arm. He held a towel in his other hand. She hastily averted her gaze, but not before memorizing every detail of that flawless male body, from the golden-furred planes of his hard chest to the rippling muscles of his shoulders, torso and legs. A surging ache rose from deep inside her as she longed to be held in his arms and to let her fingers glide over the moist warmth of his flushed skin.

Treacherous thought! Dear Lord! But it had been so long—two years—since she'd known anything other than the agonizing loneliness of living like a single woman—two years since she'd experienced the thrilling fulfillment only Nick could give her.

And she'd told herself that that night after Jack's service had meant nothing to her and that she wanted Nick out of her life forever!

She gasped, acutely conscious of the implied intimacy of finding Nick naked in a bedroom, even their son's.

Nick heard the sound. Amused blue eyes discovered her in the darkness and studied her mercilessly.

Amy wanted to die. Or at least to run.

She remained frozen where she was.

His throaty chuckle sent a tremor down her spine. "Well, well. Things seem to be going even better than I planned. I never expected you to come to me. And so soon."

Amy let out a low growl of fury. "I should have known you'd take this in the worst possible way."

"Or the best. Our viewpoints differ, as usual." He grinned that white-toothed, loathsome grin that could have such a devastating effect on her nerves. "Tell me, what is it you need from me? I'm always happy to be of service—to such a beautiful lady, who just happens to be my wife." He tossed his towel on the bed. His mocking tone, combined with his utter nakedness and perverse lack of modesty, gave his seemingly innocent remark an unpleasant double meaning.

Her face turned as red as a wine grape. "I don't need anything from you," she snapped. "I'll be in the living room, thank you."

"You'll stay right here," he commanded, taking a menacing step toward her.

"Not when you don't have a stitch on."

"That situation can easily be remedied," he said softly, "if you really want it to be."

She regarded him with cool silence. "You're crazy if you think I'm going to stand here and watch you dress."

Amused blue eyes sparkled. "So you prefer me nude? I had hoped so."

She emitted a muted cry. "Damn you. Stop twisting everything I say."

"Okay, okay. Look, if I don't mind dressing in front of you, why should you mind watching? It's not as if you haven't seen it all before."

"That's hardly something I want to be reminded of."

"Really?" An eyebrow arched and met the wayward lock of gold that tumbled over his brow. He looked boyish and mischievous, and so dangerously attractive that she blushed again. "Then why did you come in here?"

She was backing toward the door. "I knocked, you ... you ..." She searched for the worst insult in her repertoire, only to find them all hopelessly inadequate.

"Why don't you save that particular compliment for later?" he asked in a velvety, hypnotic tone.

"Compliment?" she shrieked. She had almost reached the door to the hall. "I was about to call you a bastard!"

"In my case that's only the truth. Remember?" he teased, not in the least perturbed.

She had one foot out the door.

"If you go, I'll only come after you," he taunted softly.

"Without any clothes?"

"I swear, I will."

She hesitated, recalling how he liked nothing better than to back up his obnoxious promises.

"You may remember that I love running around the house nude," he added, "especially if I'm chasing you."

"For your information I've struggled to forget everything about your odious personal habits just as I've tried to forget everything about our short-lived marriage."

He moved closer.

"Why do you keep strutting around naked?" she cried. "Why don't you get dressed?"

Without bothering to search for his underwear, he pulled on the black slacks. They hugged his male shape as tightly as a glove. She watched his bronzed hand tug the zipper up.

"I'm flattered it's been such a struggle—to forget me," he said, letting his gaze linger on her face.

Her own gaze was resting hungrily on the tanned expanse of that gold-furred chest. "You are so arrogant. You're flattered even when I insult you!"

He laughed boldly. "You could do worse, you know, than to have a man who thrives on your insults—since you love to dish them out." Then he said huskily, "Some men are not so easily pleased. You're lucky I have such a sweet disposition."

Sweet! That was the last adjective she would have applied to him. "Just get dressed," she muttered.

Feeling trapped, Amy turned her back on him and studied Triple's gruesome collection of pets while Nick took what seemed an interminable time to dress. In one jar was a tarantula. Normally its hairy legs in motion would have evoked a mild shiver of horror in Amy at the very least, but she was too wary of the dangerous man behind her. In another jar there was an immense chrysalis, which Triple inspected first thing every morning when he jumped out of bed. There were frogs, beetles, turtles and other spiders.

From behind her came the taunt of Nick's raspy voice. "It's safe to look now."

"I prefer not to." Her eyes remained glued on the hairy black legs of Triple's tarantula. Perhaps if she ignored him, Nick would leave her alone.

Nick lifted a jar of scrambling spiders. "Our Triple's certainly all boy," he said, refusing to be ignored.

Our. Why did the word make Amy tremble and want to slink away?

"Like his father," Nick murmured, his low voice a silken caress. He moved nearer. She caught his clean male scent. His voice grew even softer. "You weren't always made of ice. Don't you ever get lonely, Amy?"

"No!" She spoke sharply, breathlessly. She didn't dare to turn around.

"I do." His tone was oddly warm and gentle.

Her heartbeats sped crazily. "I'm sure there are many women..." She broke off, finding the thought surprisingly painful.

"There are, but I'm not interested."

"Maybe you should develop new interests."

Her sideways glance sought his carved profile in the dim light. His mouth was set in grim lines.

"Believe me, I've told myself that more than once, but I'm not ready to give up on you and me."

"Nick, please, I don't want to talk about us."

"You never do." He spoke quietly, but with a biting cynicism. "Amy, all my life people have shut me out. First my mother did, because I was the bastard that ruined her life. When I was a kid I knew something was wrong with me, but it took the school-yard bully to spell it out with brutal unforgettable clarity. Mother never told me anything. Then when my father found out, it took his family a long time to accept me. All my life I've had to fight for anything I wanted."

Nick's expression had turned dark and bitter as he remembered the pain of his childhood. As always, thinking of him suffering as an innocent child affected Amy, even though she knew the story by heart.

Nick's father, Wayne Jackson, was a rancher in south Texas and the king of a million acres scattered around the world. When Wayne had been separated from his wife Mercedes, he'd had a brief affair with Nick's mother, Ticia Browning. By the time Ticia realized she was pregnant, Wayne was reunited with his wife. Nick felt that he'd had to fight his way into the family and battle for acceptance.

Amy turned to face him. "I can't explain. I just can't," she said desperately.

"You mean you won't."

"Why can't you understand that it's too late? Explanations won't make any difference."

He studied her pale, frightened face, and was as puzzled as he always was every time he tried to get to the bottom of what had gone wrong between them. She looked terrified. Of him. Why? That was the question.

"All right. For now," he replied gently, not wanting to push her too far, too soon.

Although Nick had already studied the hodgepodge collection on Triple's shelves, he did so again to give Amy a chance to recover. He felt a heady mixture of fatherly pride and love. Every photograph Nick had ever sent Triple was tacked prominently to his bulletin board. The makeshift gallery was overflowing onto the walls.

There was a jumble of curling yellow articles about Nick's sailing triumphs and glossy color pictures of Nick and his trophies, all dangling at crazy angles from lemon-yellow tacks. He smiled faintly, suddenly reminded that his younger half brother, Jack, had also kept all the pictures and articles about Nick's sailing triumphs just as proudly when they'd been kids.

In many ways Triple reminded Nick of Jack. The boy definitely had Jack's lust for life, his wildness, and Triple was all the more precious to him now that Jack was gone. Triple would need a strong guiding hand, and Amy, for all her dedication, tended to spoil those she mothered.

Nick studied Amy for a minute. "Thank you for letting my son keep all these pictures of me out like this."

"They mean a lot to him," Amy said.

"They mean a lot to me," came that raspy silken tone.

His sincerity caused a warm, wonderful confusion to envelop her.

"There's no reason to thank me," she said stiffly.

His dark gaze narrowed. "You could have turned Triple against me, but you didn't. A lot of women who felt the way you did would have."

"That wouldn't have been the fair thing to do."

"And I'm grateful."

She fought to avoid the blue infinity of his eyes. Instead of looking at him she kept studying the writhing legs in the spiders' jar. "I did it for Triple," she whispered brokenly, "not you. Boys need to be proud of their fathers."

"Perhaps you should amend that to boys need their fathers," he said, his voice dry and sardonic.

"You never miss a chance, do you?"

"I try not to," he said.

Their eyes met and held for an instant, until she looked away.

Nick broke the awkward silence, changing the subject. "Who's been feeding all of Triple's ... er ... pets while he's been sick?"

"Probably no one."

"Then I'll take over that responsibility," Nick said. "What do they eat?"

She turned and looked at the beasts scrambling in their jars. She grimaced. "Each other."

Amy had spoken with loathing and disgust, but behind her, Nick burst into laughter. Even as the pleasant sound shivered down her spine, she turned in surprise, intensely conscious of how attractive he was. She couldn't resist a giggle of her own.

Soon the deep rich sounds of their mingled joy filled the room. It was the first time in years that they'd laughed together.

Amy giggled until tears sparkled in her eyes. In his delight, Nick reached out and took her arms, instinctively drawing her close and hugging her. She felt the brush of his jaw and chin against her hair, and an electric current shot through her.

Too late she realized what she had done. She stopped laughing, and so did he, but they continued to cling to each other a little breathlessly. Treacherous sensations of intimacy flowed through Amy. She pressed her hands against his shoulders and arched away from his chest. He let her go, and she backed away clumsily. But the spontaneous moment of shared humor had touched her more than she'd wanted it to. She felt shy and embarrassed. She couldn't stop herself from recalling how delicious it was to be folded against the warmth of Nick's body. It was all too easy to remember how charming and fun loving he could be—too easy to remember how deeply she'd once loved him.

"I'm serious, Nick," she said, trying to be. "They do eat each other, but you'll have to ask Triple who eats who."

Nick lifted a wire-screened box from a shelf to examine it more closely. "What's in here?"

"Careful," Amy said with a shiver. "That's Geronimo."

"Geronimo?"

"Triple's snake," she whispered.

"His cage is practically falling apart," Nick said. "If Geronimo doesn't get a square meal before long, he's going to slip out one of these cracks where the lid's warped."

"At the moment Geronimo is the least of my worries."

"I know what you mean," Nick said gently. "Why don't we call the hospital and check on Triple? If he's okay, we'll eat and rest a bit and then go back."

She didn't resist when he touched her waist possessively, guiding her out of their son's bedroom. It never occurred to her to marvel at how quickly and ruthlessly he was zeroing in on his targets—her heart and soul.

Five

———

Triple was doing well at the hospital, so Amy and Nick enjoyed a late dinner with Sam. They spread out plates of cold cuts and fruit in the informal dining room that overlooked the Pacific. Lights from the boats offshore flickered against the darkness.

Lorrie had not come home. Amy wondered guiltily if she had sensed Nick would be there and was avoiding him. Ever since Amy had married Nick, Lorrie had been terrified he'd find some way to move in with them.

Sitting across the table from Amy, Nick was stunning. The lapis color of his dress shirt turned his eyes a most dazzling shade of blue. Amy tried not to look at him because every time she did, she felt the warmth of his intense gaze skimming over her, caressing her, and she would quiver in response to this pleasantly disturbing sensation. She would glance down quickly at her plate, but not so quickly that Nick didn't realize how he had affected her. She knew if she glanced up at such a time, she would catch the knowing flash of one of his frequent white smiles.

"I am always delighted by the view in this room," Sam said.

Nick smiled lazily. "So am I."

Sam was looking at the glistening ocean. Nick was watching Amy eat strawberries with her fingers. He seemed to take great pleasure as her white teeth nipped the red skin of the berries and sank delicately into the luscious pink fruit. He smiled every time she licked a pearly droplet of sweet juice from her fingers.

Amy's gaze lifted to his during this sticky process. Nick was regarding her with a gaze of sheer aesthetic appreciation, as if he considered her an opulent masterpiece of female flesh. She had finished licking her fingertips. Her tongue was flicking tidily over her lips, leaving them moist and luminously soft. His eyes grew hot, and his hungry look made her creamy skin glow as pinkly as that of the lush strawberries she'd been nibbling. Embarrassed, she brought her napkin to her lips, hiding the lower part of her face from his view as seductively as a beautiful houri in a Muslim harem. She lowered her long-lashed eyes and ate no more.

His gaze lingered.

After dinner Apolonia served mugs of hot chocolate topped with whipped cream and cups of steaming black coffee.

"Tomorrow morning I go to grocery store and do the shopping, Mr. Nick," Apolonia apologized. "Tomorrow night I serve you hot meal."

Nick beamed at her. "This was wonderful. Especially the strawberries."

Amy blushed, but no one other than Nick saw it. He noticed everything.

Apolonia, who seemed younger and prettier than usual, was chattering gaily. She was wearing a frilly, girlish apron that Amy had never seen before. She had even put on lipstick, and she smiled almost as often as Nick did.

When Apolonia had returned to the kitchen, Sam said to Amy, "It always amazes me how different Apolonia is around Nick. She can be so difficult."

"That's a talent I need to hone in the near future," Nick said carefully, looking at his wife. "There's a certain difficult woman I'm set on charming." Nick's slow tone was laced with sardonic amusement.

A chill settled over Amy. Although she made no comment, she couldn't keep her heart from fluttering, or her senses from stirring.

Time passed uneventfully as they finished dinner. Lorrie did not come home. Nick was unusually quiet. He seemed content to lean back and listen to father and daughter tease one another affectionately. From time to time Amy wondered uneasily what Nick was thinking.

As he watched Sam and Amy, a warmth invaded Nick's soul. Amy's life had always been filled with people, and he'd enjoyed being part of the hubbub when they'd dated. She still lived with her child, her father and her sister. His own life was empty by comparison. For years he'd let himself believe all she'd wanted was money. Now he could no longer justify that shallow assumption he'd made as a sop to his own wounded ego when she'd rejected him as a man. For all her hardness as a businesswoman, Amy had always known how to fill her life with love and people, and although Nick was an extrovert, he didn't.

He'd built himself a beautiful house that overlooked San Francisco Bay, but it was so vast and lonely, he rarely spent time there. He was always flying from city to city alone to check on the far-flung branches of South Sails. He'd been able to throw himself into the America's Cup campaign with a vengeance because it was no sacrifice for him to give himself completely to the effort that cost most men their families. No one cared if Nick Browning sailed fourteen hours a day, seven days a week, month after month, for two to three years.

As Nick watched Amy and Sam, he realized how sick he was of no one caring. Why should he live alone when he had a wife and child? He'd lost a lot of time being angry at Amy for the way she'd used him, but that was over. Maybe she'd wanted his money, but he'd always hungered for the love that permeated her life. Suddenly he was determined to have it again.

After dinner Nick drove Amy to the hospital, and they looked in on their child and found him sleeping peacefully. His progress was so favorable that Nick found it easy to persuade Amy to return home and get a full-night's sleep in her own bed.

It was almost midnight when they returned. Nick seemed to realize how tired she was and let her go to her own room at once.

Alone, Amy quickly took her hair down and changed into an old-fashioned flannel nightgown, buttoning it to her throat. When she heard the jaunty sounds of Nick singing to himself in his own, tuneless, raucous way, she turned on her radio to shut him out. She didn't like dwelling on the unpleasant fact that he'd be sleeping next to her in Triple's bedroom.

Later, sinking into her bed, Amy was so exhausted she expected to fall asleep at once. But she lay awake for hours. It was strange that the night before, in Nick's arms on a narrow couch in a hospital waiting room, sleep had come so easily.

Tonight her thoughts tumbled restlessly over each other.
She kept thinking of Nick, recalling how his blue shirt had
hugged his lithe body, how his eyes had sparkled every time
he'd looked at her from across the table. She remembered
his kiss, how his mouth had covered hers in the hospital and
how wantonly she'd welcomed his passion. She remembered as well how tenderly they'd laughed together later in
their son's room. It was suddenly difficult to remember the
terrible reasons why she had to resist him.

She envisioned him standing resplendently naked in
Triple's bedroom. She recalled as well their last night together two years before. Nick had been so devastated in his
grief, so alone, with none of his family there. Her heart had
gone out to him. She'd been so afraid for him. She'd wanted
only to ease his pain when she'd welcomed him into her
arms, never dreaming she would respond to his touch again.
To her amazement she'd found an ecstasy and a thrilling
completeness in his lovemaking beyond anything she'd ever
imagined. Afterward she'd come frighteningly close to for-
giving him. The hardest thing she'd ever done was to leave
the next morning and face the loneliness and sorrow of
knowing she could never have him.

Never... The word seemed to repeat itself in her weary
mind.

Long ago she'd made a promise to Lorrie. Because of it
she was now doomed to lead her life separately from Nick's.
She had to protect not only herself, but the two people she
loved most.

There was no way to go back, to rethink whether what she
had done was right or wrong. There were no second
chances. The one thing she knew was that she had to get
Nick out of her life as soon as possible.

But how? He seemed so determined to stay.

At last Amy threw off her sheets and got up. She pulled on her thick terry robe and stepped out onto her balcony, into the shining darkness.

The night was crisp and cold. A sliver of moon hung in a black and starless sky. She went to the railing and gazed out upon the glistening ocean and the mansions that hugged its edge.

"Guilty conscience?" The low, raspy voice came from behind her, following her train of thought much too closely for comfort.

She started. "I couldn't sleep; that's all."

Nick was lounging against the railing in front of Triple's door. Moonlight outlined his body and she strained to look at him. "Neither could I," he said.

She wanted to rush back into her room, to try to make some sense of her troubled thoughts, but that was out of the question. Nick read her mind, approaching her lazily, cutting off her avenue of escape.

"Beautiful night," he murmured.

"Yes."

His eyes sparkled. "Beautiful woman."

A warm flush ran through Amy, terrifying in its pleasure; a driving physical need, astonishing in its intensity.

"There's something so peaceful about the aftermath of a storm," he said.

She nodded in silent agreement, glad that he didn't seem to expect her to speak.

"Or the aftermath of a lovers' quarrel." The conversation had shifted to a more dangerous topic. "I guess it's a natural pattern—violence followed by a peaceful interlude. Do you remember the way we used to fight?"

Amy remembered all too well. Shifting uneasily, she tried to concentrate on the moon that was blazing in its glory.

"We'd make up, and there would be a beautiful closeness between us," he said softly, dangerously.

She told herself not to listen, but she was drawn by the sound of his voice. His words wove a spell and time seemed to slide backward.

"I remember another night like this one, after a storm, when the ocean was washed with moonlight," he said.

Oh, Amy thought, so did she. Her fingernails dug into the soft wood of the railing as she fought to deny the poignant memory. It was no use. The feelings he'd aroused were overwhelming.

"We were young and in love."

"Nick, don't . . ." she whispered desperately.

"We were sailing Sebastian's *Marauder* offshore when a storm blew up, and we had to seek shelter behind the leeward side of an uninhabited Island."

He said no more, but he didn't have to. What had happened had been wonderful, unforgettable. She'd been a virgin, and she'd never meant to let him make love to her. But he had, and it had been too natural, too beautiful and too perfect to regret. That night had been their beginning. It was only later, after he'd betrayed her and she'd learned how little she'd really meant to him, that she was sorry.

"You don't know how hard I've tried to forget everything about you," she said bitterly.

"No harder than I've tried. There was a time—before Jack's funeral—that I thought I'd succeeded. Now I know I never will. What happened to us, Amy? Why won't you tell me?"

Because the answers to those questions could destroy too many lives, she thought.

"Do you know what's bothered me the most all these years?" he asked.

"I can't imagine."

"When you found out you were pregnant, you didn't come to me."

Amy was suddenly terribly afraid. In the empty chasm of silence, her heart thundered violently.

She heard a sound like a door shutting softly near Lorrie's room. Had she only imagined it?

Amy couldn't look at Nick. She couldn't face him. He found her too easy to read.

"I never understood that," he continued. "You'd always been so open with me. Everything was fine between us until I went away to Berkeley at the end of the summer. You were supposed to come, too, but you didn't. I didn't know what to think. Why did you promise to come as soon as you finished your job as lifeguard if you never meant to? Why didn't you call? Why didn't you come? All you would say was that you'd changed your mind. Amy, why haven't you ever been willing to tell me what happened?"

At first she hadn't wanted to hear anything he had to say, but later, when she'd known for certain about the baby, she'd wanted to. She'd almost gone to him that once, and that mistake had nearly cost her everything. She watched the waves roll against the distant beach and shivered.

If Nick ever discovered that the mother of her son was not Amy but the immature Lorrie, he might find a way to take Triple from her.

"Amy?"

She wanted to turn to him, to tell him everything, but that was something she could never do.

Long ago she'd decided that her only defense with him was silence.

There was only the sound of the surf. And the frightened shuddering of her heart.

At last he spoke again. "When I came back to L.A. to find you, you and Lorrie were gone. No one would tell me where. It wasn't until a year later that Sebastian had a few too many beers after a hard race and accidentally let the cat out of the bag. He told me you had a ten-month-old baby and that he'd been helping you. He let me have it right there in the Riviera Yacht Club bar, practically accusing me of getting you pregnant, of abandoning you. He demanded to know when I was going to make things right between us.''

Dear Sebastian, she thought. How could he have known that telling Nick was the worst possible thing he could have done?

''I came to you at once, of course. I'll never forget the look of hate in your eyes when you opened the door with Triple in your arms and saw that it was me. We'd been so careful, it had never occurred to me you might get pregnant. When I asked you if the baby was mine, you didn't have to say anything. The truth was in your eyes. By then you'd already graduated from UCLA with honors on the scholarships Sebastian had helped you get. He'd hired you, so you had no use for me. I know you would have thrown me out, if I hadn't forced my way into the house. Why?''

Amy's eyes were glittering. She spoke softly. ''Because it was over between us, Nick. I didn't love you anymore. I just wanted you out of my life.''

''But there was more to it than that. I felt it in my gut, just as I feel it now. Amy, I can't live like this anymore—not knowing what went wrong. I want a real marriage.''

''Then you should have married someone else.''

''But I loved you. And you were the mother of my child. No other woman could have given me that.''

She flinched, and her face went even whiter than the moon. Again, her nails scored the railing. ''Even so, it was wrong of you to force me to marry you,'' she managed quietly.

"You should have known I couldn't let Triple grow up illegitimate the way I had—nameless, feeling like he didn't fit in anywhere. He had to know he had a father who loved him—and his mother."

It would be so easy to believe his pretty words. Too easy. It was more difficult to remember how he'd gone away to Berkeley, how he'd called only once to ask her why she hadn't come, how casually he'd seemed to accept her change of plans, how indifferent he'd been until he'd found out about Triple. Perhaps, in his way, he did love her, but her way was not so casual and never so cruel.

"It's over, Nick." A sob caught in her throat. "It's been over for years."

He laughed in the darkness. "That's what you keep telling me. At the moment I can think of only one way to convince you that you're wrong."

He touched her, and she shivered. "What are you so afraid of, Amy?" His fingers ran lightly down her body, reaching inside her terry wrapper and leaving in their wake a quicksilver, tingling awareness of him.

She could have stopped him if he'd been savage, but he wasn't. He was infinitely gentle, and his gentleness beguiled her. She wanted him so much. There was a look in his eyes she'd seen there before, an urgency, a wanting, a desperation. Only tonight his determination burned more fiercely than it ever had in the past.

She felt hot, keenly alive, and in that moment everything that stood between them was as nothing. There was only passion, dark need, desire. He pulled her into his arms, his male hardness pressing into her thighs. His hand slid over her body, caressing her. She moaned softly as she felt herself succumbing to the powerful force of his magnetism. He coiled a black length of her loose hair between his fingers and held her face so close she could feel the warmth of his breath tickle the skin above her mouth.

"You've haunted me, Amy," he muttered in a strange harsh voice. "You'll never know how many times I've imagined you, heavy with my child, desperate and alone. I will never forgive myself for that. Never. Let me make it up to you. Give us a chance, Amy. Maybe you don't love me now, but for God's sake, give us a chance."

She felt a rush of guilt. But he kissed her, and there was a ferocity in him that she had never known. His lips sought to draw her into the vortex of his passion. His kisses seemed to go on endlessly. Her arms encircled his neck. She felt the thunder of his heart as a piercing wild hunger swept through them both.

The moonlight glinted off the water; the salt smell of the ocean enveloped them.

His lips left her mouth, and she felt their heat as he trailed kisses over her cheek into the smooth downy softness of her hairline.

She laid her head against his chest, and her raven hair streamed over his shoulders like a silken veil, wrapping around the bare skin of his throat as the feathery wisps blew on the cool breeze that came off the water. She caught his clean musky scent, and the slow ache that began in the middle of her belly seemed to spread throughout her body.

He pushed the edges of her robe aside, and only thin flannel separated his exploring hands from her body as he caressed her soft belly. His hands slid upward ever so slowly. She heard the catch of his indrawn breath as he found the soft velvet mounds of her breasts and fondled them until their fleshy tips hardened.

"Oh, Amy," he groaned, his callused palms seeking and exploring the warm, yearning womanliness of her.

She sighed and plunged her hands into the glorious thickness of his golden hair, pulling his face and mouth closer again, wanting nothing more than to be consumed by the white heat of his frenzied kisses, by his velvet torrid touching.

His touch alone was splendor and beauty. Never had she wanted any other man. She was glad of the darkness, glad that there was nothing to distract her from the warm, live contact of his mouth against her skin, of his body pressed into hers. He was beauty. And she was beauty. And the whirl of emotion he aroused was beauty.

He continued to kiss her in that mad, wonderful intimate way until she was breathless, until some new nakedness deep within her stirred, and she knew she was opening herself to him again, surrendering not only her body but her soul.

Along with the passion came the sweetness of her love for him, that same dangerous sweetness that had seduced her so many years before. Only she wasn't the naive girl she'd been then. She was a woman who'd known not only the full force of love, but the terrible pain of betrayal.

Her world was spinning out of control. There was only Nick, and her love, and in that moment the wrongness of loving him didn't matter anymore.

A soft moan of pleasure was rising in her throat as he led her toward her bedroom door. She had to open her eyes to find her way. Dimly, far beneath, Amy became aware of a fluttery movement on the beach. A woman with golden hair was walking aimlessly along the water's edge. She was bundled in white furs against the chill, but filmy white skirts swirled around her slender ankles. Rhinestone slippers dangled from her fingers.

The thought flickered in the back of Amy's mind that it was odd for a woman in an evening gown to do such a thing on such a cold night—even in Malibu. She focused her attention on the woman. The wind swept the girl's hair back from a fragile face.

Lorrie! Only Lorrie would do such a thing! Lorrie must have come home. She must have seen them on the balcony together. She had been frightened. Amy realized how extremely upset Lorrie must be to go near the water.

An image from the past rose in Amy's mind: that golden hair matted in seaweed, that delicate face lying white and lifeless in the roiling surf, that body limp and frozen as it was stirred by the waves. "My fault..." Amy whispered dully, remembering the agony of that night. "My fault..."

Lorrie must have come home tonight and somehow discovered that Nick was here. Amy saw it all so clearly. Lorrie hadn't been able to deal with his presence in the house. She probably thought that Amy had wanted him here, that she'd even asked him here. Lorrie had felt lost and confused. Whenever she felt threatened she went down to the water. It was something she'd done ever since the tragic boating accident, once with near fatal consequences.

Amy pushed anxiously against Nick's shoulders. "You have to stop," she whispered, panic in her low tone. "I can't... I just can't."

"What?" His hands on her body tightened. Then he let her go. She could feel his eyes, intense, questioning.

She turned anyway, ashamed that she'd come so close to losing control. Her life and the life of her family had been shattered twice—once by death, once by love. Both times she'd felt terrified by the feeling that there were no rules, no control, that she was helpless to change her destiny.

Never again.

Once she'd made the mistake of loving the same man her sister had loved, and she'd nearly wrecked all of their lives.

She couldn't allow Nick to destroy them all over again.

From some deep reserve of inner strength she summoned the willpower to push him away.

She leaned against the railing feeling dazed and breathless.

All he had to do was touch her again, and she would have been lost.

But he didn't touch her. For a long moment they stared at one another. His face was dark, closed, but the blazing passion in his eyes jolted through her and left her shaken.

"Amy." Nick's voice was low and charged with emotion.

"If you force me tonight, I swear I'll never forgive you," she whispered.

He expelled a long breath of angry frustration. "So what's new?" But he backed away from her, widening the distance between them in order to resist the impulse to drag her into his arms again. "Why, Amy?" he demanded hoarsely. "Why? I'm not leaving until I know."

Lorrie was standing directly beneath them in the shadows. Amy looked from her sister to Nick.

"Why are you so determined to torture me with these questions?" came Amy's sobbing cry. "By making love to me?"

"I don't want to torture you. I want to love you."

"No." She shook her head. The pain splintering through her body was too great to be borne. "You never loved me. You don't even know the meaning of that emotion. You don't love. You only make love," she said, weeping angrily. "And I hate you! Do you understand? I've hated you for years!"

She was shaking, and tears were streaming down her cheeks. Amy Browning never, never, screamed at people. She never cried. Only Nick could shatter the shield of bitter control she hid behind.

Only Nick.

She turned to run. His hand gripped her shoulder to stop her.

"You don't hate me," he taunted softly. His fingers cut into her flesh. "You love me."

She twisted out of his reach and dashed toward the door to her room, slamming it and bolting it once she was inside.

His fist pounded against the glass, but she refused to let him in.

"Go away!" she moaned.

If she opened the door, there would be no stopping him. Wrong! There would be no stopping herself.

She sagged against the wall and hugged her body with her arms. Slowly she sank to the floor and wept bitterly.

For the man she still wanted despite everything.

For the man she must never let herself have.

Six

Amy awoke the next morning feeling even more exhausted than when she'd collapsed on her bed the night before. After she showered, she took great pains to make up her face, attempting to conceal the black circles beneath her eyes. She braided her hair and wound the braids into a sedate knot at the nape of her neck. Then she put on her most severely tailored black suit, a shapeless garment she knew Nick would hate, and headed for the kitchen hoping to drink a cup of coffee before she had to face either him or Lorrie.

On her way she discovered Lorrie's door ajar. Amy pushed it open, calling to her sister softly, but Lorrie was gone. Her bed hadn't even been slept in. Wondering where Lorrie might have spent the night, Amy felt a fresh tug of guilt for having let Nick reenter their lives and cause problems.

Even if Amy could forgive Nick, he would never be accepted by Lorrie. Lorrie had been changed by that night with Nick, and Amy's deep protective feelings for her sister had been outraged. The last thing she wanted to do now was to hurt her. Amy wished that she'd had the strength to go to Lorrie last night and talk to her, but she hadn't been able to.

Amy closed Lorrie's door and hoped that Nick wasn't up, that he hadn't gone down to the kitchen yet.

But he was already there, lounging in one of her kitchen chairs, drinking her coffee, and reading her paper. He was wearing the blue dress shirt that always made his eyes so dazzling. Only this morning, he'd added a navy silk tie.

Sections of newspaper were scattered carelessly across the counters, the table and the chairs. No man messed up a newspaper more thoroughly than Nick.

He was reading the business section, her favorite part of the paper.

He glanced up. She wanted to run. Instead she endured his smile and his sardonic, "Good morning," as if it were the most natural thing in the world for the two of them to share a kitchen.

She felt the cynical blaze of his eyes as he appraised her from the top of her shining black head to the pointed tips of her unfashionable shoes. He let his eyes linger appreciatively in all the wrong places until she flushed. She took a cup down from the cabinet.

He smiled again. "That's got to be the ugliest dress you own."

"I put it on just for you," she retorted, grimacing.

He chuckled. "The urge to rip clothes from your body was never stronger."

Her cup rattled against the blue Formica counter top. "You wouldn't dare!"

Once again his winning grin flashed across his dark face. "Don't tempt me," he murmured, leaning toward her, his brilliant eyes recklessly touching her mouth, her breasts, her thighs. He was a man of lusty, unashamed appetites. With his eyes alone, from across the kitchen, he could devour a woman.

Flames of confusion engulfed her. The white-tiled walls seemed to close in and suffocate her.

Why had she never noticed before how tiny her kitchen was? Or was it that it only seemed so, with his virile presence in the center of it? He dominated the room like a giant golden spider happy to have discovered some hapless creature tangled in its web.

Flustered, she poured herself a cup of coffee.

"You obviously woke up on the wrong side of the bed," he said, his smile broadening.

She found his insolence and cheerfulness equally maddening. "And whose fault is that?"

"Yours entirely, darling. I offered. You refused. Next time..."

"There won't be a next time!" she snapped. "And I'm not in the mood for this sort of conversation."

"But I am. I can't stand a woman who sulks over breakfast. "I'm determined to cheer you up."

"You're not doing a very good job."

"Then I'll have to try harder." His blue eyes danced in merciless merriment.

"Please, just leave me alone."

"That's the last thing I intend to do," taunted his soft, well-modulated voice.

She snatched the business section from him and attempted to read an article, but the words ran together in a blur of tiny black print. She was too vividly aware of that indolent male sprawl of arms and legs across the table, of those avid eyes watching every move she made with excessive interest.

Finally she put the paper down and scowled at him. "I can't concentrate with you staring at me like that."

"There's nothing of interest," he said mildly. His gaze fell to her heaving breasts. "In the paper, I mean."

"This house is too small for the two of us," she whispered feverishly.

"You just haven't gotten used to me," he replied, smiling placidly.

"I don't intend to."

"Then we're at cross-purposes—as usual." The fact didn't seem to bother him in the least.

When she picked up another section of newspaper, he said softly, "I called the hospital."

Instantly her hostility died. Her eyes softened with love and motherly concern. "And?"

"I thought that would get your attention."

"Tell me, damn it!"

"Can you believe Triple's himself again and trying to run the show as he always does. He made them move him out of the intensive care unit this morning. He was eating breakfast when I talked to him and complaining because his cinnamon roll was too mushy. It was all I could do to talk him out of going down to the kitchen and teaching the chef..."

"Oh dear! We've got to get to the hospital," Amy cried, pushing her coffee cup away. "There's nothing more dangerous than Triple unsupervised—when he's not on his deathbed. He can get into trouble faster than any child I've ever known."

"He reminds me of me," Nick said fondly.

"Unfortunately," came her dry retort. "Why couldn't he have been just a little like my side of the family?"

"Maybe when we have a girl," Nick tossed hopefully.

A look of horror flashed across her face. "No..."

Nick merely laughed good-naturedly. "Whenever you're ready, I'll drive you, darling."

She was about to object to this last statement on several points when he pulled her into his arms. His hands plunged into her hair. She could feel his fingers quickly, deftly, unpinning the thick braids looped at her neck.

"What are you doing?"

"Improving the scenery," came his husky tone. Her hair fell in showers of black silk down her shoulders. Gently he ran his fingers through it. "There, that's better."

"Nick, you have no right . . ."

He gave her a searing look as he undid the top button of her blouse.

"Don't remind me of my rights, honey, unless you want me to exercise a few of them."

Her senses rocked in alarm as she felt the full power of his earthy appeal. "No," she protested raggedly.

Ever so gently he brushed the leaping pulse in her throat with a callused fingertip, and beneath the velvet warmth of this most casual touch, her heart beat all the faster. "Just be glad I don't have time to strip you, darling," he whispered.

"Don't call me—"

"I keep forgetting, darling," he said.

His fingertip remained on her throat. He stared down at her intimately, impertinently, but instead of the fury she wanted to feel, she felt herself melting. Nevertheless, she managed a stern tone. "You're impossible!"

"Like our son. You love him. Why can't you love me?"

For a breathless eternity they stared into one another's eyes. Then his long fingers wound into her thick hair, pulling her head back so that the curve of her slender neck was exposed. Like one mesmerized, Amy watched the slow descent of his mouth. In a dream she felt the light caress of his lips graze hers, and she tasted the flavor of his tongue as it met her own.

Their mouths parted.

"I love you, Amy. I always have, and I always will."

She didn't want to believe him. She couldn't let herself. Nevertheless, her fingers came up and curled around his collar, among the golden tendrils of his hair, and she kissed him back.

Abruptly he released her. For a long moment she kept her eyes closed. At first because she was too stupefied with pleasure to do otherwise. Then, because she was too mortified to face him.

When at last she let them flutter open, she found to her surprise that Nick seemed almost as stupefied as she.

He had been watching her covertly, a look of wonder on his dark face. Then, when she opened her eyes, an impenetrable mask came over his features as if he could not allow himself to believe the emotion he thought he'd read in her languorous expression.

He grabbed her hand and said in a low harsh tone, "Why don't we go?"

When he went to get the car, Amy phoned Triple to make sure he was all right and to give him orders not to get out of bed. Much to her surprise, Lorrie answered.

Amy felt a deep relief to know her sister was safe.

"Lorrie, what are you doing at the hospital?" Amy asked gently.

"I was worried about Triple. You were home ... with Nick."

Amy knew it wasn't deliberate, but Lorrie's soft voice lacerated Amy's conscience.

"It isn't like you think ..."

Silence.

"Lorrie, I'm sorry."

Silence.

"Please say something," Amy pleaded desperately. "Can you tell me at least if Triple's okay?"

Lorrie hesitated and then began in her weakest voice. "He doesn't even seem sick. He wants me to take him down to the kitchen so he can complain about his breakfast."

"Lorrie, please, you don't have to worry about Nick. He won't be around that long. He only came because of Triple. Just don't let Triple out of your sight. I'm on my way. We can talk when..."

"I don't want to talk."

The line went dead.

When Nick and Amy opened the door to Triple's hospital room, Nick stared in horror at Triple's empty room.

Amy felt only mildly dismayed. She should have known Lorrie couldn't keep Triple here. Lorrie was always putty in the boy's hands. Even at six, his was a strong, fully developed personality, and he knew exactly how to turn an adult's weakness to his own advantage.

"Looks like our little monster's been busy," Amy said, "and I see Lorrie brought him a present from the gift shop."

"Why do you say that?"

"Look!"

Amy pointed to the bright bits of blue foil and streamers of white satin ribbon littering the chairs, the floor, and the bed. In one corner a demolished cardboard box lay askew.

Amy knelt and investigated the torn box. It appeared to have been ripped open by an explosion and then to have belched tiny cars and trucks everywhere.

Nick picked up a discarded miniature red Porsche that had rolled under the bed and set it on the nightstand beside what was left of a half-eaten cinnamon roll.

Other than stuffed animals, Triple had never taken the slightest interest in most toys, a fact Lorrie had never been observant enough to have noticed.

"Where do you think he is?" Nick asked.

"Wherever he can get into the most trouble the quickest," Amy said calmly, sinking into a chair and relaxing for the first time in days. "Lorrie has obviously been as careless as usual and turned her back on him. I wish that could have been avoided, but if Triple is strong enough to seek mischief, he's definitely on the mend."

"We've got to find him," Nick said, alarmed. "Anything could happen to him. Night before last he was at death's door."

"Save your concern for the unlucky person Triple decides to pester."

"How can you be so sure he's all right?" Nick demanded.

"Experience." At Nick's blank look of shock, Amy gave a faint smile. "Never mind. Before long, there will be such a hue and cry that the proper authorities will find him."

Nick paced the room. At every sound in the hall, he would rush to the door. "I don't know how you can take this so coolly," he said.

"I got used to things like this years ago. You forget Triple is not a typical six-year-old. Believe me, the hapless souls who are forced to participate in his adventures are always anxious to return him."

"I can't just stay here and wait. I've got to try to find him."

"Suit yourself," Amy said, closing her eyes. "Why don't you check the kitchen first?"

Nick hadn't been gone long when an army of tight-lipped nurses marched purposefully into the room. At the head of this formidable battalion, Triple was being pushed in a wheelchair. His demeanor was as imperious as that of an Oriental potentate being carried on a litter by an escort of slaves. He was clearly in charge. In each of his hands he tightly clutched two large jars, as if he considered them treasures of vast worth. Several of the nurses were also carrying jars, which they quickly set down on the nearest window ledge seeming only too happy to be rid of them.

Although he looked white-faced and thin, Triple's high-pitched voice rang as exuberantly as usual.

"Mom, I saw a baby being born!"

"You should see what he's done to the kitchen," said one of the nurses.

Amy took this information as calmly as she usually did when faced with one of Triple's adventures. "What were you doing out of your room, dear?"

"No one told me I was supposed to stay in it, Mom."

"You were," Amy said firmly. "I specifically told your Aunt Lorrie..."

"She had to make a phone call."

Amy removed the jars from his hands so the nurses could help him back to bed. In the jars, gray spongy objects hung suspended in formaldehyde.

"What are these, anyway?" Amy asked, setting the disgusting jars in the window.

"Oh, just some tonsils and an appendix a couple of guys had cut out and..."

"I see," Amy said. "Where did you get them?"

"A doctor gave them to me."

"Oh, he did." She helped her son into bed.

"He said I could have them if I'd promise to stay in my room and look at them. Hey, Mom, was he really supposed to spank the baby and make her scream like that? He turned purple when I asked him that. Mom, did it hurt like that when you had me?"

Amy reddened. "Let's not talk about babies right now."

"Mom..."

"Never mind, dear. You're not nearly as strong as you think you are. Why don't you lie back and put your head on the pillow?"

A breathless Nick stumbled into the room. His tie swung from his collar at a rakish angle. A lock of golden hair fell across his brow. Amy imagined him racing down miles and miles of hospital corridors. Nick looked even more worried than he had when he'd dashed off to find Triple. "I couldn't find him anywhere."

"That's because I'm right here, Dad," Triple chirped from the bed.

"Triple!" Nick gave a shout and ran to his bed. "Are you okay, son?"

"I saw a baby..."

"No more about that baby, Triple," Amy said sternly.

"Okay, Mom." Triple grinned so guilelessly that Amy was immediately suspicious of his intentions.

After the nurses left, Triple lay against the pillow looking pale and exhausted. His eyelids drooped, and sitting beside him quietly, Amy knew he'd soon be asleep.

"Did you spend the night at home, Dad?" Triple murmured.

"I slept in your room, son."

"My room, huh? Right next to Mom's?" Triple grinned wanly. "It was almost worth getting sick so we could be a real family."

A real family. The thought hovered in Amy's mind like an elusive, tantalizing dream before it trailed away. Amy's eyes met Nick's for a charged moment that seemed an infinity. His eyes were shining with an intense emotion she couldn't read. Quickly she looked away, determined to break the spell.

Reluctantly Nick turned back to Triple. "Son, don't you go having any harebrained ideas about not getting well—just to keep me here." His voice was husky, and his eyes were disarmingly gentle as they slid from his son's to Amy's face. "Nothing anyone can do or say is going to drive me away again."

Amy stared at him wordlessly as his hand covered hers. She didn't pull away as his callused thumb caressed the soft inner flesh of her palm.

The hospital door opened and closed, allowing a beautiful blonde dressed in white silk, white fur, and white rhinestones to sweep inside on a breath of perfume.

"Hi, Aunt Lorrie."

Lorrie looked ethereal, like a figment from a dream.

Amy and Nick sprang apart instantly. Amy's face darkened guiltily. Nick looked annoyed.

Lorrie ignored Triple's greeting. She ignored her sister as well. "Hello, Nick," she said softly, attempting to bridge the awkwardness. "A-Amy... told me you were here."

Nick glanced toward Lorrie with a look of cool indifference, and a white-faced Lorrie dropped her eyes.

Nick saw Amy's stricken expression. She was staring dazedly at him. When the seconds ticked by and no one spoke, Lorrie tried to cover the awkward moment by talking about her acting career. All she did was make Nick more aware that something was wrong.

For the next half hour, while Lorrie spoke of her latest audition for a television sitcom, Nick was acutely aware of Amy's subtle change of mood. She seemed tired, drained, depleted, curiously on edge, and he was at a loss to understand why. In the past Amy had always adored her younger sister to a fault and been overly protective of her.

Amy seemed to retreat within herself. It was almost as if she weren't there, and he was alone in the room with Lorrie and Triple.

"Well, it's time I went. I just had to come by and check on you, Triple," Lorrie said, patting Triple's hand and clinging to it. "You know how special you are to me since I'll never be able..." Lorrie's voice broke.

Triple's eyes were closed. He was pretending to be asleep. Nick, who'd been studying his wife and only half listening, saw Amy whiten with pain.

"You see, Nick," Lorrie said. "A few years ago, shortly after you left, I was ill. So ill, I'll never be able to have a baby of my own. Triple's all I have."

Nick was watching Amy, who looked utterly bleak.

"I'm sorry," Nick said quietly.

Amy pressed her eyes tightly shut and turned away. "I...I think I'll leave you two to watch Triple for a while," she said, her low voice curt with repressed pain.

"I'll go with you," Nick offered.

"No!" Amy turned wildly, refusing to so much as look at either of them. "I have to be alone!" She stumbled toward the door. "You belong here, Nick. With Lorrie and Triple."

Nick would have rushed after her, if Lorrie hadn't stopped him. "Can't you see she doesn't want you?"

"Hell, yes, I see." He felt impatient, on the verge of something momentous, and Lorrie was deliberately detaining him. "I've got to go after her," he snapped. "I've got to find out what's wrong."

"Let her go, Nick," Lorrie said softly. "Haven't you hurt her enough?"

"All I ever wanted to do was love her. Maybe I made a few mistakes along the way..."

Lorrie blanched.

She opened her mouth, but he didn't wait for her reply. "Watch Triple a minute, will you? Only this time do something right for a change and really watch him." He spun on his heel and was gone.

Though he searched everywhere, Nick couldn't find Amy. She had chosen her hiding place too well. Nor could he force her to tell him what was wrong when she returned to Triple's room hours later.

It was as if her heart and soul had turned to ice.

She was colder to Nick than she'd ever been before.

Amy sat rigidly at her desk, scribbling notes as fast as she could, which wasn't fast enough because Sebastian was barking orders over the phone at an even faster rate.

Two uneventful days had passed since Triple had run loose in the hospital. Since that time, Amy and Nick had taken turns staying with him.

This strategy had been Amy's idea. She liked it because it served a double purpose. Not only was Triple supervised, but she didn't have to see Nick except for the few minutes their shifts overlapped.

Thus there had been no more sticky moonlit conversations, no more sharing of her kitchen and her morning newspaper with him, and no more having to watch Lorrie and him together.

Today Triple was coming home from the hospital.

Today Nick had to leave—for good; before he became firmly entrenched; before he became set on staying forever!

Nick had gone to pick up Triple from the hospital. Amy had planned to go with him, but Sebastian had called, and Sam had offered to go in her place.

Sebastian continued shouting in his excitement. "Of all the times for that kid of yours to pull one of his stunts, this is the absolute worst!"

"I don't usually defend Triple, but not even he could help getting sick, Sebastian."

"Maybe not, but you have to admit drama stalks that kid. I need you, Amy! I don't know the first thing about running Crackle!"

Sebastian was upset because he'd followed one of Amy's hunches and caught two of his key executives embezzling at his potato-chip factory at Long Beach and fired them.

"It's your company."

"One of many, and one I hired you to take care of. I've been here all week. I feel like I'm drowning in potato chips! I can't give you another day off! You've got to be on the premises until you can find someone to replace those two weasels, Beashel and Sheldon. I leave in two days to close that land deal in Australia."

"Then you could give me at least one more day. Triple—"

"Triple's fine. I checked on him myself yesterday. Nick was there. He and the doctor told me Triple's recovery verges on the miraculous. Once that kid's home, he'll be tearing the place apart in no time."

"That's what I'm afraid of. Apolonia's down with the flu again. She went out in the garden during the storm. Sam's not up to chasing Triple."

"Then let Nick chase him! He's offered to."

"He what?"

"And I accepted his generous offer—on your behalf, naturally. He seemed so thrilled, I was touched. So was Triple, for that matter. If you were smart, you'd be thrilled, too. Forgive Nick. Use this opportunity to—"

"Sebastian!"

For all his outward gruffness, Sebastian was an incurable romantic.

"You know I'm right."

"Sebastian, you're meddling in my life—"

"No. I'm merely putting my own affairs in order. I'm going to Australia. You're going to work. Nick stays, and that's final!"

With that, he hung up. For a long moment Amy stared out the window, weighing her options.

There weren't many.

It would do no good to call Sebastian again. He never backed down once he'd made a decision. She tried to think of just one baby-sitter she could call, but all the good ones had told her not to call again.

Nevertheless, she was determined about one thing. Nick was not staying.

The front door banged open with such a violent thud that the whole house shook. Triple's shout reverberated off the tile floors and redwood ceilings.

"Mom!"

She heard the sound of shattering glass.

"I'm coming, dear." She rushed down the hall toward the front door to find a remorseful Triple studying the fragments of a crystal ashtray.

"I bumped into it by accident. Honest, Mom."

He looked so troubled, her heart went out to him. "Never mind, dear."

Triple threw himself into her arms. "Guess what?"

She looked down at him, the ashtray forgotten. A tender smile tugged the corners of her lips.

"Dad says he's staying! For a whole week! Till I get really well! And look what he got me!"

In one hand Triple was holding an immense toy sailboat that was almost as tall as he was. An antenna was attached to the tip of its mast. "He's going to use it to teach me to sail."

"Triple, you've been very sick. I'm not about to let you near the water."

Triple was starting to protest when Nick and Sam came through the door together. Nick was laden down with suitcases and a huge stuffed gorilla he had given Triple as a gift. Sam was carrying the rest of his grandson's possessions. They were laughing over some bit of shared humor.

"Private joke?" Amy asked.

"I was just saying I never saw a hospital process a bill faster," Nick replied. "Triple certainly made a name for himself."

"That was a fun place," Triple said.

"Triple, why don't you take your boat and gorilla and go to your room and lie down?" Amy said, determined to talk to Nick alone.

"I will . . ." Triple glanced earnestly at his mother. "But only if you promise not to make Dad go."

"Triple!"

"Go on, son," Nick said.

Triple squared his jaw mutinously, exactly as Nick did when he was determined to have his own way. Then he ran to his father.

"Don't worry, son," Nick said softly, rumpling the tawny curls. "I can handle your mother."

Triple regarded his father dubiously and remained where he was.

Nick's blazing blue eyes met hers. Amy felt acutely uncomfortable. Still, she managed to speak gently. "I'd really like to thank you for all you've done the past few days, Nick."

"You're welcome," he said, his voice as deceptively soft as hers.

"But, I really think that since Triple's home now, and so much better, we don't need to impose on you any longer."

"Believe me, it's no imposition," Nick replied in that same silken tone.

"I'm sure you must be worried about South Sails," Amy persisted.

"Why? I've been in touch with the office every day. I have complete faith in my staff. If you hire the right team, a company will run itself.

She sent a small, forced smile in his direction. "How very fortunate," she retorted.

His gaze narrowed. "Yes, isn't it?"

"What I was trying to say, Nick, is that you must have a million important things to do."

"I do. You and Triple head the list."

"Why must you always be deliberately obtuse?" she muttered.

There was a watchful stillness in his expression. "Is it so wrong of me to want to help my wife and son when they need me?"

A frown of exasperation swept across her brow. "But we don't need you! Dad can look after Triple."

Sam had listened thus far in silence, but he shook his white head in vigorous dismay at the idea of baby-sitting Triple full time.

"Dad, please..."

"I suppose I could do all right if I had Nick here to back me up," Sam said at last in a conspiratorial tone.

"Dad, Lorrie can help out," Amy pleaded.

"Honey, you know as well as I do that when Lorrie helps she only makes things more difficult. It's best not to count on her for much."

Amy stared hard at her son, her husband, and her father. Never had three male faces been set in more stubborn lines. She couldn't fight them all.

"Mom, he can stay in my room." Triple's eyes were shining with hope.

"He can bunk in with me," Sam countered with equal enthusiasm.

All eyes focused on her, as if everyone expected her to invite Nick into her bedroom, and Amy blushed.

"Oh, that won't be necessary," Nick replied grandly, having prolonged the embarrassing moment as long as possible. "I'll just move my suitcase into that little guest room off the garage. I don't expect to share a room...or a bed...with anyone." He was staring pointedly at his wife.

Nick was enjoying himself. The devil, she thought furiously, for having put her in such a difficult position. But how could she break Triple's heart or disappoint her father after all they'd been through? Triple's recovery was truly miraculous, and she didn't want to do anything that might risk complications.

"Then it's settled," Nick declared triumphantly. "I'm staying. At least for a week." His brilliant eyes touched hers. "Maybe even longer."

"Oh, boy!" Triple cried. "Thanks, Mom."

Triple threw himself into her arms and hugged her.

Glad as she was to have her little boy safely home once more, Amy could feel nothing but horror at the insurrection taking place in her own household.

Nick moved closer and put his arm around Triple and Amy.

She glanced up, seeking Nick's eyes. His fingers tightened on her body, and she shivered.

An undercurrent of electricity flowed between them, its tingling existence such a tangible truth, there was no way to ignore it.

"You won't be sorry," Nick whispered over Triple's head, smiling at her in that way of his that made her feel, despite everything she knew to be true, that she was the only woman in the world for him.

His gaze zeroed in on her parted lips. "I think this calls for a kiss—to seal our bargain, so to speak," he murmured.

She was blinded by the dazzling light in his eyes.

"No..." She reeled away, swallowing convulsively, afraid for him to see how shaken she was.

Trembling, she clung to Triple.

She heard the velvet resonance of Nick's voice. "Soon," he murmured. "Soon." His tenderness reached out and seemed to enfold her with his warmth. "We have a week."

Amy lowered her dark eyes to the tousled gold-brown head of the son they both held in their arms.

She knew suddenly that the most horrible thing of all was the insurrection in her own heart.

Seven

The glass doors to the swimming pool stood open when Amy came downstairs three days later. She knew what those open doors meant, and a painful pulse beat low in her stomach.

Triple and his father were already up, practicing sailing techniques with the remote-control, miniature twelve-meter Nick had given Triple.

Dear Lord! How was it possible that Nick had fit into her life so easily and smoothly? Like Triple, Nick had boundless energy, and he'd made himself incredibly useful. If he wasn't playing chess with Sam or nursing Apolonia, or singing those raucous tuneless songs of his while he cooked in the kitchen, Nick was entertaining Triple by the hour. Only Lorrie was upset by Nick's presence, so upset she'd packed a bag and gone to stay with a friend until he left. Not that her defection seemed to bother Nick or anyone else, except Amy.

Nick was too busy teaching his son sailing theory and chess, helping him learn to read, and helping him care for his pets. Last night, Triple's discovery that Geronimo had slithered out of his poorly constructed cage, Nick had shown Triple how to make the necessary repairs to the screened box, just in case they found the snake.

Father and son were inseparable, and it bothered Amy that Triple had become so emotionally dependent on his father. It was going to break Triple's heart when Nick had to go.

Though she knew she should grab a cup of coffee and hit the freeways before rush hour, Amy was too curious to pass the doors without peeping inside. She stopped, edging cautiously toward the shadowed doorway so they wouldn't notice her.

Near the diving board Nick had positioned a huge fan to simulate wind. He could roll the fan to different spots whenever he desired a new wind direction. Every day father and son practiced for hours with the boat.

Inside the room, the air was warm and dense with humidity and the scent of chlorine. Sunlight glittered on the dancing water of the pool.

Triple was reclining in a chaise lounge, his head propped against a mound of plump red pillows, the little boat's remote-control device clutched tightly in one fist. Nick's giant golden form was crouched beside him, and Nick was whispering instructions and helpful comments. As always Amy marveled that such an impatient man could be so patient with a child.

Triple was listening to his father with such rapt attention that he wasn't watching the sailboat. Suddenly the twelve-meter hit a gust from the fan and lurched saucily, its sails dipping into the water, and its bow ramming the side of the pool at maximum speed. Triple gave a yelp of rage that was so loud it shook the glass walls. Then he jumped up, raced to the edge, and yanked the boat that had been drifting helplessly on its side out of the glimmering waters and examined the damage.

"Dumb boat! What did it do that for?" he bellowed.

For a minute Amy thought he would throw it.

Then she heard Nick's low soothing voice. "We all make mistakes, son. The thing we have to do is learn from them. You've got to figure out what you did wrong and take corrective measures."

The wind chose that moment to snap the open door against the glass wall where Amy was standing. Nick glanced up, and when he saw her, a wistful expression passed fleetingly over his dark face.

His eyes held hers, and her stomach went weightless as he murmured, "Believe me, son, I've made a mistake I'd give my life to straighten out."

Amy knew that this last remark was meant solely for her, and she was moved by it—much more than she wanted to be.

Nick rose slowly to his full height. As usual he was costumed outrageously. This morning he wore a flamboyantly flowered Hawaiian ensemble that made his skin seem darker and his eyes more brilliant. In the morning sunlight, his thick hair was wispy, spun silver and gold as the fan tossed it back and forth across his brow. His bronzed thighs were thrust widely apart, and in his swimming trunks and unbuttoned tropical shirt, he looked boldly piratical.

Amy felt the blue blaze of his eager gaze roaming across her shapely length as surely as if he had touched her. She wanted to run, but she stood transfixed. The heat of her blood rose as that treacherous part of her nature that found him irresistible flared to life.

She turned blindly, bent on escape, but his deep resonant drawl stopped her.

"Amy, why don't you stay for a minute, so Triple can show you what he's learned?"

Amy glanced away wildly. The blue Pacific stretched placidly toward the horizon. Palm fronds danced lazily in the light winter breezes. Surely there was no danger in such a peaceful setting.

Triple was looking at her, his eyes bright and expectant. "Hey, Mom, watch this!" Triple leaned over, eagerly replacing the boat in the water and nudging it gently into the middle of the pool.

More than anything, she wanted to stay.

"I have to go to work," she said in a tight, constricted voice.

"It'll only take a second, Mom."

As she turned and began to retreat silently down the stairs, she heard a whispered curse. She was aware of Nick's rapid footsteps clamoring behind her.

She stopped. It was no use trying to run from him. Her white-knuckled fingers gripped the railing as he caught up to her.

They were outside, near sugar-white dunes in the brilliant glare of the morning sunshine with its fresh smells and sounds of the sea.

They were alone, where Triple couldn't see them.

"Why won't you stay?" Nick demanded.

She clung even more tightly to the banister. Her head whipped around defiantly, and there Nick was, closer than she'd realized, with his golden, windblown hair and his incredible blue eyes. His loose shirt whipped about him, and a great deal of his hard-muscled chest was revealed.

"You just can't take no for an answer, can you?" Her voice was as thin as a thread.

His hand closed over her shoulder, and he backed her against the railing until its round edge bit into her hip. His own large body loomed against hers.

"You didn't answer my question," he insisted softly. The warmth of his breath slid against her throat like a sensuous caress. "Why won't you watch?"

She felt the darkly veiled intensity of his gaze scanning her face—searching for something.

"Because if I come in," she began, "if I watch you together, it would seem too much like we're a real family."

Blue eyes bored into hers. "That's what we are."

Something in his low voice mesmerized her.

"No," she cried. "And we can't ever be! I don't want Triple to get the wrong idea."

Nick's hand tightened on her shoulder. He moved a half step closer. She had to leave, but there was no way she could, caught as she was between the flimsy banister and the blistering warmth of his body.

She could smell his scent, the mixture of salt and sea combining with the tangy smell of his skin. It was his habit to jog every morning along the beach, work out, and then swim laps in the pool.

"Maybe it's you who has the wrong idea," he murmured huskily. Nick's hand stole around her waist, drawing her into the shelter of his chest and arm. His lips moved down to the hollow beneath her jaw and whispered near her ear, "If we didn't feel so right together, I don't think you'd be half as afraid as you are."

"I'm not afraid."

He studied her shadowed face with its downcast trembling eyes, its half-parted, trembling lips. His hand skimmed the satin softness of her cheek, and her pulse leaped erratically.

"Oh, yes you are." His voice had grown softer. It was the tone he used with women, and some intimacy in his low gravelly voice seeped inside her. A callused fingertip trailed across her quivering mouth.

"You think you're so smart," she cried desperately.

"I know about some things," he murmured.

"Such as?"

"You." A long pause while his eyes studied her. "And me."

She brought up her hand to push him away, but it inadvertently touched his chest, uncovered by his blowing shirt. She felt the bristly whorls of bleached gold that formed a gilded cloud against the darker bronze of his chest. His skin was smooth and warm beneath her fingers.

Her eyes rose to his face. His tanned features were expressionless. His inscrutable gaze met her faltering one. Something electric passed between them.

She knew she should pull her hand away. When instead she let it stay, she realized she was losing the fierce inward battle against the physical arousal of her senses.

A hoarse sob clogged her throat. "I don't like Triple's becoming so emotionally dependent on you."

"Is that so wrong?" he said gently. "After all, I am his father."

"But you'll be leaving soon."

To that Nick said nothing. The intense emotion in his eyes alone spoke to her heart.

"Why can't you see?" she began. "He's always worshiped you from afar. Now you're using his adoration to make him think you can be a part of his life you can never be."

"I don't use people," Nick muttered, letting her go and turning away from her in anger. "That's your specialty, remember?"

She whitened. "Maybe you aren't doing it on purpose," she whispered at last, "but can't you see that if Triple's so thrilled to have you around now, he'll be equally miserable when you leave? Nick, I've been watching him. I can see how hard he's trying to change for you. He'll do anything to please you, even things he normally hates."

"If only his mother were more like him." Nick's smooth tone and quick white smile had their customary devastating impact on her senses.

"Damn you," she whispered.

"Is it so bad that Triple wants to please me?" Nick demanded.

"If he's on his best behavior just because he's hoping to maneuver things so you end up staying, what's going to happen when you leave?"

"Look, all I'm trying to do is make the most of the time I have with him." Nick hesitated. "Triple hates reading and spelling. You told me you frustrate him when you try to help him, but I've got him working happily on those two for an hour every day. Since I have dyslexia myself, I have a deeper understanding of the problem than you; therefore, it's easier for me to help him. I used to help Jack the same way."

"Nick..."

"Has it ever occurred to you that I can give things to Triple you can never give him, just as you can help him in ways I can't? That by keeping me out of his life, you're cheating him? Have you ever wondered why he's always been such a little hellion? Has it ever occurred to you he's starving for something he's not getting—my attention? You're too soft with him, Amy. He needs a firm hand. You spoil him, exactly like you've always spoiled Lorrie. Have you noticed that he hasn't pulled one of his stunts in the last three days? He needs a father to relate to full-time, not just one month out of the year."

Every word Nick spoke was tearing her apart.

"Amy, I love Triple just as much as you do. That's all I'm trying to say. Why is that so wrong?"

A dark, overpowering emotion filled her. "Because... your love was the most destructive force I've ever encountered. Because..." Sunlight glistened in the swirling surf. Amy stopped herself, stunned. The answer had been on the tip of her tongue.

She whirled away. She couldn't explain—ever. She owed Nicholas Browning nothing.

"Triple needs me," Nick said. "You're asking me to neglect my own son, and that's something I won't do—even for you."

She clenched her hands tightly together. She agreed in part, and it upset her that she could agree with him about something so important. Triple was starved for a man's attention. Why hadn't she anticipated that as Triple grew up he would want a father? It was just that she had been so busy going to school, being a mother, and getting ahead in her career that she hadn't taken the time for men.

"You need a man in your life, too," Nick said softly. "I think you crave a man's affection and love just as desperately as Triple does. Amy, you spoil everyone you love. Why won't you let me spoil you?"

He started to touch her. She had been looking at the beach. With a moan she jerked away. "No!"

He stood stock-still, his handsome face dark with hurt.

A muted cry of pain sprang from her soul, only to die on her lips.

His golden hair blew carelessly across his dark brow; his blue eyes were bleak with pain.

Oh, why did he have to be built like a god? With an almost physical ache she remembered what it was to know his hands on her, his lips caressing hers.

A part of her felt like weeping hysterically. Never had she been more tempted to give in to the powerful feelings he evoked.

She must not think of him like that, she told herself angrily.

"Yes," she whispered, "I do need a man, but it can't be you. Never you. You belong to a past I have to bury forever. All I'll ever want from you is a...a divorce."

The word seemed to echo in the hushed silence. His dark face turned ashen, and Amy's blood froze in her veins. What had she said? Her heart throbbed dully with numb stupefied pain.

"A divorce! The hell you say!" Nick whispered. His eyes narrowed to slits of cold blue steel as he lunged for her and snapped her against his hard body as if she were nothing. "That's the last thing you'll ever get from me."

"How can you stop me?"

"Don't ask a question like that unless you want the answer," he said roughly, winding his hands in her hair, and yanking her head back so abruptly that a shower of pins rained onto the stairs.

She fought to twist away from the cruel hands that tugged at her hair, from the cruel mouth that descended toward hers. "Can't you see, I have to get on with my own life," she pleaded, frantic. "It's time I gave Triple a father. It's time I found a real husband."

"You have a real husband." A bitter, uncontrolled fury swept over Nick, and he forced her body harder against his own. "Is this real enough for you?" he mumbled thickly. His callused hands positioned her female body intimately against his own hardening male shape.

She gasped as she realized the extent of his arousal. For the briefest second his gaze skimmed the pleading softness of her white face, the terror in her huge eyes and trembling mouth. Tenderness flickered across his face and was gone. Then she shut her eyes helplessly as his lips claimed hers in a hard and brutal kiss.

With his mouth and body he made her his. Hotly he fused their lips together, their bodies, their souls until there was no part of her that did not belong to him. No part of her that did not yearn for him. He kissed her lips, her face, her earlobes, her slender throat, until she was panting and breathless. She was filled with the scent and taste of him. Her blood turned to fire. She felt dizzy, drugged.

"Mom! Dad!" Triple shouted impatiently from the pool.

Slowly, reluctantly, Nick released her. He raked his hands through his hair to smooth it. He fought to control his ragged breathing.

Near faint with desire, Amy sagged wearily against the railing and let the cool ocean breezes fan the long, mussed black waves of her hair.

"Mom!"

Amy couldn't look at Nick. She could feel her pulse pounding in her throat. She felt bruised, shamed. Wanton. Her every impulse directed her to escape quickly.

"Come back and watch him, Amy," Nick said quietly. "I swear I won't bother you again if you do." There was a note of desperate hopelessness in his low, hoarse voice. "Just for a minute," he said. "Whatever I did a moment ago, there's still nothing wrong about a little boy loving both his parents. There's nothing wrong with us taking pride in his accomplishments together. It's something he needs. It's something I want very much to give him."

Hearing it put like that, no matter how much she wanted to, Amy could not say no.

"All right," she agreed softly.

"Thank you." Nick took her hand and pressed it tightly in his as he led her inside. "And Amy?"

"What?" The single word was barely audible.

"No divorce." Passion blazed from his eyes. "Never, between us."

She walked blindly through the glass doors. The small boat was skimming up and down across turquoise waters in a series of zigzag maneuvers, executing one successful tack after the other, but Amy did not see it.

"Watch that, Mom!" Triple shouted. She tried, but her vision was too blurred. "I never would have learned that without Dad. Gosh, it's great having Dad home, isn't it?"

She felt Nick's eyes on her, watching her, waiting for her answer.

Her vision went even blurrier. Her throat was as dry as dust.

"What happened to your hair, Mom?"

"The wind," she muttered even as she felt the telltale color staining her cheeks.

Triple cocked his head inquisitively. "I like it," he said. "It makes you look pretty. I think you're just as glad Dad's home as I am."

Father and son were both looking at her. She tried to speak, but she couldn't. Some emotion that she did not want and would not name had entered her heart, crushing her with its intensity, suffocating her, consuming her in its flame.

After that morning at the pool, Amy worked very hard to avoid Nick, but he worked just as hard to make that impossible. He made her feel that she was fighting a war of wills in her own home, a war that she was losing. Although this far Lorrie had avoided him, he had won her father's, her son's, and Apolonia's allegiances. Thus, if Nick was not working directly on her, one of his confederates was. They loved Nick as passionately as she was determined to despise him, and they wanted him to stay—permanently. They did not understand why he couldn't, and she could not explain. They did not understand that hers was a house of carefully guarded secrets, and it was too dangerous to have Nick around trying to unlock its mysteries. He had to go, and quickly.

One evening after work Amy became upset when she caught Nick browsing through her photograph albums. He was in the den, his golden head bent over an open page. The cabinet doors behind him stood ajar, and the shelves were empty. One glance at the orderly stacks of loose pictures and the mountain of albums littering the sofa and carpet made Amy's blood run cold. He had been going through them all!

Wondering what he was about, she tiptoed stealthily into the room and peered over his shoulder.

Dear Lord! A painful sigh escaped her as she glimpsed an all-too-familiar enlargement of Jack and Lorrie and herself. That picture alone instantly brought back the fateful summer that had almost ruined the lives of everyone Amy loved.

Amy's breath caught at the sight of Lorrie in her gold bikini. Jack and Lorrie were locked in a torrid embrace while anxious big-sister Amy looked on. It was funny how much older and more sophisticated than Amy the glamorous Lorrie, who'd only been sixteen at the time, looked. Nick had snapped the picture and given it to Amy, and across the bottom edge he'd scrawled playfully, "Bet you're frowning 'cause you want to be kissed like that! Anytime..."

Amy fought against a flash of bitter memories. Oh, how she wished she'd been strong enough to resist dating him. Maybe... It had been her fault, everything that happened.

Amy grabbed the album from him and shut it. The last thing she wanted to remember was that summer.

"I should have torn that picture up!" she muttered angrily.

Nick's blue gaze lifted to hers. His rough masculine features filled her vision, leaving room for little else. He seemed suddenly too close, his intense eyes reading her much too easily, and alarm made her heart flutter. If only she'd gone to her room and left him alone.

"You don't really think by slamming that album shut you can forget that summer, do you?" Nick sounded amazingly calm as he made the low challenge.

"You have no business snooping among my things," she whispered tautly, replacing the album in the back of the cabinet.

Nick regarded her with lazy indulgence rather than anger. "Triple wanted to show me these albums."

"He doesn't seem to be around at the moment."

Nick shrugged. "I think he got bored. He's playing chess with Sam."

"And you didn't?"

"No. But then I like looking at pictures of you." He lifted a single photograph of her on a Windsurfer and studied it. "You look good in a bikini." The smoldering heat of his eyes engulfed her.

She flushed hotly and tried to grab the snapshot, but he quickly pocketed it next to his heart. His gaze seemed to strip her clothes from her body. Shaken, she dug her fingers tightly into the soft upholstery of the couch.

He was watching her, something flickering in his keen look. "I had forgotten about Lorrie and Jack."

"So had I," she lied warily, still not looking at him.

"You didn't like them dating," Nick persisted.

"Lorrie was so young," Amy replied too quickly. "Besides, she wasn't serious about Jack."

"That was your theory. You thought they were too young for each other. I realized later you were right about that, but she was special to Jack. He never got over her. Sometimes I wonder about Lorrie. She's never married . . ."

Amy felt sick. "Th-they were a bad combination," she stammered. "Each seemed to bring out the wildness in the other."

"And is that so bad?" Nick queried softly. "That's the way you've always affected me." He smiled at her.

She felt her pulse quicken with unwanted excitement. Her low voice was shaky. "Why must you always turn everything into a seductive remark of some sort?"

"I would think the answer was obvious," he murmured. "Because I want to seduce you. If you'd only let me, maybe I'd stop."

"Thank you, but no thank you," she retorted.

He flashed her one of his charming white grins. "Back to Jack and Lorrie, then."

"I don't want to get back to them."

"But I do." He grinned. "I never felt responsible for my younger brother the way you felt for your sister. Jack always thought he could handle anything that came along."

"So he thought."

"Yes... Maybe I should have done things differently, but I let him live his own life his own way," Nick said gravely. "You never believed Lorrie should do that. You were always in a state of panic that she would get in too deep, that she would get into some relationship she couldn't cope with. She went a little wild there at the end of the summer, but at least now she's all grown up, and you don't have to worry about her anymore."

"Y-yes." Amy gazed out the window, pretending an indifference to the subject she was far from feeling.

Nick swung a lazy glance to her. "Then why are you so upset every time her name is mentioned?"

Her teeth clenched together. "I'm not—upset."

He swore under his breath. "Liar."

He came to her, and she felt his hands grip her bare arms lightly, then more firmly. He turned her around, and his eyes probed into hers. She felt drained.

"If Lorrie's part of what's wrong between us," he said, "Why can't we talk about it? I don't think she liked us dating. She's hardly spoken to me since I came. Don't you think it's time we were honest with each other for a change—about everything?"

Amy felt truly frightened. It was too late for honesty; far too late.

"Do you really think anything you could do or say at this point could make any difference anyway?" she whispered.

"Damn!" His voice was low and angry. Amy always deliberately shut him out. His grip tightened on her arms. When she stiffened from his rough touch, he let her go.

"We are going to talk about it."

"No!"

"Lorrie didn't say something about that last night did she? She didn't twist things around so that you blamed me? She promised me . . . *She did say something!* I can see it in your eyes. Surely you don't blame me for what happened?"

He asked these questions so guiltlessly, Amy felt a sickening feeling of nausea. Did he really blame Lorrie for his own weakness of character?

There was nothing she could say. Terror was scrawled across her white face. She stood poised at the doorway to run.

His voice followed after her. "What in the hell are you so afraid of, Amy? The truth isn't something to fear. It's something to face. Run while you can, because that's a liberty I won't allow you much longer. I'm not leaving Los Angeles until I find out what's going on. Six-and-a-half years ago I was too proud to fight for you when you rejected me. I'd never been in love before, never been hurt like that. I couldn't handle it. Not after the way I'd been raised. It was like a repeat of the past when I'd loved my father and mother and they couldn't love me the way I wanted. When you didn't come to Berkeley—when you were so cold over the phone when I asked you why, I thought the hell with her. If she doesn't want me, I don't want her, either. Because I didn't know about Triple, I let you guard your silence. But no more. You spoiled Lorrie. That's part of why she did what she did. She was pretty and pampered, and that's a lethal combination when a girl sets out to seduce a man. Maybe we should confront Lorrie together."

"No! She's suffered enough at your hands."

"What the hell's that supposed to mean? I never did a damn thing but try to help her."

His last words were shouted to an empty room. Amy had run away.

It was four o'clock in the morning. Nick's questions about Lorrie and the past had been so disturbing that Amy hadn't been able to sleep. She had stolen down to the pool to swim.

Moonlight silvered the darkened warm waters of the pool as Amy tossed her filmy cover-up on the tiled floor and stepped into the shallow end. She hadn't turned on the pool lights or the overhead lights because she didn't want anyone to know she was there.

Sparkling waters closed over her. She began to swim an endless number of slow, languid laps, and slowly she felt the tension drain out of her. She finished the last lap in the shallow end.

Amy kept seeing Nick's face. He'd looked so sincere so unafraid, as though he'd had nothing to hide. She kept hearing his words. *The truth isn't something to fear. It's something to face.*

A terrible, unspeakable question had formed in her mind. Perhaps it had always been there, she thought.

Had Lorrie lied in some way about Nick, about everything? The one time Amy had doubted Lorrie's story and had almost gone to Nick, Lorrie had run away and almost died. Her nearly lifeless body had been discovered in the surf. Amy had never dared to question her sister again.

But had she lied?

Lorrie had told little white lies as a child occasionally, lies like the one to Nick about her age all those years ago. But they'd been silly little fibs. Surely she hadn't told a lie about anything so important.

Had she?

Amy felt numb. Cold logic told her she'd never even given Nick a chance to defend himself. Because she'd been so upset, because she'd always protected her sister, Amy had accepted Lorrie's story as gospel.

Stepping out of the pool to retrieve her towel, Amy became aware of a tall, darkened shadow in the doorway.

A scream bubbled from her throat.

"Hush," whispered Nick's raspy voice through the velvet darkness. "There's no reason to be afraid. Not of me."

There was every reason to be afraid.

She wrapped the thick towel around her body protectively. "W-what are you doing here?"

"I thought I heard something, so I came outside to check."

"Well, now that you know who it is, you can leave."

He chuckled. "Now that I know who it is, I'm determined to stay."

"Nick!"

He moved silently toward her. The moonlight made silver ribbons in his golden hair.

"Why won't you go and leave me alone?"

"I've won over everyone but you," he murmured.

"And?"

"It's time I won you," he said softly.

"That's something you'll never do." Amy scampered lightly to the far end of the pool even as he came after her. "I don't want you."

"Yes, you do," he murmured softly, beguilingly. "Tonight I'm going to prove it to you."

"If you dare to force—"

"Oh, I won't need force."

"If you think you can just turn on the charm and have everything your way, you're wrong."

He laughed. "Am I?"

She shrieked at the shock of her wet skin pressed against ice cold glass and steel. She had reached the farthest glass wall, and there was nowhere to run.

His shadow fell across her frightened face, as he caught her wrist and drew her into the hard circle of his arms.

"J-just what do you think you're doing?" she whispered.

"I'm turning on the charm so I can have everything my own way," he murmured huskily. "Thanks for the suggestion."

He brought her close against his body. He was dry and hot, fully clothed; she was wet and warm, and nearly naked.

He held her tightly, not caring that she ruined his silk shirt and wool cashmere slacks. For an instant she was too stunned by the magnitude of what he was doing to react, and then it was too late because she was responding to him as she always had. She felt keenly alive, on the edge of something wonderful and incredibly exciting. She'd been starved so long for the thrill of his lovemaking that she could not resist him.

Tilting her face so that the moonlight fell across it and he could see it properly, he very gently smoothed the damp strands of hair from her eyes. "When I stood there watching you swim, I knew you wanted to be alone. I knew I'd driven you here. I told myself to go, that you didn't want me, that you'd never wanted me." His voice was desperate, agonized. "But I didn't have the strength; I never have where you're concerned. There's never been anyone else for me."

Some part of her wanted to believe him. The past, his betrayal and all the lies and secrets were as nothing. All that mattered was the terrifying emotion in her heart.

She could not stop herself from smiling at him, an achingly sweet smile that must have touched him to the heart because the smile that answered hers was just as sweet in its own masculine way.

"All week I've wondered if you could ever be soft and gentle in my arms again," he murmured. "I'd almost given up hope."

"I'm sorry," she heard the alien, dreamy creature who now possessed her body reply.

Amy stared wordlessly at him as his finger tilted her chin even more, and he bent his golden head to hers and brushed a velvet kiss across her mouth.

The touch of his mouth was heady. She felt dizzy, and her hands slid from his chest to his shoulders to steady herself. The feel of his mouth, firm and hot against hers, the softness of his shirt beneath her fingers, the warmth of his body against her own sent a quiver of bewildering sensation through her.

She drew a quick breath and tentatively dared to kiss him back. Nicholas had already begun to pull away when he felt the faint movement of her lips beneath his. He stood statue-still, his eyes darkening as they met hers. Then something over which he had no control seemed to break inside him, and he crushed her to him fiercely, bending his mouth to hers with more determination than before, his kisses harder this time, and hotter.

His arms tightened around her, drawing her up against himself until they were pressed so closely together that it seemed the flame of his body would burn them into one.

His mouth moved against hers, his tongue moist and seeking as it slid between her parted lips, tasting the molten flesh of her lower lip before nibbling it and sucking it inside his own mouth. Then his tongue slid deeper, and Amy's knees turned to butter as the hot, dark night seemed to revolve around her.

She was drowning; she was dying. And for the first time in years she was really alive.

He was bending her backward, and Amy had to cling tightly to his neck. His tongue touched hers, mated with it, tantalized it. Passionately Amy returned the intimate caress.

Against her flattened breasts she could feel the sudden thunder of his heart. She no longer knew what she did; what he did. She only knew that her tongue was in his mouth, tasting the pleasant warm flavor that was his alone. That his great body was trembling, and suddenly so was hers.

She was hardly conscious of what he did after that, so seduced was she by the ecstasy of sensation his mouth aroused. His hand slid to her breast, shaped it expertly, his fingers brushing against her nipple until it grew rigid. The exquisite pleasure of his touch rippled like hot fluid waves through every part of her.

She stiffened. He was the enemy. Her eyes flashed opened. But was he? Had Lorrie lied? Oh, had she?

Nick kissed Amy again. Whatever he had done, he was her love, and she could not fight him. The same tide of passion sweeping him, swept her.

One taste from the cup of desire and she had to drink more deeply.

Her arms tightened around his neck. Her lashes, fluttered shut, and she was ready to surrender heart and soul to the man she'd despised for more than six years.

When he finally released her, Amy swayed against him. She opened her eyes. Her lips felt moist and swollen from his kisses. Her heart was racing at an unnatural rhythm. She didn't know what to do or say.

Slowly he untied her bikini top, and it fell soundlessly to the tile floor beside her towel.

His dark soft eyes raked her body where her smooth shoulders flowed into lush breasts. "My wife, my darling," he whispered. "You are so beautiful." His hand skimmed lightly over her breasts. Then he caressed her narrow waist and her taut flat belly. His touch was ecstasy. His low voice mesmerized her. "It seems incredible that a body as perfect as yours has ever given birth to a child. To my child."

To Amy the reverently spoken words seemed part of her worst nightmare. Her curved palm flew to her lips, and she gave a little cry of mingled pain and horror. With that single sentence, he broke the spell that had bound her to him, and the past with all its shame and bitterness came back to her.

Though she loved him and he was her husband, he could never be her lover. Never again.

Without bothering to retrieve her towel or the bra of her bikini, she turned and ran.

He was too stunned by her reaction to do anything other than watch her slender form slip away and disappear in the shimmering darkness.

Eight

———

The bedroom door opened, cracking the stillness. Amy leaped to her feet as if she'd been shot.

"Nick?" Her voice was breathy, terrified.

He made no answer. There was only darkness and silence.

She didn't dare make another sound. She had been too upset to think that he might follow her, too upset to remember to lock her door.

Nick paused at the threshold, one large hand on the frame. His gaze was fixed on Amy, his heavy eyes shuttered to conceal their expression.

Amy's breath caught in her throat. Would he be furious or tender? Loving or brutal?

He moved inside and shut the door. She heard the metallic snapping of the bolt as it slid into place. In the darkness he seemed immense.

Amy ran her tongue over her dry lips. She felt the perspiration bead her brow as she shrank back against the bed. Her trembling fingers pulled the warm velvet robe protectively around her naked body.

He came nearer. "Why did you run?" His voice fell softly rather than threateningly, and yet that only made him seem all the more dangerous.

"Because," she gasped. "Oh, Nick. I can't tell you! I—I... I should never have kissed you that way. I should never have led you on."

"But you did."

"I'm sorry."

"I'm not. And this time I'm not going to let you run away."

He strode silently across the room, and pulled her from the bed into his arms. Her wet black hair spilled down the back of her velvet robe, dampening the thick cloth with cold rivulets of water.

"What are you so afraid of?" he demanded.

"I can't tell you—ever."

"Damnation, woman!" he erupted furiously, bitterly, yanking her against his body. "You're enough to try the patience of a saint. And heaven knows, I'm no saint." His fingers dug into her arms, and he shook her until her teeth rattled. "Tell me. Was having my baby alone so awful?"

She merely stared at him helplessly, terrified. His expression seeming to blaze in the darkness, was infinitely tender. Surely no man could look at a woman like that and not be sincere.

"If only you'd told me, I would have been there," he said.

Had Lorrie lied about him? About everything? Oh, had she?

Fear knotted Amy's stomach. Never had she felt more terribly confused. Had she wronged Nick more horribly than any man ever deserved to be wronged?

Deeply ashamed, she began to weep, strong, proud Amy who almost never wept. Oh, if she'd been wrong, she'd never be able to face him.

For an instant he was so stunned he didn't know what to do. At the sight of her tears, the fierce red haze of emotion that had driven him to treat her so brutally died. His breathing slowed and his rough hands gentled.

A terrible guilt assailed him. He had ruined her life by making her pregnant, by forcing her into a marriage she didn't want, by refusing her a divorce. Tonight, he'd used force again. She didn't want him. She never would. He loathed himself for having brought the woman he loved so much pain.

Softly, soothingly, he spoke her name. "There, there, darling. Shh, Amy, sweetheart," he murmured, sliding his fingers through her flowing wet hair, stroking her back.

"Oh, Nick," she whispered, clinging to him tightly, forgetting for the moment her need to fear him. "If only I could have found the strength to stop loving you. If only... Why did you have to come back?"

He hesitated, staring down at her in wonder, only half believing what he heard. *Loving*... She had said she loved him.

After an endless moment she felt his lips on her eyes, kissing away her tears, and slowly her sobs subsided until she rested quietly against him.

As she calmed, he grew aware of her body against his. Her robe had come loose, and only his clothes lay between his skin and her naked body. He could feel her soft breasts pressed against his shirt. He could feel her nipples tighten. She wanted him as much as he wanted her. He could feel it.

They were alone, together, in her bedroom. A man and a woman, and neither had had a mate for two years.

He still couldn't believe the marvel of what she'd admitted. She didn't hate him as he'd feared in his most agonized moments of doubt. She loved him.

"Whatever I've made you suffer, you have to believe that I came back because I wanted to help you," Nick said. "Triple nearly died, and you were all alone. Can't you see that I'll do everything in my power to help you? Whatever it is that's wrong between us, if you'd only tell me what it is, we could work it out. I shouldn't have blamed Lorrie earlier today. I know things aren't that simple."

"No..." The word was a low choked sob. "The only thing you can do is to leave me alone and accept the fact that we can't have a relationship."

"You can't mean that you still want a divorce?"

"Y-yes."

"Look at me, darling," Nick commanded.

Unhappily she lifted her chin an inch, knowing there was no way she could conceal her love for him. It was still shining in her eyes. Gently his hand turned her face to his. His gaze was deep and dark as he accurately read her desperately vulnerable expression. A triumphant smile parted his lips.

"Even though you love me, you want to end our marriage?" he said, incredulous.

"Y-yes."

"Not until I know why."

With a sob she lowered her head. More than anything she longed to seize Triple and have the three of them run away somewhere where they could start over. But even that wouldn't work. The past would always be there to haunt them, to destroy them. "It's not something I can explain," she said tautly.

"Can't you see that you're asking an awful lot?"

"There's too much against us." Her voice quivered with defeat. "We never had a real marriage anyway. You only married me because of Triple. And I only married you because you forced me to. You threatened that paternity suit. You..."

She could feel his muscles tighten; an icy tension froze her heart.

"I remember everything I did then, and I won't give up now, no matter what you say or do," he said angrily. His fingers dug into her arms again and he yanked her viciously against his body. "Even if you won't fight for us, for our happiness, I will."

"It's no use, Nick. There are too many lies. Too..." She stopped herself.

"What are you talking about?"

She buried her face in his shoulder.

He knew of only one weapon to combat her stubborn resistance, and that weapon was his love. His hand traced the length of her slender throat, turning her face once more toward his. She seemed to stop breathing as his gaze explored the lovely radiance of her frightened face. She had expected some harsh argument from him but instead she felt herself being irresistibly drawn by his tenderness.

She felt the pressure of his hand against the small of her back as he arched her body into his, and she sighed. Very slowly his mouth took hers, kissing her lightly at first.

Hesitantly her arms lifted around his shoulders. She opened her lips and let his tongue inside. She was so scared she was shaking like a frightened animal. He crushed her against his body. She could feel the thunder of his heart, but it was racing no faster than her own. The pressure of his mouth hardened, deepened. Gently he stroked and caressed her, his fingers sliding over her arms, her waist, down her back.

Wildfire raced through her veins. She felt dizzy. It was as though some part of her were dissolving into him. She was quivering, trembling. As her fingers dug into the wavy golden silk that curled against his collar, he dragged his mouth reluctantly from hers.

"I love you," he said. "That's the only reason I married you. Triple was just the excuse I used. I would have done anything to make you mine. My life's been hell because you wouldn't have me."

Amy cried out softly. Then she stared back at him dazedly, feeling aroused, lost, frightened. They had both suffered. She wanted him. Nothing else mattered. Not tonight.

Would she later accuse him of forcing her? he wondered. It didn't matter. Nothing mattered. He had to have her.

He stared at her for a long tense moment. The drowsy look of sensuality on her face aroused him more than anything. Her lush lips were parted and swollen from his kisses. Her bewildered amber eyes glowed with desire. The soft gentleness of surrender was in her features.

He felt her fingers remove his shirt from his waistband and slide erotically across the warm skin of his belly. Her touch left a tingly trail of fire.

His eyes darkened to a stormy blue. There was passion in his tense, brown face.

She smiled that sweet, shy smile that made his insides melt, looking at him through her thick lashes. Her hands made lazy caressing circles on his brown skin.

His whole body trembled at the warmth of her soft, sensual touch. For an instant his intense gaze devoured the loveliness of her. Then something inside him broke. He'd gone too long without a woman. Without *his* woman. He needed Amy. He had to have her, or some vital part of him would perish forever.

"Amy; darling, Amy." Gently he wrapped his arms around her and kissed her sweetly, tenderly.

He felt her fingers loosening the buttons of his shirt, sliding the shirt from his shoulders. His arms encircled her like an iron band and he crushed her against the hot, naked wall of his chest. Then he picked her up and carried her to the bed. Her robe opened and his body pressed into hers.

He kissed her until she could hardly breathe. He gripped her arms so hard they hurt, yet his fierce passion sent tremors through her as his mouth slid from her lips, down her throat against the pointed nipples that budded when his wet tongue touched them.

At last he stopped kissing her and stood up to remove the rest of his clothes. She watched him with tremulous fascination, unable to tear her eyes from those broad shoulders, from the exquisite maleness of him.

Slowly he helped her slip out of her robe. Then he lowered his body once more to hers. Every inch of him, every nerve seemed to touch her, and she was enthralled by a new throbbingly alive awareness of him.

His mouth devoured hers. His lips touched her throat, hot against her flesh. His hands played over her breasts. She excited him, and he had to force himself to go slowly.

Gently he drew her close to his chest and stroked her long flowing hair down over her shoulders. As his caresses grew more intense, her body gradually relaxed against his, and a tiny moan escaped her lips.

When he came into her, gently at first, and then more fiercely, she cried out against his shoulder. He felt her fingernails dig into his skin. Nick forced himself to stop, and he held her closely as he waited for her to grow accustomed to him. He kissed her brow tenderly; then he murmured something low and inaudible against her ear.

He whispered her name. "Amy. Are you all right?"

"Yes." The single word was a throb of desire that quickened his own savage longing. For years he'd lived without her, without this, without any woman, because he wanted no woman but her, and now she was his. As she pressed her hands into the small of his back and drew him closer, he made a silent vow to himself that he'd never lose her again.

Stirred past reason by her acceptance of him, he could restrain himself no longer. He began to move again, driving into her with a wild, urgent force. An answering excitement rose within her, mounting higher and higher as he sought to please her. Her lips half opened, and her teeth came together in a strange agony of delight as a dazzling tide of emotion flamed through her. She clung to him desperately.

He was hot, and she was hot. It was as if their love were a flame and they were consumed by it.

Giving a short, hoarse cry, he thrust inside her one last time, ending the deep hard rhythm, holding her tightly to his body. She clung to him, almost unconscious in her own pleasure as violent sensations exploded in every soft tissue of her being.

For one keen, exhilarating moment they were one.

As she held on to him fiercely, a joy Nick had never known before pierced him. Amy had gone wild in his arms.

Then it was over, and the glorious moment slipped away, dissolving too quickly into a hazy, warm memory of desire. His body loosened its clasp on hers.

She slid to the other side of the bed, silently rolling over and turning her back to him. He heard her as she began to sob quietly in the darkness, and all the ecstasy he'd known only a minute before drained from his heart.

His loving her had changed nothing.

Amy awoke to the startling image of Nick's golden head bathed in glorious sunlight, but she did not at first comprehend that there was anything abnormal about waking in his arms. The room was warm, the cotton sheets soft against her body, and she felt enveloped in a cocoon of sated sensuality.

Her raven hair flowed over his arms like glistening skeins of spilled silk. His body heat had been like a magnet in the night, drawing her close, and at some point she had snuggled against his shoulder.

Slowly it came to her that although it was delicious lying with him, it was something she should never have done. Amy swallowed hard and averted her eyes from Nick.

She was naked, her arms and legs tangled intimately in his. One of his thighs was sprawled across her stomach, locking her tightly beneath him. His fingers were curved possessively over her breast. Her freshly awakened body felt throbbingly aware of him.

As she remembered what she had done, remorse washed over her. At the same time she felt every flutter and subtle nuance of sensation at his slightest movement.

Why? Why had she let it happen?

How could she have stopped it?

Hadn't she known that from the moment he'd returned, such a night as the one they'd shared was inevitable?

Trying not to awaken him, she made an attempt to shift out of his embrace, but that was not possible. He had only been pretending to sleep. He caught her playfully by the wrist and pulled her back.

"Good morning," his sleepy voice rasped lovingly.

His thigh was rock hard against her hip bone. His fingers were tongues of flame upon her slender wrist as he drew her nearer.

As Nick's indolent gaze swept the length of her womanly form, the warm tremor of desire made his eyes light hotly.

Her eyes met his, and she saw at once that it would never be possible to convince him that what had happened had been no more than an irresistible moment of madness, that it must never, never happen again. His eyes staked his claim to a fresh and torrid passion.

His mouth lowered to hers, and he kissed her with such bewildering tenderness, that all her thoughts of protest died. Hands that might have fought to push him away, trembled and then slid around his neck and clasped him passionately. A low moan escaped her lips.

He kissed her lips, her throat, her breasts, his mouth moving ever lower, stirring her, awakening in her the old aching need.

How could it seem like forever since she'd been loved when it had only been a few short hours?

With his mouth he worshiped her, and soon nothing mattered but his lips and the flame of desire flaring in the center of her being.

His golden head nestled into her belly. Gently he forced her thighs apart. She felt the roughness of his cheeks as they slid rhythmically against her velvet skin. He drove her wild.

Her body writhed shamelessly. Her fingers curled into the golden thickness of his hair and pulled him even closer until she felt the building of an elemental and primitive explosion from deep within her being.

"Nick." His name was a raw agonized sound.

Dear Lord! How she loved him! She was frantic for him. Her cry rent the air as rapture flooded every living cell of her body.

Afterward they lay quietly for a long time. She was ashamed of how completely she had surrendered herself to him, of how deeply she adored him.

Vaguely she wondered how she would ever find the strength to fight the battle that lay before her.

It was Nick who got out of bed first. "I'd forgotten how hot-blooded you are," he said on a low, self-satisfied chuckle. He grabbed her hand and pulled her up.

"I had forgotten, too," she admitted, unable to deny his power.

It was something she had struggled to forget.

"Next time," he whispered, "it will be your turn to make love to me."

His eyes were brilliant, and the answering excitement his words aroused filled her with dread. There couldn't be a next time. There mustn't be . . .

But even as she thought of how she must deny him, she turned her lips to his and let him claim them in a passionate kiss.

She loved him, no matter what he'd done. But if she had been misled all those years ago, if it was *she* who had wronged *him*, would his love for her be as strong?

When Nick and Amy came into the kitchen, they were astonished to find Sam and Triple already there, having waited for them before eating breakfast. A mood of celebration hung in the air. Sam usually didn't cook, but he was up and about, whistling and smiling by the stove, his cane forgotten against the wall.

On the counter was a generous platter of fried ham and eggs, English muffins, and glasses of fresh orange juice. A radiant Triple was rushing around the kitchen, carrying plates and silverware, and setting the table, showing an unusual amount of exuberance for a task he normally found tedious. Only Lorrie was absent.

The minute Nick and Amy stepped inside, an embarrassed hush fell, then Sam boisterously greeted them. "Great morning!"

"Couldn't be better," Nick replied on a bold vibrant note, smiling broadly as he encircled a glowing Amy with his arms and drew her close. Triple watched with shining eyes as his father tenderly kissed his blushing mother on the forehead. Nick's lovingly reverent expression was such that no one but a blind person could have mistaken the change in their relationship since the night before. If Nick had shouted it from the rooftops, he could not have gotten his message across more clearly.

As Triple danced across the kitchen to get the paper napkins and set them out, the boy began to sing to himself in that raucous off-key way that so reminded Amy of Nick. Suddenly Triple gave a cry of joy and threw himself into his parents' arms. "Are we a real family now? Is Dad going to stay for good?"

Amy could only clutch her child tightly with shaking fingers. She heard Nick's voice, deep and gentle, filled with love.

"Yes, I'll be staying—for good."

"Is he, Mom? I mean—really?"

She felt Nick's arms around her. She looked down at Triple. She wanted it to be true so much that she could not deny it.

"Really, son," Nick said softly.

"Breakfast's ready!" Sam said.

"Sit down everyone," Nick murmured. He sat at the head of the table and began shoveling eggs and ham and a muffin onto everybody's plates.

Amy couldn't look at him. Her eyes were swimming with tears of happiness. A fragile hope was beginning to take root in her heart.

Nick began to make plans. "Of course, this means I'll have to make some changes, but I've already spoken to Sebastian about moving the headquarters of South Sails to L.A., and he has no objections."

"You were that sure?" Amy whispered, looking at Nick wonderingly from across the table.

He merely smiled at her boldly in that confident way of his. "After breakfast, I'm going to call my father and Mercedes. I want them to come immediately. And maybe I'll even invite Jeb," he said smiling ruefully.

Jeb was Nick's older half brother, and there had always been a friendly rivalry between them, instead of the closeness that had existed between Nick and Jack.

"Oh boy! Grandfather and Mercedes and Uncle Jeb are coming!"

Triple knew his father's relatives because every July Nick had dutifully flown his son to Texas to their ranch for a week.

"Why don't we go to the ranch and see them, Dad! Mercedes wrote me at Christmas that she'd bought a pony named Nugget. He's small enough for me to ride. She said he's as sweet and gentle as a puppy and comes up to you to be petted. She said Nugget can talk and Nugget wants me to come because there's nobody there little enough to ride him. He gets lonely for a kid to play with."

"Soon," Nick said, grinning. "First you have to get well and catch up on your schoolwork."

Amy said, "Nick, don't you think, maybe...you're rushing things? Maybe we should get used to one another..."

"I'm not rushing things. We've been married five years, and you've never met my family. We have the rest of our lives to get used to one another."

"You'll like them, Mom!"

Nick and Sam and Triple kept talking enthusiastically of all the things they would do as a family. Amy toyed with her food, twisting her fork in her egg as she listened to them. She felt weighed down by doubt. Nevertheless, she wanted to believe what they all believed—that she and Nick could really become a normal married couple with in-laws and family breakfasts like this one, that the past and a long-ago lie would not tear up all their lives again.

She had been alone too long. She wanted to be happy, but before that was possible, she had to see Lorrie.

Nick called his family in Texas. Later he went out to see Sebastian to arrange the South Sails move. It was with some difficulty that Amy convinced Triple he had to go back to his bed and rest. He agreed when she allowed him to take two jars filled with spiders and his chrysalis to bed. Only after Nick had gone and Triple was settled, did Amy dare to call Lorrie.

Lorrie's voice was immediately defensive and so faint Amy could hardly hear it. "He told you something, didn't he? That's why you called."

Amy's hands felt clammy. Had Lorrie really lied? Amy almost blurted the question before she realized she had to proceed cautiously. "We've got to talk."

"I don't want to see...*him*," Lorrie continued in the same fearful defensive tone.

Amy had to steel herself. "He'll be out all day."

"I don't want—"

"If I have to, I'll come over there." Amy had never spoken to her sister so firmly.

"A-Amy—"

"It's time we faced the truth. I have to know...
everything. I want you to come to the house and talk to
me."

Lorrie only made a strangled, guttural sound.

Their phone call had been over for an hour before Lorrie
came. Amy had paced the floor impatiently, wondering as
the hour grew later, if Lorrie's faint courage had failed her.
Then Amy heard her sister outside.

Amy threw open the door. The day was full of brilliant
sunshine. Lorrie stood on tiptoe as if poised for flight. She
was standing in the shadows, her face white with panic.

"Oh, Lorrie." Amy hugged her gently. "There's no reason for you to be afraid—not of me."

At her kindness, Lorrie seemed to shrink even more
deeply into the shadows.

A telling glance passed between the two sisters before
Lorrie allowed herself to be led wordlessly inside. Amy's
face was flushed and radiant. Lorrie looked pale and
haunted.

Amy fought to ignore the twist of guilt brought by the
knowledge that she was the cause of her sister's anguish.

"You look different," Lorrie said in a trembling voice,
taking in Amy's brilliant eyes and her glowing expression.
"It's *him*."

Amy could not deny it. She whispered breathlessly,
"Yes."

When Amy closed the door to the den so that they could
be alone, she didn't notice that the door didn't quite latch,
that it fell back from the jamb an inch or so.

"I-it's the way you were before," Lorrie stammered hesitantly, not quite daring to look at Amy, "that summer...
when you were planning to go away with him."

"I love him."

Lorrie's eyes were immense. "But..." She was trembling as though on the verge of hysteria.

Amy saw the agony in her sister's eyes, and it was all she could do to quell the powerful maternal feelings that swelled in her heart. She had always taken care of Lorrie and had never willfully caused her pain. "I don't care what he did. He wants to put the past behind us."

"You really love him...more..."

"More than anything. I can't deny it any longer, even though I know it brings you pain. That doesn't mean I don't love you, Lorrie. Or Triple. It's just that Nick's first. Even after...what happened. I have to know about that night...when you were together. Yesterday he tried to talk to me about it, but I wouldn't let him. He seemed so honest, so forthright, and because of our lie to him, I couldn't talk to him."

Lorrie began to shiver. She looked like a worried child who knew she'd done wrong and was afraid of being punished.

"I wanted to talk to you first—alone," Amy said. "I want a real marriage with him. That's why we—all of us—have to face the whole truth about that night. You want me to be happy, don't you?"

Lorrie's fearful eyes had grown even larger, and she looked more deeply troubled and uncertain than ever. "I—I want you to be happy," Lorrie began slowly, "and I've known you weren't—not for a long time. It's all my fault, too. But I've never known what to do about it. I'm not brave like you. I've always been such a ninny."

Amy took Lorrie's cold hands in hers and kissed them. "I don't blame you."

Lorrie's face was taut and drawn as she regarded Amy closely. "But what about Triple?" Lorrie whispered. "What about him?"

"I said we have to tell Nick the whole truth."

"You can't mean—"

There was a gulf of silence. Amy's face grew as ashen and doubt-filled as Lorrie's.

"We have to tell him that you're really Triple's natural mother, Lorrie."

The silence between them deepened as Lorrie stared at her in mute horror.

Neither spoke. Neither moved. It was as if a freezing fear held them both in its paralyzing grip.

"You know we do!" Amy said.

Lorrie pulled her hands free. "But you promised we'd never," she shouted, "that no one would ever know that you weren't his real mother."

Amy went on talking. "We have to tell him that when we found out you were pregnant with his child, you wouldn't let me go to him. So I went to Sebastian instead and said I was in trouble. We went away together. You pretended to be me. You used my identification. You dyed your hair black. We have to tell him everything, every single detail." Amy swallowed back the lump in her throat. "How difficult the birth was; how the doctor said you should never have another child."

"No..." Lorrie turned away. "We can't. We just can't."

"Nick has to know. We can't make a true, fresh start unless we deal with this honestly."

Lorrie was standing at the window. She turned. Her white face was drawn with horror.

"We can't ever do that! Don't you see? We can't ever!" Tears were streaming down her face.

"Why not?"

"Because you'll lose both Triple and Nick for sure, if you do."

"That's a risk I have to take."

"You still don't get it, do you?"

"Get what?" Amy whispered, dreading the answer, wondering, doubting, half hoping.

"There's something you don't know. Something I never told you. Something so awful that you'll hate me forever when I tell you. I only did it because..." Lorrie wrung her hands. Her eyes pleaded for an understanding Amy couldn't give her.

A terrible knot began to form in Amy's stomach. She felt queasy with fear. "What are you saying?"

Lorrie's eyes fell guiltily. "Nick didn't sleep with me! It was Jack! Not Nick! Nick came home and found us together. He sent Jack away. Nick stayed and talked to me. He told me Jack and I were too young for that sort of relationship, that we weren't old enough to accept the responsibilities that went along with it. He told me how worried you were about me—that I was to tell you everything. I looked up and saw you. He told me he loved you, that he was going to marry you, that someday when I was older I would find a man who would love me in the same way. When you ran away, I began to see a way."

"No..." For a moment Amy stood petrified, her face as bloodless as if she were a statue cut from some pale, cold slab of marble.

"I know it was wrong, what I did, to sleep with Jack, to lie," Lorrie said quietly. "I've known it for years, but I didn't know how to make it right again. Maybe I didn't want to make it right. I've never had your ability to fight...for anything. I was sixteen. I was jealous and scared of Nick. All I knew was that he was going to take you away. I'd lost Mother. Daddy was never there for me. You were all I had. You were like my mother, only sweeter. You always put me first, spoiled me. I couldn't lose you, Amy. Oh, I was wrong. I loved you so much, but I ruined your life. There've been times I've come close to telling you, but I never could. I thought I was doing the right thing. I thought you'd forget him. Maybe I would have told you the truth, but then I got pregnant. I let you assume Nick was the father, and the lie went on and on. I was too young to be a mother. I couldn't face bringing up a baby. You said we had to tell Nick the truth because it was his child, and I got so scared I ran away."

"N-no..."

"I wanted to die that night. I walked along those slippery rocks and fell into the ocean. I wanted to die like Mother, but I didn't. You were so scared for me, so sweet to me, and I made you promise you wouldn't ever go to Nick. So you went to Sebastian. Then Nick found out, and forced you to marry him. Everything got so twisted and mixed up, and I just couldn't see any way we'd ever straighten it out. But don't you see, you can't tell Nick the truth. Not now. He's not Triple's father at all. He'll only hate us both."

Amy studied her sister, seeing her fragile, childlike face and yet not seeing it, realizing for the first time in a kind of dazed amazement that she had lived with Lorrie for years and had never known her true character.

Oh, the terrible, terrible weapons of the weak.

"Say something, Amy, p-please... Forgive..."

Amy kept looking at her sister, whose tear-filled eyes were downcast, whose bright head dropped disconsolately with shame.

A tight band closed around Amy's heart. She could hardly breathe.

Sickened with a mixture of remorse, disgust, and shame, she whirled away and said nothing.

What was there she could say? Lorrie wasn't a little girl anymore, though she still acted like one far too often. This wasn't a childish bit of mischief that could be instantly forgiven or forgotten. Amy saw how wrong she had been to spoil her. How wrong...

Nick was innocent. He'd never been unfaithful to her. Amy had believed Lorrie. Amy's heart felt near bursting with the pain of it all. Oh, why had she? Was it just that she was used to always believing her younger sister, to always protecting her? That was no excuse. Amy had hardened her heart with hatred toward an innocent man, a man who'd loved her. She'd had so little faith in herself, so little faith in him, she'd never given him a chance to defend himself. She'd been so selfish and blind with her own hurt that she'd built up a case against him to soothe her wounds. She'd posed as the mother of his child, accepting money from Sebastian, accepting marriage from Nick, and everything she'd done was based on a horrendous lie. She'd lived on hate. She treated him cruelly, deliberately keeping him from Triple. She'd thought he'd destroyed all their lives, but he hadn't. She had.

He would never forgive her.

She would never be able to forgive herself.

Through the haze of her pain, Amy heard Lorrie's voice. It was indistinct, blurred, but Amy caught every word.

"Don't you see? You can't tell him. You've been unhappy for so long. You deserve happiness. Don't tell him, and everything will be all right."

That was the same destructive pattern of thinking that had gotten them all into such trouble.

A dull hammer pounded in Amy's temple. Nothing would ever be all right again.

If she didn't tell the truth, she would hate herself forever.

If she told the truth, she would lose Nick forever.

A lonely, black despair closed over her.

She wasn't even aware that Lorrie had slipped quietly out of the house.

Nine

The afternoon sun cast filaments of fire upon the glimmering waves. Purple shadows slanted across the beach.

Amy sat motionless in the brooding silence of her bedroom and waited for Nick to come home. She had to tell him everything—as soon as possible.

But how was she ever going to convince him that she had believed she was doing right by going to Sebastian and telling him *she* was pregnant? Amy had been used to shouldering responsibility, to fighting her sister's battles. Besides, from the day Amy had first lifted Triple into her arms in the hospital, she'd wanted him to be her child more than anything. From that first moment, when his tiny hand had curled around her little finger and clung, she'd been his mother. Everything else had seemed insignificant. The shame of letting everyone believe her an unwed mother had seemed as nothing when compared to the prospect of putting him up for adoption. She'd loved him with all the fierce, protective loyalty only a mother could feel.

Amy had married Nick when he'd threatened a custody battle, only because she'd been afraid that he might somehow find out the truth about Triple's parentage. If Nick had found out then that she wasn't Triple's natural mother, she thought he might have taken the child away form her.

She'd misjudged Nick. She only hoped there was some way to make up for it.

An eternity later the front door banged open, and she heard Nick's heavy tread in the hall. Her heart lurched as his footsteps approached her bedroom. Then he paused, and the house became silent. What was he doing?

The minutes ticked by, one by one, and he didn't come. Where was he? What was he doing? She twisted her hands. Then she leaped to her feet. She would rather face being drawn and quartered than tell the man she loved what she'd done, but she had to get it over with. She left her room and went downstairs.

Standing outside the den, Amy heard the whisper of excited male voices. Silently she opened the door a crack and peered in. Nick and Sam were sitting on the couch, huddled over a new computer chess board resting on a low table. Nick's raspy voice was a murmur of patient explanation.

Her heart contracted in fresh shame as she watched this latest example of Nick's kindness. He was very busy with the South Sails move, but he had taken the time to buy her father a gift.

"I need to talk to you, Nick," she said so quietly her words didn't quite carry across the room.

He glanced up quizzically. A glare of copper-gold light flooded into the room. Her hair was tumbling about her shoulders in fire-tipped waves, her bosom heaving nervously. He flashed her a dazzling smile.

"Come here, darling," he said, "and see what I found for Sam."

As he continued to look at her steadily, she felt the warm glow of his love, and her hand fluttered to her heart with new misgivings.

"I—I was worried—you were gone so long," she murmured, too ashamed to say more.

"I had to look in several stores to find this," he said, pulling her down beside him. Tenderly his lips grazed her icy brow. "I was just telling Sam that Mercedes, Dad and Jeb are coming tomorrow."

"Tomorrow..." The word died halfway up her throat.

Misinterpreting her anguished tone to be lack of enthusiasm at the prospect of his parents' imminent visit, Nick folded her freezing cold hands in his. "I know there's not much time for you to get ready, darling, but Apolonia's better now. And we'll do a lot of eating out. I'll pitch in. I tried to find Triple to tell him, but I couldn't find him anywhere. His room was as silent as a tomb and as tidily arranged as a museum. It's obvious he hasn't been near it in hours. His twelve-meter is lying on its side by the pool."

"It's always a bad sign when Triple doesn't mess up his room or when he gets quiet and goes off by himself," Amy said.

Normally Amy would have been more worried about Triple's odd disappearance, but she was too preoccupied with her own problem to give it the attention it deserved.

She turned away from Nick and her father, from the dancing red lights of the computer board as they moved the chess pieces. There was no way she could spoil Nick's family's visit by telling him the truth now. She would have to wait.

Triple's behavior remained strange even after Jeb, Mercedes and Wayne Jackson arrived. Though they brought Triple presents and made a fuss over him, he kept to his room as much as possible. In the past when Triple had a quiet period, it had usually been a lull before the storm.

Amy immediately loved Nick's family, and because she did, her problem was magnified. It was as if her secret were growing to affect them.

Wayne Jackson was an older, almost exact replica of Nick. He had Nick's same restless, excessive energy, his indomitable will, the same pale hair—silvered now—and brilliant blue eyes. Wayne was larger than life, stomping around Malibu in his jeans, custom-made boots and Stetson. He was a Texan to the core, outgoing and friendly to a fault, stopping strangers on the beach with a howdy and a smile, and treating them to long, drawn-out conversation, Texas-style. At first they would stare at him in wonder and listen with more wonder, privacy being the most highly prized of all Malibu commodities. But soon he had them up at the house for a drink, introducing Amy to neighbors she'd lived near for years and never met.

Mercedes was quieter, darker and lovely, even though she was almost sixty. She had the slender, graceful figure of a girl, and a beautiful way of moving. She had formerly been Mercedes Montez, the great Mexican ballerina, before giving up her career to marry Wayne. Her long, black hair was streaked with ribbons of silver. She was not so blatantly a Texan as Wayne and Jeb. She was more sophisticated, having lived all over the world. Mercedes had a melodious Spanish accent, rather than a flat Texas drawl, but for all her outward softness and femininity, Amy sensed in her a formidable will the equal of her husband's.

Jeb was dark and quiet, more like his mother than his father; yet he was a mixture of both these strong personali-

ties. He was tall and bold, heavily muscled and strong. He
exuded an aura of command and managed an empire bigger than many countries. In some indefinable way he reminded her of Nick. There was a restlessness in Jeb. It
seemed as if he were in conflict with himself, as if despite
everything he had, there was something missing in his life.
Amy sensed a deep affection between the two brothers, yet
she was immediately aware of their rivalry.

"Amy's too pretty and smart to be your wife," Jeb had
drawled lazily on first meeting her, pulling her into his arms
before he tipped his hat back and kissed her. "No wonder
you haven't brought her to Texas to meet your big brother."

"That wasn't why."

A look flashed between the brothers.

"Easy, boy," Jeb said, letting her go. "Just welcoming
her into the family Texas-style."

Amy found herself in the possessive iron grip of her husband's arms.

"Maybe it's time you got married again," Nick said.

Jeb's warm, black eyes lingered on Amy. "Maybe so.
You've certainly proved that finding the right wife could be
a worthwhile enterprise."

Nick was careful not to leave Amy and Jeb alone together for long.

Amy wasn't able to resist teasing Nick.

"Surely you trust your own brother."

"Of course, I trust him. About as far as I can throw
him."

"Nick..."

"Jeb's the oldest Jackson son. He thinks he's a king. He
rules a world. He has to know he's not a king here. Not in
my house."

"He's your brother."

"My half brother. A legitimate son. Neither of us has ever been able to forget that."

"You love him?"

"That goes without saying. But love doesn't have to blind you to the defects in someone's character. He used to resent me when I was a kid, when I came to Texas—and I resented him. I thought he had everything—a father and mother who loved and wanted him, the ranch. He could do everything better than me. There's nobody that knows more about horses, cows and oil than Jeb. He belonged in the family. I didn't. But I've carved out a life of my own. You're mine, not his. He can have the ranch. He can have everything else. All I want is you."

Nick had made love to her so passionately that night that Amy had almost been glad of his jealousy.

Mercedes was a natural matchmaker. She was obviously thrilled to find Nick so happy. Once when the men had gone out with Sebastian to sail on Sebastian's *Marauder*, taking Triple with them, Mercedes caught Amy alone.

Apolonia was busy as usual in the garden, so they made tea themselves and carried their cups down to the pergola where they could watch the water and the glamorous people meandering along the beach, waving effusively to one another but rarely speaking. Mercedes and Amy talked of general things for a while, joking that dinner might be late if Apolonia didn't abandon her gardening for the kitchen. At last a comfortable silence fell between them.

"This may be my only chance to talk to you privately," Mercedes said gently. "I wanted to say that I'm happy you and Nick are together at last. I knew, of course, about your marriage, your separation. When there was no divorce, I could not help hoping there wouldn't ever be one."

There was such a motherly warmth about Mercedes that Amy did not mind the personal turn of the conversation.

"We still have problems," Amy said, biting her bottom lip. "I'm not sure we can work them out."

"You will," Mercedes said softly. "I can tell by the way you look at each other. Sometimes it takes a while." She hesitated. "Wayne and I were separated once. I'm sure Nick told you. We nearly lost each other because of a terrible misunderstanding. It was all my fault, but of course, I didn't see it that way at the time. Injured feelings have a way of blinding one to the truth. Wayne even turned to another woman during that time, and the result was Nick. When I learned that I had been wrong about Wayne, I had to swallow my pride and go to him and beg his forgiveness. Neither of us knew about Nick for a long time."

"And Wayne forgave you?"

"Not immediately. It took time. The first months of a reconciliation are the most difficult. Sometimes it isn't easy for two people to find each other no matter how much they want to. And when we found out about Nick, it wasn't long before I was even glad about him. Do you know that he's more like Wayne than any of my other three sons were? I have come to love him so much, sometimes I have to remind myself he's not my son. One need not give birth to a child to feel like his mother. Nick has been alone too long. Make him happy, my dear. You have your child. It's too bad you had to come so close to losing Triple before Nick and you could find each other again."

"Triple was very sick. I was so frightened until Nick came. He's been... wonderful."

"Sometimes it takes a crisis to help us put life into perspective." Mercedes's eyes were moist. "I know all about the fear of losing a child. Such an experience has a powerful effect. I've lost two, you know."

"Of course, I knew about Jack."

"Years ago, I lost my only little girl, Julia. We never found her..."

"Nick never told me."

"It's not something any of us have spoken of, but I've never forgotten her. I've always wondered if she was dead or alive."

"That must be dreadful."

"When you're as old as I, you will know that life is filled with both sorrow and happiness. Without the one, you cannot appreciate the other. The tragedies brought me closer to my husband and the children I have left. I have much to be thankful for. So do you. Make Nick happy."

If only it were that simple, Amy thought.

The Jacksons' presence in their lives increased Amy's awareness of how wonderful being truly married to Nick could be—if only she was not constantly haunted by the guilt of her secret. It ate at her heart, robbing her of genuine happiness. The Jacksons liked her and trusted her, and sometimes a pressure built in her to shout that nothing was the way they thought it was. But she kept her silence.

To entertain the Jacksons, they went sailing, dined in the best restaurants so that Mercedes could stargaze, and went sight-seeing. Jeb and Wayne proved to be as reckless behind the wheel of a car as Nick was. From time to time when they didn't know she was listening, she would hear them singing in the same raucous off-key manner Nick had when he was alone. Even if Nick had been born a bastard, he was one of them.

Mercedes told Triple she'd brought him an autographed picture of Nugget, the little horse she'd bought for him.

"Horses can't write," Triple had said.

"Nugget is a very special pony." Mercedes turned the picture over. "He writes in his own way." On the photograph's back was a hoofprint.

Triple burst into laughter. "I have to come to Texas, soon."

It was a whirlwind, fun-filled visit. Triple remained quiet, which was fortunate in a way because he was on his best behavior. Nick was a marvelous host. He told Amy that soon he would take her to Australia to meet Tad, his other brother, who ran the Australian cattle stations that belonged to the Jackson Ranch.

Triple kept asking about the Jackson jet. Saturday afternoon Wayne and Jeb took Triple and Amy to the airport to meet their pilot who was a beautiful redhead named Megan MacKay. She'd grown up on the Jackson Ranch. Megan took Triple aboard and gave him a tour of the jet. For the first time Triple was his old energetic self, and Amy knew he would soon make a complete recovery.

Triple took great interest in examining everything. There was a lot of excitement for a while when he got lost somewhere at the airport. Then he popped up. He seemed quite pleased when he came home that evening, and he did not go to his room until he was made to.

On Sunday it was time for the Jacksons to leave. Amy and Nick drove them to the airport to see them off. Because it was late and Triple said he wasn't feeling well and wanted to go to bed, Amy and Nick had gone to the airport alone.

When they returned they were happy, but a little sad, too, because the Jacksons were gone. Amy was exhausted, both emotionally and physically from their visit.

Nick and Amy were in their bedroom undressing for bed, and as Amy stared at her impassive pale face in the mirror she made a silent vow. "Tomorrow... Tomorrow when I'm rested, I'll tell him everything."

Nick came up from behind her, and his golden head bent over her dark one. "My family loves you," he said huskily. "Just as I do."

"And I love them."

"I think we have the beginnings of a real marriage."

She turned away and bit her bottom lip.

"More than the beginnings," he went on in the same velvet tone. "Have you ever asked yourself what has held us together for all these years, even when we almost never saw each other? Was it only our child? Or was there something more, some deeper reason why neither of us took the steps to end our relationship?"

She was silent. Her heart hammered against her rib cage. She could not say anything. If he knew the truth—

"I want another child," he said.

"You keep rushing me."

He came close to her again. She had taken off everything but her silk slip. His hands glided slowly over her spine to press her against his hard lithe body. His voice was soft against her ear, his mouth brushing the bottom edge of her earlobe. "Because I love you. Because I sense that even now you're not completely mine. There are still some barriers between us. If we had another child and could share everything about the experience..."

Her head was spinning as he kissed the back of her neck. "N-no. That's not the answer."

"This time it will be different," he murmured. "I'll be there with you. I've always wondered what you went through having Triple."

He was turning her. His mouth followed the wildly pulsing vein in her neck to the sensitive hollow of her throat.

"Nick..."

He let her go.

His expression was grave as he studied her. "You've never talked about it. Was it a difficult birth?" He misunderstood the silent agony in her eyes, and his demand became more passionate. "Tell me. I have to know."

"Y-yes. It was difficult." That wasn't exactly a lie, but it wasn't the whole truth, either. Dear God! She had to do better than that. "Nick, tomorrow...we'll talk. I'll tell you everything," she said desperately.

Oh, what would he think of her when he found it was Lorrie's pregnancy, not hers he would be hearing about? After Lorrie had nearly drowned, her pregnancy had been difficult. The baby had come early. Lorrie had been terrified, childlike, so hysterical the nurses had let Amy stay with her. Amy could still remember Lorrie's piercing screams. They had torn her heart out.

Nick was watching Amy, reading the emotions on her face. Then his arms wrapped around her. She breathed in the intoxicating smell of him. He crushed her face against his so that the moist softness of her cheek scraped the rough stubble of his beard. "It always upsets me when I think of you facing all of that alone. Never again, my love. I will always be with you. You must believe that."

Suddenly she was sobbing.

"Why are you crying?"

"B-because I love you so much, and I'm so afraid of losing you."

"You'll never lose me."

He crushed her lips beneath his mouth, devouring them in a rapturous assault of passion that left her breathless and dazed.

He kissed her again and again. Deftly his hands slid the straps of her slip down her bare arms so that the flimsy silk fell to her waist. He cupped her breasts lovingly.

She was hardly conscious of what he did after that. Desire flooded her mind and body, sweeping her away on a dizzying tide of emotion. Amy forgot the monumental lie that stood between them. She wanted the oblivion of forgetfulness.

As he drew her down upon the bed, she forgot everything but his dominating kisses and the fierce, keen urgency to belong to him.

Nick fell asleep at once, but she couldn't. As the warmth of her passion ebbed, the old icy fear stole over her heart. Amy knew what Lorrie must have felt through the years. She was beginning to realize that if she didn't tell Nick the truth, the misery would never stop. It would always be there, twisting everything, marring with guilt even the happiest moments of their marriage.

She got up, pulled on her robe, and went out onto the balcony. Tomorrow... How would she ever find the strength to tell him? How could she face the risk of losing him? Where would she start?

Nick, there's a little matter we have to talk about. It's nothing really. It's just that I'm not really Triple's mother. She imagined his look of blank shock. *And that's not all. You're not his father, either. You never should have married me...*

Dear Lord, she thought. How unbearable it would be to watch Nick's love turn to hate.

She looked out to sea, then across the length of the shadowed balcony, as if somehow she would find the answers she sought from that still, black infinity.

It was then that she noticed Triple's open door. Slowly it dawned on her that something was wrong.

She rushed across the balcony to his room, remembering how he had said he wasn't feeling well enough to go to the airport, how he'd insisted on going to bed before it was even dark, before they'd left for the airport. Even though he'd kept to his room more than usual lately, that had been a first. Recuperating or not, Triple had never once in his brief, active life volunteered to go to bed early.

Amy stepped into his room and for an instant felt immediate relief when she saw her little boy's form nestled peacefully beneath his covers.

The room was ice-cold. She went to him. No one could sleep in such a room. Unless... Fear gripped her heart.

He was so still, so soundless.

No... Triple had to be all right!

As she bent down to touch him, she saw that the figure in the bed had the gigantic head of a stuffed gorilla.

She screamed. Then she flipped on the light and yanked back the bedspread.

There was nothing but a carefully arranged mound of pillows and stuffed animals.

Triple was gone.

She was almost relieved.

Even as she stared at the empty bed, she saw the note on the bedside table. Triple never wrote anything unless he had something important to say.

She picked up the note. It was horribly misspelled, but it's meaning was all too clear. *Yuore not my parnets! You dnot love me!*

It could mean only one thing. Triple had found out the truth somehow.

She should have told Nick. Oh, why hadn't she?

The note fell through her stiff fingers as Nick rushed into the room.

"I heard your scream. Where's..."

She shuddered at the dark grimness of his features. "Gone..." Her voice trailed away. "He left...this."

She picked up the note and handed it to him.

"This doesn't explain anything! What the hell's going on? If you know something, tell me."

She felt tense, afraid to speak, afraid not to. She stared at him, drinking in the carved glory of his male face, realizing

in that moment how very much she had always loved him.
She was so terribly close to losing him. "Oh, Nick," she
sobbed helplessly.

Instantly he pulled her into his arms. "We're in this together, darling. We'll find him. It isn't as if this is the first
time he's pulled something like this."

With a gasping cry of pain, she pushed him away. Bitter
tears filled her eyes. She felt his strong arms try to pull her
back against his chest. Even though she longed for the heat
of his body to warm her, she pivoted and turned away. She
was glad her back was to him, and he couldn't see the agony and pain in her eyes. "I don't deserve your love."

Again he tried to draw her into his arms and she wouldn't
let him. He looked hurt, baffled. He couldn't know it wasn't
his touch she feared, but his anger.

"Triple's run away, and it's my fault," she said. "Nick,
I've kept a terrible secret from you, and somehow Triple
found out. He's so little. He can't understand. If anything
happens to him, I'll never forgive myself. You should have
divorced me when you had the chance."

"So we're back to that. The first crisis, and it's, good-bye,
Nick." His face hardened. "I told you I'd give you a divorce only when you told me the truth."

"I don't know where to begin."

"Damn it!" Anger was in every controlled move he made.
"Why don't you say whatever it is and get it over with! It
couldn't be any worse than this hellish suspense of wondering what's wrong."

"It's about Triple." The remaining color drained from
her cheeks. She bit her bottom lip until it bled.

"What about him?" Nick demanded in a tautly edged
voice.

Seconds ticked by in silence.

Her frightened eyes met the harsh brilliance of Nick's. There was a hideous expectancy about him. She felt as if she were sitting on the edge of a volcano with an eruption only seconds away. Her world was about to disintegrate.

"I'm not really his mother," she whispered.

Although Nick didn't move, he seemed to loom nearer. "I don't believe you," he rasped. "Next you'll be saying he's not my son."

"H-he's not." Bitter tears of remorse filled her eyes. "Oh, Nick, I thought he was. For years I believed it!"

"You're lying!"

"If only I were. I'm telling the truth."

"No!" he shouted. He grabbed her by the shoulders and began to shake her. Then he seemed to realize what he was doing and let her go.

"Triple is Lorrie and your brother Jack's son, not ours! When she got pregnant, she told me he was your child. I believed her without even asking you. Don't you see—"

"No! I don't see a damned thing!" he thundered.

"Lorrie told me she slept with you that last night you were in L.A. I believed her. That's why I didn't go to Berkeley. That's why I was so cold to you afterward, why I hated you."

"I slept with *you* that last night!"

"But I went to your apartment after that. I saw you with Lorrie. I believed . . . what I thought I saw. I was so hurt, I hated you so much that I couldn't think straight."

"Your hatred was nothing but a cover for your own guilt."

"No . . ." She blurted out every horrible detail in a tear-choked voice, and as he listened, his expression took on a deathly calm.

"Why?" he whispered. "Why did you go to Sebastian in the first place and give him the impression you were the one

in trouble? Why did you let me believe all these years you
were Triple's mother?''

"Because I am his mother in every way that really counts.
Because I believed you were his father.''

"The hell you say. That's some stupid excuse you and
Lorrie concocted to cover up a coldly calculated plan. Sebastian liked you. He trusted you. He didn't even know
Lorrie. You knew Jack was too young and irresponsible to
marry. You could never have pulled the wool over my eyes,
so you didn't tell me.''

"I *did* believe you were his father—until a few days ago.''

"You set me up to marry you. And you weren't even his
mother. For years I've lived with the guilt of what I believed I'd done to you. It killed me every time I thought of
you pregnant and alone.'' He laughed bitterly. "Even tonight you let me go on believing all that.''

"I wanted to tell you the truth. Oh, Nick, I wanted to so
much. But I didn't want to ruin your parents' visit, and after they left I was too tired.''

"I've done everything in my power to try to make up to
you for the wrong I thought I'd done you. You went to Sebastian, took his money, and turned him against me. You let
me marry you, knowing—'' He paused. "I remember the
way you and Lorrie were so impressed with the moneyed
world, how ambitious you were—to make it on your own,
you said. Hell! Not when you saw an easier way. You deliberately used Triple, Jack's son, to get your start in the business world. You took money from Sebastian, from me. And
Triple's not even yours.''

"I thought I had to go to Sebastian. I had to get the
money to take care of Lorrie. There was no one else I could
turn to. After Triple was born, I couldn't have loved him
more if he'd been my real son. I didn't marry you for your
money. I married you because I thought you had a better

claim to him than I did. You might have found out I was only his aunt. There was a nurse...who knew the truth. He wasn't even legally mine. You could have taken him.''

The thrust of his frozen gaze pierced her like the coldest blade.

''And when Jack died, why did you come to me then and bind me to you with your warmth and love? You must have seen how vulnerable I was. You knew exactly how to keep me on the hook, loving you, paying... What a fool I've been.''

''It wasn't like that, I swear it. You were so desperate, I was afraid for you that night. I wanted you so much the next morning, I almost told you everything. But I couldn't because I still believed Lorrie.''

''I don't want to hear any more.''

A tiny sob escaped from Amy's lips. She turned away. ''I—I can't blame you.''

Nick reread Triple's note. ''So he found out the truth? How can a child understand any of this if I can't? He's out there somewhere, hurting badly. Jack's son. I've got to find him.''

''I'll help...''

Nick's mouth thinned into a cruel line, all savagery and pride. He stared down at her for a long moment. ''No, thank you, darling,'' he muttered viciously. ''Haven't you already done more than enough for us all?''

''Nick, please... Try to understand.''

He broke his gaze away from the pleading look in her eyes, cutting her out of his world as if she no longer existed.

''I do understand,'' he said coldly. ''That's the problem. You should have told me before. If something happens to Triple because you didn't—''

He let his unfinished statement linger in her mind like a shard of horror.

He turned and was gone.

She had lost him.

Ten

A phone rang in the house, and someone picked it up. Then silence reigned again.

The balcony door was still open. Moonlight whitened the surf that rushed onto the pale crescent of world-famous beach. Amy held her face up to the cold ocean breeze. Her tears felt frozen to her cheeks.

The front door swung open and slammed. She heard Nick's footsteps rushing down the hall toward her, and she sensed the controlled violence in his every movement.

She was still in Triple's room, still sitting in the silent darkness, hugging Triple's stuffed gorilla. She felt numb, paralyzed. She'd been there for hours, worrying about Triple, grieving over Nick, yet knowing she would feel even worse when the paralyzing numbness damming up her most piercing emotions broke.

She hadn't gone to look for Triple because Nick hadn't wanted her to, and because never before had she succeeded in rescuing Triple from one of his adventures. When Triple was ready, Triple rescued himself.

"Amy!"

"In here," she called weakly.

He threw open their bedroom door and slammed it. She heard other doors, opening and being thrown violently shut as he reached for her. Lights flashed on and were extinguished.

"Amy! Damn it! Answer me!"

"I'm in Triple's room!"

She bit her lip. Her hands started to shake again. Why was it that now that she knew the bliss of sharing a life and home with Nick and Triple, she had lost it all? She wanted more than anything else to make Nick happy and all she'd ever done was make him miserable.

The door to Triple's room crashed open.

All she could see of Nick was his golden hair shining in the moonlight, but even before he stepped inside or spoke, she felt the smoldering fury of his presence.

"So you're still here?" His voice was harsh, cold.

Inside she was dying. As he came closer, she searched his face for some sign of his former love for her.

White-gold hair, bronzed skin stretched taut across cheekbones and jawline, the cruel line of his mouth, cold haunted eyes, his slow, tigerlike grace struck her with the powerful force of a blow to the gut.

Gasping, she wanted to close her eyes against the shattering pain in her heart, but his cold gaze locked onto hers and wouldn't let go.

"Triple? D-did you find him?" There was an agonizing tightness in her throat.

"Yes. It wasn't so hard once I got to figuring. There was only one place he could have gone."

So that was the only reason Nick had come to her, she thought.

"Thank God. He's all right, then?"

"He's fine," came Nick's cold, low tone.

She was relieved that her son was safe, but her heart was breaking. Only pride kept her shoulders squared and her head held high.

"Where is he?" she managed.

"In Texas. Somehow he got himself to the airport and stowed away in Dad's jet. Megan just called me back a few minutes ago. She found him in a compartment in the back of the jet. Triple was running away, but now that he's there, it's not as great as he thought it would be. He got scared on the plane. He's homesick. He even cried on the phone."

"He's never been away—except to be with you," Amy said softly.

Her eyes met Nick's pleadingly, and he turned away, as if he were determined to ignore the mute appeal.

"I guess he didn't know how lonely he'd feel until he left," Nick said flatly.

"Only Triple could pull off something so dramatic."

"Oh, I don't know." Nick's cynical gaze swept her. "He comes from a wild bunch. It's in his genes."

"Thank you for telling me where he is. I've been so worried."

"Megan could fly him back, but I think it's important we go after him—together. Megan's flying the jet to pick us up in the morning."

"Together? W-why? I thought you were through with me."

He cursed under his breath, his face taut with suppressed anger. "I could kill you for what you've done, but you're the only mother Triple's ever known."

Hurt and humiliation swelled inside her.

"And I'm the only father he's ever known," Nick continued in the same flat, harsh tone. "We have to make him understand that we love him as much as we ever did."

"You mean, you aren't going to turn your back on Triple?"

His jaw tightened ominously. He lifted his hand. But he only raked it through his golden hair in a weary, defeated gesture. "Damn you, Amy," he muttered. "What kind of man do you take me for? You aren't Triple's biological mother, but you love him with a mother's love. Is it so hard to believe I could feel the same way? For years I thought Triple was my son. Do you think anything you could say or do would ever change my feelings for him? I'm crazy about Triple. No matter what you've done, he'll always be mine. He's even more precious to me now that I know he's part of Jack. I lost my brother. I don't want to lose Triple, and right now he's in Texas feeling confused and alone. I came back for you only because when I told him I was coming, he begged me to bring you, too."

Her heart constricted. So it was really over. Nick wanted Triple, but he'd never want her. She had hurt him too deeply. What she'd done wasn't something that could be easily forgiven or forgotten.

"Go to bed," he said. "I'll spend what's left of the night on the couch."

When the sun came up, Nick came into her bedroom with a cup of coffee. Amy was red eyed and pale from lack of sleep.

"Get dressed." His voice and eyes were as cold as the night before. "Megan will be here in an hour."

Amy didn't dare disobey. She dressed quickly, silently. He didn't stay to watch.

They drove in silence to the airport. Except for greeting Megan briefly before she seated herself in the cockpit, Amy and Nick maintained their tense silence. Nick was always especially nervous on airplanes, but he was more so today. When they took off and the jet careened over the blue Pacific, his tan hands clutched the armrest of his seat. Moisture beaded his brow.

Before she thought better of it, Amy had reached across and touched his hand in reassurance. Abruptly he jerked his hand free from hers, got up, and left her, vanishing into the cockpit to join Megan.

Left alone in the cabin, Amy felt jealous and left out. She knew Nick had known the beautiful Megan for years. As a child when Nick had spent his summers in Texas, Megan had always been there. Her mother had run off first, then later, her father. Her older brother had moved overseas. Megan had been raised on the ranch during that difficult period, and Amy knew Nick had the greatest admiration for her. He had always spoken of her affectionately, saying that she was wild and fun loving, that she'd been the only one on the ranch who ever dared to disobey Jeb.

Amy could hear Nick and Megan talking and laughing together. For once Nick seemed to have found a means of distracting himself from his fear of flying. Nick was snubbing Amy, treating her as though she didn't exist.

Perhaps the beautiful Megan had made him forget her completely.

Amy couldn't endure it.

But she had to.

By the time Nick and Amy got to the ranch it was noon. Amy had never been to Texas and was stunned by the vastness of the open mesquite range spreading out beneath an endless blue sky. A ribbon of blacktop with heat waves

shimmering off it seemed endless, too, as the road mean-
dered into the distance. Amy thought the ranch had a stark,
lonesome beauty unlike anything she'd ever seen before.
They drove for miles, after passing through the front gate,
beneath billowing white clouds, through tangled oak motts,
beside oil wells, and past herds of Santa Gertrudis and An-
gus cattle before reaching the white Big House.

"It doesn't look all that impressive," Nick said coolly,
"but beneath all those cow hooves and cactus thorns and
that dry caked dirt there are millions and millions of bar-
rels of oil. I guess Texas was built on its bigness, brag, and
oil. At least that's what this ranch is founded on, along with
my brother Jeb."

Amy made no comment. She could see that the Jackson
Ranch was a world unto itself, an empire carved out of the
desert land between the Rio Grande and the Gulf of Mexico.

Mercedes greeted them warmly, offered them coffee, and
told them that Triple was at the corral. Kirk MacKay, Megan's brother, was teaching him to ride.

"You mean you've turned Triple loose on a cowboy?"
Amy asked dubiously.

Mercedes's smile was indulgent. "Kirk's our horse-
program manager, and he's no ordinary cowboy."

"Kirk's a former CIA agent," Nick said dryly. "For once
Triple has a competent sitter."

As soon as they could, Nick and Amy left Mercedes. As
they approached the pasture nearest the corral, they saw a
tall, powerfully built, Indian-dark man leading a little boy
on a docile, velvet-brown pony. Except for having the same
green eyes, Kirk bore little resemblance to his red-haired
sister. Megan was all spirit and fire. There was a coiled
tenseness about this silent man, a fierce, indefinable rug-
gedness about him as if there was nothing on earth that

could frighten him—ever again. And yet there was a quiet
gentleness in him when he turned his attention to the horse
and child. When Kirk saw them, he waved in greeting.
Sensing their need to be alone with their child, he cocked his
Stetson in a salute and lifted Triple down from the saddle
before leading the pony back to the barn.

Triple hesitated, looking torn and uncertain. Behind him
a windmill groaned as its blades whirred in the wind. A
mother quail was leading her feathered nestlings in a parade across the road.

Triple stood in the pasture with the wind ruffling his
golden-brown hair. He hesitated, a tiny figure in a vast
world, and his proud, aloof stance clawed at Amy's heart.

"Triple!" she cried out, her voice choked with emotion.
She opened her arms. Her face was illuminated with a
mother's unmistakable love for her child.

For a long moment Triple held himself rigid, his troubled eyes betraying a heart in turmoil. Then he could hold
back no longer. Suddenly he was running through the dry,
waving grasses. He threw himself into his parents' arms in
his eagerness to see them, having forgotten that they were
the very pair he had run from.

"Triple, why did you run away?" Amy asked gently after a while, tousling his curls and hugging his sturdy little
breathless body as she knelt beside him. Her eyes were filled
with tears of joy.

"I wanted to fly. But then it was awful. I was scared. It
was so bumpy."

Nick smiled grimly. His eyes were brilliant with a keen
understanding. Amy saw his brown hand tighten on Triple's
shoulder. "Son, for anyone with a drop of Jackson blood,
flying's hell."

"Why did you run away?" Amy repeated.

Triple looked from his mother to his father, and the warmth and understanding the child saw in their faces seemed to reassure him.

"I heard you talking to Aunt Lorrie. I didn't think I was your little boy anymore, and maybe you wouldn't love me anymore."

Gently Amy tilted his face up to hers. "I will always love you. Always," she said.

"I don't want Aunt Lorrie for a mother."

Amy's fingers lovingly caressed Triple's cheek. "I will always be your mother." Her gaze swung to Nick, who seemed so uncomfortably silent. "Just as Nick will always be your father."

Triple glanced dubiously toward his father and then back to his mother. "Really?"

"Yes," she whispered fervently. "Nothing will ever change that. Nothing in the past. Nothing in the future. He loves you as much as I do. You are our little boy. You have to believe that."

"And I can live with both of you? All the time? Can everything be the way it was?" Triple's small hand tightened its grip on his mother's fingers pleadingly.

Amy's imploring eyes met Nick's. A small, agonized sound slipped through the constricted muscles of her throat. More than anything she longed to give her child the answer he wanted to hear, but she couldn't.

It was Nick's voice that broke the silence.

"Yes," Nick said. "We'll all be together. All the time."

"Really, Dad?"

"Really." Nick was folding Triple into his arms, and Triple was staring trustingly into his father's eyes.

"Don't lie to him," Amy pleaded desperately. "Please, no more lies."

She couldn't bear to hope, for Triple to hope, if there was no chance. It would be too cruel.

Nick's grim gaze met hers. "Trust me," he whispered softly, ironically.

She gave a swift silent nod, and then got up and left them together. It was very important that Triple know how much Nick wanted him.

Amy hadn't walked far when Triple gave a shriek of pure joy. She whirled and saw that Kirk had returned and was lifting Triple into the saddle again while Nick watched.

Suddenly Nick's gaze riveted itself to the solitary woman standing apart from them.

"Amy!" he shouted, calling her back.

She wanted to run to him, to believe that he'd meant it when he'd promised they would always be together. She wanted to stand with him, to hold his hand, to watch their son as he rode Nugget. Nick's tall, bronzed form blurred through the mist of her intense emotion.

She turned away and began to run from them, blindly, stumbling through the deep grasses. Behind her she could hear the muffled thunder of Nick's heavy boots chasing after her. He caught her just short of the Big House and spun her around in his arms.

"Let me go!" she wept.

"Shut up!" His raspy voice was harsh and angry.

Amy strained to push him away, but he merely tightened his brutal grip. "Don't come after me if you don't want me!"

She licked her dry lips.

A muscle jumped convulsively at the corner of his mouth. Rage glittered in his eyes. "Why the hell did you run?" Nick jerked her onto her tiptoes. "You've been running from me, turning your back on me for years and years. Don't ever do it again." He covered her mouth with his in a savage kiss that betrayed a bewildering mixture of emotions—rage, desire, tenderness.

Amy shuddered away from his touch with a moan, but he pressed his body into hers, and she felt the rigid contours of his taut, male body.

Just as abruptly as he'd seized her, Nick released her. He pushed her beneath the dense shade of a gnarled live oak. Her slender, graceful figure was dwarfed by the immense size of him.

"What do you think you're doing?" Amy demanded, trying to hide her trembling from him.

"We've got to talk." His raspy voice was harsh. His lips were clamped so tightly together that there were white lines beside the edges.

"Y-you shouldn't have lied to Triple about us all being together." Her words seem to tremble uncontrollably. Her eyes were golden and luminous, mute in their appeal.

His expression softened as he cupped her face. She felt his other hand wrap around her throat. To her amazement his hands were shaking.

"I wasn't lying," he said. "Do you really think I could live without you? I've tried that. The one thing I learned was that no matter how much I wanted to forget you, I couldn't crush all the memories. I couldn't block out the smell and the taste and the feel of you. The harder I tried to, the more I wanted you. I want you too badly, still, to give you up."

It had been the same for her.

"I didn't use Triple to get money from you or Sebastian, Nick," she whispered. "I needed the money for Triple, not for myself."

His hands held her face still, and he read the agony in her eyes.

"I believe you," he said quietly at last. "I believe you."

"But can you ever forgive me?" Her low voice throbbed. "What I did was so wrong. My only excuse is that I thought I was protecting my family."

As Amy gazed up at him her pain seemed to reach out and touch him, hurting him as much as it hurt her. Then she buried her face in the hollow of his neck, drawing a deep, shaking breath and closing her eyes.

He groaned. Then he drew her closer, his hands moving over her body caressingly, soothingly. "We've all suffered—you no less than I. I can't blame you. You did what you believed was right. Hating you is like hating part of myself. I've never felt as alone as I felt last night. Losing you, finding you, losing you again. It was unbearable."

"For me as well," she said.

"I told Triple we would legally adopt him. He would be our little boy. Ours alone. Just as he's always been. He couldn't be any more precious if he were my own son." Nick's eyes were shining. "Darling, don't you see, you have given me back something of Jack."

"Do you really think we're going to be...a real family?"

"Yes, darling, I do," he said hoarsely. "That's what I've always wanted and never had—to be at the center of a real family."

He kissed her throat gently and then her lips more passionately.

"We're going to have to find someplace to be alone," she whispered after a long time.

He smiled down at her. "Believe me, darling, that's not too hard in Texas."

It was the second lay day of Antigua Race week, and a lazy stillness pervaded the sultry Caribbean island. In some hotel or thatched hut nestled behind a wall of lush purple bougainvillea and crotons, reggae music was playing. It was a dull, throbbing, repetitive sound that seemed to go on and on, endlessly crooning just as the aqua waves endlessly caressed the sugar-white sand.

The tiny harbor was overcrowded. A multitude of expensive racing yachts from all over the world were jammed side by side and docked. Sebastian's *Marauder*, the sixty-five-foot Swan ketch that Nick was racing in the series, was anchored out in English Harbour, a safe distance from the other yachts that were also anchored in the still green-blue waters of Antigua's Hurricane Hole.

Not a breath of air stirred the protected waters. Amy and Nick were alone on the deck of the gleaming yacht drinking iced drinks, relaxing for the first time after days of hectic racing. Triple had gone ashore to participate in the lay day dinghy races for children. The rest of the crew had gone as well, encouraged by Nick to participate in the sail-bag races, drinking contests, or the lascivious-leg contest. Mercedes and Wayne were ashore, too, ensconced in the lavish splendor of their air-conditioned hotel suite.

"Whoever heard of bringing a child on a honeymoon?" Nick teased, his gaze drifting over his wife like an intimate caress.

Her eyes sparkled. "Some honeymoon. Whoever heard of bringing an entire crew along—as well as your parents."

"We need the crew to race," Nick declared practically.

"That's just the point. We're supposed to be honeymooning. Not racing."

He flashed her a hot, eager look. "Thank you for reminding me," he said, pulling her into his arms.

The glow radiating from his face was warm and intense and Amy basked in its loving light. In the months that had

followed their reconciliation, she had never known a more
complete and serene happiness.

"I had to race," he murmured. "Sebastian's orders. I
couldn't leave you behind. Do you really mind...so much?"

"I really mind," she whispered, drawing his open palm
to her lips and kissing his fingers. "All I want...is to be
alone with you. When you're racing, you never think of
me."

"And when I'm not, I never think of anything else but
you." He gathered her close to him in a fierce, possessive
embrace, and she reveled in his nearness. His golden head
lowered gently to hers, his mouth claiming hers in a passionate kiss that rocked her senses. A wild, hot glory filled
her. She didn't mind anything as long as she was with him.

She was breathless when the kiss was over, and the tingling sensation remained as Nick nuzzled his face into her
raven black hair, his mouth trailing kisses of fire along the
sensitive skin of her throat. A tremor shook him, and she
knew he was no more immune to the sensual thrill of their
embrace than she was.

"I love you," she said softly.

"I love you, too," he murmured. "Maybe we'd better go
below..."

"In a minute. There's a little confession I need to make
first. A little something I haven't told you."

"A little something..." He was remembering her last
confession all those months ago when Nick had learned
their son's true parentage. Nick pulled away and as he
studied her suddenly grave face, he grew even more alarmed.
"Dear God! Not another secret! Not again."

"Yes."

"What? I thought you'd learned your lesson."

She smiled softly into his startled face. "We're going to have a baby. You and I..."

His fingers lightly touched her cheek. The expression on his dark face was incredulous. "For a minute there..." His brows drew together. "What the hell have you been doing on this boat working as hard as the men?"

"I was just going along with your idea of a honeymoon."

"Not anymore," he pronounced emphatically. "The men can tail the jib sheets without you. You should have told me sooner, sweetheart."

"I'm not made of glass, you know."

"I'm not letting you take any chances. We'll get you a hotel room. No more hot nights on this boat."

"Nick," she protested softly, laughing at him. "I like our hot nights."

"No argument," he insisted arrogantly. "You and our baby are much too precious to risk." His arms encircled her gently, lovingly. "This is the happiest day of my life." Gently he traced the lines of her face with his fingers. "I never dreamed...it could be like this. Our child—a beautiful, black-haired little girl like you."

Amy laughed. "I was sort of hoping for a golden-haired little boy. We could call him Sebastian."

"Sebastian, hell! What's wrong with Nicholas?" Nick bent his head and kissed her—a long, deep kiss. Amy slid her arms around his neck, rising on her tiptoes.

It seemed that their souls met, touched, and came together.

"Darling," he said in an aching murmur against her lips.

Once she had asked him not to call her that ever again.

But that unhappy time was a lifetime away.

The sky above the soft green island and its shimmering, azure waters was iridescent pink and blue. A golden band of sunlight trailed away into infinity.

Nick lifted his wife in his arms and carried her below.

* * * * *

EMILIE RICHARDS

THE WAY BACK HOME

As a teenager, Anna Fitzgerald fled an impossible
situation, only to discover that life on the streets was
worse. But she had survived. Now, as a woman,
she lived with the constant threat that the secrets of
her past would eventually destroy her new life.

1-55166-399-6
AVAILABLE IN PAPERBACK
FROM SEPTEMBER, 1998

JASMINE CRESSWELL

THE DAUGHTER

Maggie Slade's been on the run for seven years now.
Seven years of living without a life or a future because
she's a woman with a past. And then she meets Sean
McLeod. Maggie has two choices. She can either run,
or learn to trust again and prove her innocence.

"Romantic suspense at its finest."

—Affaire de Coeur

MIRA®

1-55166-425-9
AVAILABLE IN PAPERBACK
FROM SEPTEMBER, 1998

Jayne Ann Krentz

A Woman's Touch

He was her boss—and her lover!
Life had turned complicated for Rebecca Wade when she
met Kyle Stockbridge. He *almost* had her believing he
loved her, until she realised she was in possession
of something he wanted.

"...one of the hottest writers in romance today."

—USA Today

MIRA

1-55166-315-5
**AVAILABLE IN PAPERBACK
FROM AUGUST, 1998**

DEBBIE MACOMBER

Married in Montana

Needing a safe place for her sons to grow up, Molly
Cogan decided it was time to return home.
Home to Sweetgrass Montana.
Home to her grandfather's ranch.

*"Debbie Macomber's name on a book is a guarantee
of delightful, warm-hearted romance."*

—Jayne Ann Krentz

1-55166-400-3
AVAILABLE IN PAPERBACK
FROM AUGUST, 1998

RONA JAFFE

Five Women

Once a week, five women meet over dinner and
drinks at the Yellowbird, their favourite
Manhattan bar. To the shared table they bring
their troubled pasts; their hidden secrets.
And through their friendship, each will find
a courageous new beginning.

Five Women is an *"insightful look at female
relationships."*

—Publishers Weekly

1-55166-424-0
AVAILABLE IN PAPERBACK
FROM AUGUST, 1998

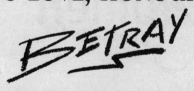

LAURA VAN WORMER

❧ ★ ❧

Just for the Summer

Nothing prepares Mary Liz for the summer she spends in
the moneyed town of East Hampton, Long Island. From
the death of one of their own, Mary Liz realises that these
stunningly beautiful people have some of the ugliest
agendas in the world.

*"Van Wormer,…has the glamorama Hampton's scene down to
a T. (Just for the Summer is) as voyeuristic as it is fun."*
—Kirkus Reviews

MIRA®

1-55166-439-9
AVAILABLE NOW IN PAPERBACK